GREEK AND ROMAN WRITERS

THE MIDDLE AGES TO THE 17TH CENTURY

GOETHE TO IBSEN

20TH CENTURY WRITERS

THE PAGEANT OF LITERATURE
20th Century Writers

Revised Edition

Emery C. Mollenhauer, F.S.C.

La Salle College, Philadelphia, Pennyslvania

The Macmillan Company   New York

ACKNOWLEDGMENTS

For permission to use material in this book, grateful acknowledgment is made
to the following:

George Allen & Unwin Ltd.: For "London Streets" and "The Pilgrim Observes
the People" from Letters from England by Karel Capek. Reprinted by permission
of the publishers, George Allen & Unwin Ltd.

Atheneum Publishers: For "A Ghost in the Subway" from Waters of the New
World by Jan de Hartog. Copyright © 1961 by Littra, A. G. Reprinted by permission of Atheneum Publishers.

Avon Book Division-The Hearst Corporation: For "The Green Kitten" by
Maxim Gorky, from 26 Men and a Girl and Other Stories, copyright © 1957
by Avon Publishers Inc. Published by arrangement with Avon Book Division-The
Hearst Corporation.

The Cummington Press and Professor Carl Niemeyer: For "Gym Period" by Rainer
Maria Rilke, from Primal Sound and Other Prose Pieces by Rainer Maria Rilke.

Babette Deutsch: For "Little Catkins" and "The Scythians" by Alexander Blok.
From A Treasury of Russian Verse, edited by Avrahm Yarmolinsky, published by
The Macmillan Company.

Doubleday and Company, Inc.: For "Four Years in a Shed" from Madame
Curie by Eve Curie. Copyright 1937 by Doubleday and Company, Inc.

E. P. Dutton & Co., Inc.: For "War" from The Medals and Other Stories by
Luigi Pirandello. Copyright, 1939, by E. P. Dutton & Co., Inc. Reprinted by per-
mission of E. P. Dutton & Co., Inc. For "Before and During Exile" from the book
Conversations with Casals by J. Ma. Corredor. Copyright, ©, 1956 by E. P. Dutton
& Co., Inc. Reprinted by permission of the publishers.

Farrar, Straus & Cudahy, Inc.: For "The Treasure," "Raw Material," and
"The Little World" from The Little World of Don Camillo by Giovanni
Guareschi. Copyright 1950 by Giovanni Guareschi. For "I Am Like a Distracted

The Macmillan Company, New York
Collier-Macmillan Canada, Ltd., Toronto, Ontario
Printed in the United States of America

CONTENTS

PRONUNCIATION KEY

The pronunciation of those authors' names which are difficult to pronounce will be found on the pages where the names first appear. The diacritical marks used are those found in *Webster's New World Dictionary*. The key to these diacritical marks follows.

a   *as in*   fat, lap
ā   *as in*   ape, date
â   *as in*   bare, care
ä   *as in*   car, father
à   *as in*   French *bal;* intermediate between a and ä

e   *as in*   ten, let
ē   *as in*   even, meet
ê   *as in*   here, dear
ẽr   *as in*   over, under
ë   *as in*   French *leur*

i   *as in*   is, hit
ī   *as in*   bite, mile

o   *as in*   lot, top
ō   *as in*   go, tone
ô   *as in*   horn, fork
o͞o   *as in*   tool, troop
oo   *as in*   book, moor
ö   *as in*   French *feu;* round the lips for ō and try to pronounce ā
ô̂   *as in*   French *coq* and German *doch*

u   *as in*   up, cut
ū   *as in*   use, cute
ü   *as in*   French *duc* and German *grün*

ə   *as in*   *a*go, umbrell*a*
n   This symbol indicates that the vowel sound immediately preceding it is nasalized, as in French *en, mon.*
th   *as in*   thin, truth
th   *as in*   then, father

INTRODUCTION

The literature of any century is an authentic and exciting guide to the understanding of that century as a whole. Through the fiction, nonfiction, poetry, and drama of the times, a reader can get a vivid picture of how the people lived, felt, thought, and acted. To read, for example, the works of Hugo, Balzac, Schiller, Tolstoy, Chekhov, and Ibsen, among many others, is to get a vast and detailed view of Western European life in the nineteenth century, including its social, historical, economic, artistic, and psychological aspects.

Each century, like a person, has its own personality and its own unique characteristics. Yet each century is also a continuation of the past and has things in common with the centuries that have gone before. To read the literature of any period, therefore, is to discover that the world at that time was different from and the same as any other time, new and old, unique and in relation.

This volume offers the reader an opportunity to understand the first half of the twentieth century in Europe through an appreciation of its literature. Reading the creative work of this period, written in languages other than English, is an integral part of the process of understanding the men and women who share with us the problems of existence today. To understand the soul and mind of the people of Western Europe who, in many ways, are like us, but who also have attitudes and ways of life that differ from ours, is of the utmost necessity today when communication among races and nations is ever increasing.

The reader will find that the years from 1900 to the present, with their turbulent and unsettling events, have had a marked effect on European writers. Their work reveals a new questioning of the road civilization is pursuing, of man's values, and of the direction his life should take. At the same time, twentieth-century writers have attempted to describe life as they see it and to record faithfully and imaginatively the hopes, fears, and dilemmas of people in our time. Perhaps the dominant note in the literature of Western Europe of this century is a feeling of *malaise* and frustration. There is a sense of searching and confusion amid the complexities of modern life.

Yet there is a striking diversity among these writers. They differ in subject matter, in the approach to their material, and in style. While reflecting the times in which they live, they also assert their individuality and particular outlook on life.

For convenience, the selections in this volume have been grouped according to the four major types of literature: fiction, nonfiction, poetry, and drama. This has been done primarily to aid the student's appreciation and understanding of the material. Each section is represented by outstanding writers in that field. Through them, the reader will get a glimpse into the mind and heart of Western Europe, while enjoying each selection for itself as a literary work.

The selections are offered objectively and do not necessarily represent attitudes or values that the reader should be encouraged to adopt. Indeed, at times, the opposite holds true. With the student's own clear perception of his Christian inheritance, however, he should emerge from reading world literature as a person better equipped to read, to evaluate, and to pursue the business of living.

FICTION

*T*WO world wars, tremendous scientific advance, a return by many people to faiths from which they had fallen away or neglected, the rise of a whole people without faith—these have made the twentieth century in Europe a time of upheaval and uncertainty—a time during which many were not sure of the value of anything. The novels and stories of the European writers have reflected these times which have called for new approaches to the art of fiction, a new viewpoint, and new techniques.

The tone of much of this fiction has been pessimistic. The writers are critical of the direction civilization is taking. Thomas Mann in Germany, for example, has vividly described the decay of the middle class. He has pictured the contrast between those having bourgeois, commonplace values and those having artistic values. Albert Camus in France has questioned whether man actually has a choice; he has also depicted man's alienation from himself and from society. Luigi Pirandello in Italy has declared that life itself is an illusion—that people can believe in nothing.

There has also been an increasing interest in exploring the inner life of man, the life that man does not realize is going on—his unconscious. Nineteenth-century writers were primarily concerned with the effect of outward events on a character; twentieth-century writers are primarily concerned with the conflicts going on within a character and what makes him act as he does. This emphasis on the interior life of a character can be seen, in particular, in the selections by Sigrid Undset and Albert Camus.

To re-create this inner world, writers have had to find new methods of presentation. One of these methods is the "stream of consciousness" technique, in which the author re-creates the thoughts, feelings, and observations that flow through the mind of a character, often without logical order or objectivity.

Many writers, such as Mann and Maxim Gorky, have continued in the tradition of the nineteenth-century realists. Other authors, however, like Andreyev and Kafka, have employed symbolism and allegory to express man's fate in the modern world. In their works, the literal meaning of the plot and what the characters say and do is

1

secondary. Just as in Aesop's *Fables*, the real meaning is contained in what the plot and the character stand for. What a character does or says may stand for an abstract idea, such as liberty or man's search for God. This makes stories like "Laughter" and "The Hunter Gracchus" more difficult reading than a realistic story, but if the author is good, the rewards are great.

As with all important works of fiction, you must be willing to make an effort to discover what the writer is trying to say. In short, you must work, in order to appreciate fully a work of art. The understanding, pleasure, and satisfaction you receive will be much greater than the amount of work you have done in getting to understand the story or novel. The stories by Andreyev and Kafka in this book are, for example, just a small fraction of the work that has been done in this style by European authors, but a careful examination of what the author was saying and the way he said it will give you an insight into the minds and attitudes of a whole type of contemporary European writers.

In general, twentieth-century European writers of fiction, like their English and American counterparts, have eliminated long paragraphs of description and exposition from their works. They have permitted the characters in a story to act, speak, and think without the aid of direct comments from the author. The emotion in a story arises solely from the dramatic presentation of an internal or external conflict which the main character is experiencing and attempting to solve.

Most important, however, in the European modern short story is the concern with the individual and his values. What will make a man happy? In attempting to answer this question, writers have again placed an increasing emphasis on man's moral obligations, on the part conscience plays in his life, on the effects of guilt, on his ethical duties to the world in which he lives. The tone of the stories in this section is serious. The authors are critical, both of the individual and of society. Yet it is clear that these writers are concerned with what happens to people and to the society in which they live, and how one affects the other. Even in their pessimism, they continue to assert that man is intensely interesting and worth a great deal of attention.

Luigi Pirandello

War

Luigi Pirandello (1867–1936), playwright, novelist, short-story writer, and poet, ranks as one of the important Italian writers of the twentieth century. He was awarded the Nobel Prize for Literature in 1936. His plays, notably *Six Characters in Search of an Author* and *Right You Are If You Think You Are,* have won him his greatest distinction, though they have been the subject of controversy and have been attacked as obscure. In his dramas, he reveals his inventiveness, his ability to create characters, and his ironical view of life. In most of his work, Pirandello expresses the pessimistic idea that life consists merely of a series of illusions; that people can be certain of nothing at all, not even truth; and that the existence of reality itself is questionable. He suggests that the characters in a play can have a life of their own over which the playwright has no control. Still, Pirandello shows a sympathy toward men and women enmeshed in this seemingly meaningless web of existence.

The short story "War" is a compact narrative that suggests the author's preoccupation with the nature of personality and reality, as well as the relation between individuals and Italian history.

*T*HE passengers who had left Rome by the night express had had to stop until dawn at the small station of Fabriano in order to continue their journey by the small old-fashioned "local" joining the main line with Sulmona.

At dawn, in a stuffy and smoky second-class carriage in which five people had already spent the night, a bulky woman in deep mourning was hoisted in—almost like a shapeless bundle. Behind her— puffing and moaning, followed her husband—a tiny man, thin and weakly, his face death-white, his eyes small and bright and looking shy and uneasy.

Having at last taken a seat he politely thanked the passengers who had helped his wife and who had made room for her; then he turned around to the woman trying to pull down the collar of her coat and politely inquired:

3

"Are you all right, dear?"

The wife, instead of answering, pulled up her collar again to her eyes, so as to hide her face.

"Nasty world," muttered the husband with a sad smile.

And he felt it his duty to explain to his traveling companions that the poor woman was to be pitied, for the war was taking away from her her only son, a boy of twenty to whom both had devoted their entire life, even breaking up their home at Sulmona to follow him to Rome where he had to go as a student, then, allowing him to volunteer for war with an assurance, however, that at least for six months he would not be sent to the front and now, all of a sudden, receiving a wire saying that he was due to leave in three days' time and asking them to go and see him off.

The woman under the big coat was twisting and wriggling, at times growling like a wild animal, feeling certain that all those explanations would not have aroused even a shadow of sympathy from those people who—most likely—were in the same plight as herself. One of them, who had been listening with particular attention, said:

"You should thank God that your son is only leaving now for the front. Mine has been sent there the first day of the war. He has already come back twice wounded and been sent back again to the front."

"What about me? I have two sons and three nephews at the front," said another passenger.

"Maybe, but in our case it is our *only* son," ventured the husband.

"What difference can it make? You may spoil your only son with excessive attention, but you cannot love him more than you would all your other children if you had any. Paternal love is not like bread that can be broken into pieces and split amongst the children in equal shares. A father gives *all* his love to each one of his children without discrimination, whether it be one or ten, and if I am suffering now for my two sons, I am not suffering half for each of them but double . . ."

"True . . . true . . ." sighed the embarrassed husband, "but suppose (of course we all hope it will never be your case) a father has two sons at the front and he loses one of them, there is still one left to console him . . . while . . ."

"Yes," answered the other, getting cross, "a son left to console him but also a son left for whom he must survive, while in the case of the father of an only son, if the son dies the father can die too and put an end to his distress. Which of the two positions is the worse? Don't you see how my case would be worse than yours?"

"Nonsense," interrupted another traveler, a fat, red-faced man with bloodshot eyes of the palest gray.

He was panting. From his bulging eyes seemed to spurt inner violence of an uncontrolled vitality which his weakened body could hardly contain.

"Nonsense," he repeated, trying to cover his mouth with his hand so as to hide the two missing front teeth. "Nonsense. Do we give life to our children for our own benefit?"

The other travelers stared at him in distress. The one who had had his son at the front since the first day of the war sighed: "You are right. Our children do not belong to us, they belong to the Country. . . ."

"Bosh," retorted the fat traveler. "Do we think of the Country when we give life to our children? Our sons are born because . . . well, because they must be born and when they come to life they take our own life with them. This is the truth. We belong to them but they never belong to us. And when they reach twenty they are exactly what we were at their age. We too had a father and mother, but there were so many other things as well . . . girls, cigarettes, illusions, new ties . . . and the Country, of course, whose call we would have answered—when we were twenty—even if father and mother had said no. Now, at our age, the love of our Country is still great, of course, but stronger than it is the love for our children. Is there any one of us here who wouldn't gladly take his son's place at the front if he could?"

There was a silence all round, everybody nodding as to approve.

"Why then," continued the fat man, "shouldn't we consider the feelings of our children when they are twenty? Isn't it natural that at their age they should consider the love for their Country (I am speaking of decent boys, of course) even greater than the love for us? Isn't it natural that it should be so, as after all they must look upon us as upon old boys who cannot move any more and must stay at home? If Country exists, if Country is a natural necessity like bread, of which each of us must eat in order not to die of hunger, somebody must go to defend it. And our sons go, when they are twenty, and they don't want tears, because if they die, they died inflamed and happy (I am speaking, of course, of decent boys). Now, if one dies young and happy, without having the ugly sides of life, the boredom of it, the pettiness, the bitterness of disillusion . . . what more can we ask for him? Everyone should stop crying: everyone should laugh, as I do . . . or at least thank God—as I do—because my son, before dying, sent me a message saying that he was dying satisfied at having ended his life in the best way he could have wished. That is why, as you see, I do not even wear mourning. . . ."

He shook his light fawn coat so as to show it; his livid lip over his missing teeth was trembling, his eyes were watery and motionless, and soon after he ended with a shrill laugh which might well have been a sob.

"Quite so . . . quite so . . ." agreed the others.

The woman who, bundled in a corner under her coat, had been sitting and listening had—for the last three months—tried to find in the words of her husband and her friends something to console her in her deep sorrow, something that might show her how a mother should resign herself to send her son not even to death but to a probably dangerous life. Yet not a word had she found amongst the many which had been said . . . and her grief had been greater in seeing that nobody—as she thought—could share her feelings.

But now the words of the traveler amazed and almost stunned her. She suddenly realized that it wasn't the others who were wrong and who could not understand her but herself who could not rise up to the same height of those fathers and mothers willing to resign themselves, without crying, not only to the departure of their sons but even to their death.

She lifted her head, she bent over from the corner trying to listen with great attention to the details which the fat man was giving to his companions about the way his son had fallen as a hero, for his King and his Country, happy and without regrets. It seemed to her that she had stumbled into a world she had never dreamt of, a world so far unknown to her and she was so pleased to hear everyone joining in congratulating that brave father who could so stoically speak of his child's death.

Then suddenly, just as if she had heard nothing of what had been said and almost as if waking up from a dream, she turned to the old man, asking him:

"Then . . . is your son really dead?"

Everybody stared at her. The old man, too, turned to look at her, fixing his great, bulging, horribly watery light gray eyes, deep in her face. For some little time he tried to answer, but words failed him. He looked and looked at her, almost as if only then—at that silly, incongruous question—he had suddenly realized at last that his son was really dead . . . gone forever . . . forever. His face contracted, became horribly distorted, then he snatched in haste a handkerchief from his pocket and, to the amazement of everyone, broke into harrowing, heart-rending, uncontrollable sobs.

For Discussion

1. Why did none of the passengers sympathize with the grieving mother? Do you think any of their arguments were valid? Why or why not?

2. Why did the first passenger who spoke thank God for what had happened? Do you agree or disagree with his reasons? Why?

3. What important change occurred in the way the mother saw other people? How do you explain the fact that the implied criticism of the fat man had a more positive effect on her than the consolation of her husband and friends?

4. What did the final sentence of the story reveal about the author's attitude toward people? Would you say it was essentially cynical or sympathetic? Explain.

5. In Pirandello's *novella* "The Deathwatch," one victim says: "I'm not suffering on my own account, or on your account. I'm suffering because life is what it is." Does "War" offer any echoes of this philosophy?

6. Discuss the way in which some of the effects of evil and suffering should be interpreted and understood by the Christian. Has the Incarnation and Redemption made a difference in the way people can react to evil and suffering? If so, how?

7. How do you explain the fact that Pirandello did not give names to any of his characters? What details contributed to the characterization of the mother, the husband, and the fat man?

8. This story was written from the omniscient point of view; that is, the author assumed the role of an all-seeing, all-knowing observer, who stood outside the situation and was able to describe and comment on what occurred, as well as reveal the characters' innermost thoughts. Why do you think Pirandello chose only to describe the inner thoughts of the mother? How would this story have differed in tone if it had been told by the husband from the first-person point of view?

For Composition

1. Write a paragraph developing the topic sentence "Paternal love is not like bread that can be broken into pieces and split amongst the children in equal shares."

2. In several well-developed paragraphs, state your views on the subject of war and the individual citizen. Support all generalizations with specific details and examples from experiences that you know people have had.

3. Write a composition in which you express your opinion of the fat man's idea of filial relationships: "We belong to them but they never belong to us." Give specific examples from this story, other stories, or from life, to support your viewpoint.

Sigrid Undset

The Loss and the Healing

Sigrid Undset (1882–1949) is known chiefly for her historical novels. In 1928, she was awarded the Nobel Prize for her trilogy, *Kristin Lavransdatter*, one of the outstanding works of Norwegian and world literature. In 1924, two years after the publication of the last volume of her trilogy, she was received into the Catholic Church, following a long period of struggle with the uncertainties of agnosticism. Almost all her novels after her conversion reflect her firm belief that, though through original sin man brought all his troubles upon himself, there is a God who will give him all the grace he needs to overcome these troubles. She was forced to flee her country when the Nazis invaded it and came to live in the United States, but returned to Norway in 1945.

The selection that follows is from Sigrid Undset's fictionalized autobiography, *The Longest Years*. Here, with a loving care for detail, she relates what happened during the summer and winter when the heroine, Ingvild, was eleven years old.

*M*AMMA came and told them one day that she had taken a house at Hvitsten for the rest of the summer vacation. Frida, her friend, had made them a present of the money for a stay in the country.

At the moment Ingvild was more shocked and ashamed than anything else. Accepting money from strangers was to her a thing unheard of. Her mother must have seen it, for she said curtly: "Your father needs a change of air." So Ingvild shook off her feeling of repugnance as well as she could. Naturally she would like awfully to go into the country. Though she was concerned about her garden— how would it get on with no one to water it—?

Once more she enjoyed a time which was outside all other time. Looking back on it she thought of forest paths over which the smooth-worn roots of firs stretched their claws, and the pits between the roots were thick with old pine needles. She remembered crevices running diagonally through rounded light-red rocks, in which grew

9

scanty sun-scorched grass and flowers with silvery grey-green leaves reminding one of the sea. The paths ended in a scrap of shelly beach, and there they undressed and ran naked over the bare rocks, which burnt the soles of their feet. It was horrid to get entangled in the seaweed which lay heaving, however calm the fjord might be— but the spot was so secluded that they could bathe without wearing dresses. And that was so lovely, as you didn't even notice you were swimming—you could move about in the water just as naturally and unthinkingly as you could walk on dry land. They were in and out, sitting on the rocks and in again, all the morning.

The country looked so fine as one lay floating on one's back and looking towards the shore. The wooded hills seemed to suck in the sunlight with every crest of fir and spruce. The little houses, pearl-grey and white and red, looked so sweet and homelike from here, they tucked themselves away in the clefts round the curve of the bay, and the old foliage trees and orchards of dark-green cherry that people had planted about their homes contrasted strongly with the pine woods at the foot of the hills surrounding the little seaside place.

Their nearest neighbour, the Customs boatman, had many children, and they were cheerful and amusing, and there was one little girl of about Ingvild's age, so she could always find some fun all day long.

What the house they lived in looked like inside, Ingvild had not the slightest recollection—it seemed as if she had scarcely been indoors the whole summer, except to sleep. There was a veranda where her father sat—they took most of their meals there. Then she and Marit sat on a couch covered with faded chintz; there was so little room that they kept pushing each other, and mamma told them to be quiet: "It annoys papa to hear you constantly quarreling." He scarcely saw them except at mealtimes.

Her mother used to send Ingvild to get things at the shop by the steamer pier. Every step of the way was amusing. It was only a track that had been worn over the rocks and through little hollows among them—the houses were scattered irregularly up and down on both sides of the path. Farther down towards the pier were some larger houses, painted white with verandas in the Swiss style, standing in big orchards. They were inhabited by shipowners and people like that.

There was also a bathing place by the pier, used by the summer visitors who lodged in the cottages round about with the fishermen and sailors' wives. Ingvild hardly saw them except in the shop and on the pier when they were waiting for the steamer. It was amusing to go down to the pier and watch the boats come and go. Her mother scolded her for making them anxious by staying away so long. But Ingvild was incorrigible in that way.

In the afternoon she went to fetch the letters. The post office was a little wooden house that stood high above the little place on a bare crag. In the evening sun people sat or lay on the rock outside, all those who had come to fetch their mail, while the postmaster was busy in his office sorting the contents of the bag that had come by the boat.

There was one girl that Ingvild couldn't keep her eyes off, she was so pretty. She wore one of those bright red felt hats that people used to call "ruffian hats," soft and untrimmed, with the brim turned straight up over the forehead. Underneath it the girl's curly mass of hair shone like bright gold in the sunlight. She had the kind of face that is boldly prominent, especially in profile, with large nose and mouth; and her complexion was peculiar, a dry white with pink roses on the high cheekbones. . . . She was always the center of a crowd of girls.

One evening Ingvild heard her say to the others in general—her voice too was uncommon, there was such a ring in it although it was a little hoarse, the hoarseness having the effect of a sort of dew upon the metallic sound of the voice:

"I know *that* very well—but I don't care. I don't give a hoot for what people say about *me!* When I know I'm going the same way as the others—"

Her friends murmured remonstrances, but in hushed and frightened tones.

"Don't I know that I shall die in my turn?" Her voice was arrogant, clear, with the strange dewy veil over it. "And I'm not afraid, I can assure you. When it's no use—"

There was a queer stillness around her. The people sitting on the rocks seemed to shrink and bowed their heads—some of them sighed and spoke to each other in shocked and horrified whispers. The girl stood enveloped by the fitful rays of the evening sun, so that her mass of hair under the fiery hat and the lines of her profile and bosom glimmered in the strong light.

Her father owned one of the finest houses right down on the

shore and he had a cutter. She was the last survivor of several brothers and sisters; the others had died of consumption. Ingvild never forgot her, as she stood that evening in the glory of the sunshine, saying she knew she was going to die.—What was her fate she never heard.

School had begun in town and most of the summer visitors had left. But Anine decided that they were to stay a few weeks longer—papa liked looking at the sea. The children rejoiced over every day they thus saw pinched from their school term. And there were masses of berries in the woods, and apples and pears cost next to nothing now that the visitors had gone, so mamma could buy all they were able to eat.

The lady from whom they rented the villa had a name for being difficult to deal with; she was lively and amusing, but had a pretty sharp tongue. Anine and she appeared to get on well. She lived in a little cottage which stood by itself in a corner of her piece of ground; it was really a studio. The young grown-up son she had living with her was good-natured. He got hold of a boat and took them for long rows inshore—to out-of-the-way coves where you found a solitary house standing back and where tall pointed junipers like the cypresses in pictures grew in lean meadows just beyond the light sand of the beach. Ingvild thought it must be lovely to live in a place like this—she had never before seen anything that looked so solitary. She had never before tried to imagine what it would be like to live in a lonely place, but she was sure she would like it, if it was on the fjord. Then she would have a boat, and she would bathe again in the evening, after the sun had gone down. Mamma generally went to bathe after papa had gone to bed; it must be particularly lovely on these autumn evenings when there was a moon. But Ingvild was not allowed to bathe after sunset.

She hadn't the slightest desire to go back to school and town and Observatory Street. But at last they had to go all the same.

Then the same old routine began again—everything! The ground under the trees in the Park was getting so light as she went to school in the morning, she waded through drifts of fallen leaves. Smooth brown horse-chestnuts lay gleaming among the leaves—Ingvild picked them up and thought of all the different things she would make of them, but when they had been lying for a day or two they lost their juicy gloss and their shells got dry and dull and shrivelled. And she was always getting bad marks at school for coming too late.

Then the mornings grew dark; black clouds and floods of cold rain. Then came the fjord fog. Then came snow, and turned to mud and slush. Ingvild thought of papa again.

Mamma sat at her sewing machine in the dining-room; there were so many things they all had to have for the winter. Papa sat in his little bedroom, so that he might be spared the hum of the sewing machine, and it wasn't very comfortable either when the table was littered with sewing. Ingvild was in his room, reading aloud. They had taken up the Icelandic sagas, but it was a Danish translation, and Danish was so ill suited to them. But she was not equal to reading them in Old Norse. Only now and then her father asked her to look up a section, a piece of dialogue or something of the sort that she had read in translation—he wanted to hear how it sounded in reality. The Old Norse editions were mostly old books printed on rough paper with uncut edges—they were lovely to turn over and the type was clear and handsome. All the saga editions were on the lowest shelves of the bookcase, so Ingvild lay face down on the carpet when she was reading sagas to papa, then she had only to reach out an arm to find the volumes he wanted.—Now and again mamma appeared in the doorway: "Can you come in for a moment, I want to try on—." Ingvild was to have a school dress of an entirely new material; mamma had bought a remnant at a sale, but Ingvild didn't like the brown color.—She went back to papa and continued her reading about the Vatsdal people, but got confused over their mutual relationships. It was rather a long way between the interesting bits in that saga.

She longed impatiently—there was Christmas to look forward to and the Christmas holidays, and then it would not be long till the Fair; she looked forward to going to that. And to the days growing longer so that she wouldn't have to get up by lamplight and find the lamps burning when she reached school. Spring and the summer holidays she looked forward to in such a way that it positively hurt her to think of them. She never imagined any change—springs and summers, when she was always out of doors and thought of nothing but her own affairs, would alternate with autumns and winters, when she kept her father company and let her mind be fed by him—.

It never occurred to her that the end might come at any time. Perhaps the grownups did not know either that it was so near.

During some dull, dark days at the end of November he was so ill that he had to stay in bed all day. The doctor, his life-long friend, came to see him morning and evening. Five or six days went by, and then it looked as if he was regaining a little strength.

It was Saturday afternoon. Mamma had to do some shopping. "Ingvild, can you sit with papa while I am out—?"

Ingvild lay down on the floor by the bookcase: "Shall I go on reading to you, papa?" He turned his head slightly on the pillow as he lay in the darkness: "Thanks, will you—"

They were doing Haavard Isfjording's saga. Olav Haavardssön, whose blood was as warm as a bear's and who was so strong and brave but handsome and kind—she imagined him as *her* Olav. It gave her a sharp pang when he was killed, but all that about how he was mourned was so beautiful, and she who was in love with him went away and no one ever heard what had become of her. When she came to the place where Olav's mother goes round to her brothers to bespeak the help of her nephews in avenging him, Ingvild looked at her father. She expected him to say that she was to read these passages again in Old Norse. But he said nothing. He must be very tired, she thought. She searched in the shelf—at any rate she would see for herself what the real words were. But she could not find any edition of Haavard Isfjording's saga in Icelandic.

Next day her mother sat with him all day long. In the course of the afternoon they had a visit from a maid who had been in their service. Which of them it was Ingvild did not remember afterwards. All she remembered was having a strange oppressive feeling that the visitor must not notice she had called inopportunely—she worked as hard as she could to keep a conversation going. Laboriously they dragged the words out of one another.—

When her mother came to the door, she saw it in her face before she had uttered a word. The visitor slipped away—and to Ingvild this was like a sign that now her old familiar life had slipped away from them. Her mother, as she had known her, was also gone—she was now another, quenched in tears. She took the children with her into the little room that they might see, their father lay in his bed and was dead.

Her memories of the time that followed were like images seen in the scattered fragments of a broken mirror.

The coffin stood in the drawing room for several days, and they passed in and out every day. The yellowish waxen image of a man lying in those snow-white surroundings was so beautiful, but so strange that she only knew it to be papa—she could not feel it. All that had been between her and her father—she had shared with another than this.—But that he had such long eyelashes she had never noticed before. And it dawned on her that a man of forty is not an old man.

She was more oppressed than afraid or saddened by the strangeness and incomprehensibility of it all. When she touched the dead he was cold in a different way from all other cold things. Ever after she knew what nonsense it is when people speak of the dead being cold as a stone or ice or anything else. The coldness of death is like no other coldness. Nearest to it was the coldness of the thick white flowers—hyacinths and lilies of the valley—which lay strewed over the body. For a long time after she could not bear the smell of hyacinths; she traced the other smell, as of rancid wax, beneath the scent of the flowers.

Her mother too would be changed in the future, she knew that already.—Each time she had to make an effort, having so many practical details to attend to after the death and in preparation for the funeral, Ingvild felt that when once she had composed herself again after this shattering time she would in many ways be unlike mamma as the children remembered her. She would take up her life again; in a sense perhaps one might say she would be more herself.—The only person to whom she had voluntarily and intentionally adapted herself was gone.

And she never forgot that in the midst of all the rest she had been delighted with her new mourning dress. It was of fine light woollen material, quite in the fashion, with a yoke and trimmed with many rows of black mohair braid. The doctor's wife had asked to be allowed to see to this and had presented all three little girls with these fine mourning frocks.

The interior of the mortuary chapel was so dismal that it gave her a new sense of the horrors of death and burial. There was such a crowd of strangers at the funeral that she could not cry—all the black top-hats and veils made her feel it would be unbearable if she were to cry in the sight of strangers. If she had even had a veil which she could pull down, as mamma did. So she sat looking at the great mountain of pale wintry flowers and stiff green palm-branches. Long, broad silk streamers with words printed on them hung from it. Most of them were glaring white, but it was a relief to look at those that were colored. Some were in the Norwegian and some in the Swedish and Danish colors, but there were other colors the meaning of which she did not know. Under this pile the coffin was hidden, and in the coffin lay her father, but she was unable to conceive it.

As they took their places behind the coffin when it was carried out of the chapel, she saw Herr Wilster. It was he who had played the organ, she knew. And now she began to cry after all, and it seemed not to matter because he was here.

The clergyman came to call on them. His name was Andreas Hansen. She thought him very kind; there was something about him which made it feel good to have him sitting in the room for an hour or so. Mamma thought the same. But Ingvild couldn't remember anything of what he said—the good was in himself.

They went to the cemetery every day during this first time. It snowed and the snow thawed again, the paths were muddy and the black trees hung with drops. The flowers on the grave were withered, nasty, and drenched with rain, the ribbons were limp and sodden. The grinning mound of yellow clay showed through more and more.

They went up there with a wreath which had arrived the day after the funeral. It was from Marit's godfather, papa's best friend in Denmark. It was of laurel leaves without a single flower; that was fine. On the broad red and white ribbon were some runes and underneath in Danish: "Few better will come after."

Ingvild knew very well where that came from—it was the conclusion of the inscription on the Tryggevaelde stone, and it was a wife who had raised it to her husband. And suddenly she seemed to see it all—men dying and dying, they had gone on dying through all the thousand of years, and among all those forgotten dead there had always been some whose loss their nearest and dearest thought irreparable and of whom they said: "Few better will come after." And then they went on living.

The whole of that winter was one long breaking-up.

Ingvild was aware that mamma did not know what they were going to live on. She would have to find some work. But it wasn't easy to say what that was to be. Even Ingvild guessed that, although her mother possessed a fund of varied knowledge and worked like a horse, for many reasons it would probably not be easy for her to find work among strangers.

In the first place they would have to look out for a small and cheap apartment and part with a great many of their things. The dining-room furniture was sold, a lot of the things from the drawing room were sold to museums and antique dealers. Other things their mother gave away to relations and friends.

Two young men who had been papa's pupils came day after day and catalogued his library, packing the books in boxes. That made the house look emptier than anything else, for there were bookcases along the walls, and when they stood there gaping and grinning with nothing on their shelves they were a dismal kind of furniture. One day the boxes of books were gone. A second-hand bookseller in Copenhagen had bought the whole lot.

One day mamma came and told Ingvild that she had been to see Fru Ragna Nielsen. Well, the fact was she couldn't afford to pay their school fees any longer, so she had given notice to withdraw the children and was going to send them to the Government school. But to that Fru Nielsen had replied that Seming's children should have education at her school gratis, all three of them, until they passed their matriculation. Seming had brought honor to the name of Norway in foreign countries; she was sure that his daughters would not disgrace their father's name.

Ingvild listened, red as fire. In other words, they were to be deadheads at the school.—Her mother guessed what was in her mind: "You understand, Ingvild, don't you—what Fru Nielsen did not say and never will say is that she expects you three to do honor to the school for your part. You know that in a way her position is a militant one, it is the new, radical principles that she champions, in some measure. And when your father and I sent you there it was because on the whole we believed in her principles and not in the ordinary old-fashioned girls' schools.—And you know that she has ambitions about her pupils. So from now on you will have to be *very industrious* at school. And you can very easily be that, if only you will take some trouble with those subjects which cost you a little effort. And which bore you."

There was nothing she could say to that. But she was not happy about it. True, she would rather go to Ragna Nielsen's school than to any other she had heard of. But even at Ragna Nielsen's school she wanted to have the right of being in opposition, and it was a heavy blow to be obliged in future to work hard at all those things that didn't amuse her.

There was nothing to be done about that. But even at that date she knew in her heart that she would never matriculate. She was now in the third middle. In the sixth middle they took their school diploma. And beyond that she would not go.

In any case there was no chance of taking up any study for which she had an inclination. Most girls who matriculated were destined to become teachers. In the Seventeenth of May procession there were always so many teachers in students' caps that it made you shudder to see them. And she would try to be independent as quickly as possible. Now that papa was dead there was no one on whom she cared to be dependent. Not even on mamma, any more than she could help —she saw this in a flash—.

This time it was no distance from the school to their new home. She was able to give mamma a good deal of help. The two younger ones were sent away to some friends.

She liked their new street the moment she saw it—yes, here she would feel at home! The house they were to live in was one of four big houses standing in a row—on the opposite side of the street there was only an old villa in a little garden, tucked away behind "Blaasen"—she would have Blaasen just outside the front door and it was only a few minutes' run to Lydersagen. She could sit at the drawing room window looking on to the little mountain with its bushes and rocks and patches of grass. And from the kitchen and dining-room she looked out over the fields she did not know—they had not yet been built over. The Bislet brook ran in a little valley and beyond it were the Idiot hills and far away the old villa gardens towards St. Hans' Hill. And it was April—and she had the whole of West Aker to roam over. This year she and Klara would be able to go to Frognersaeter as they had talked of doing last year.

The four apartment houses were not "fine" houses, she saw that at once; they were narrow and gray, without any ornaments or flourishes, the entrances were cramped and untidy. But after that horrible Observatory Street quarter where everything seemed designed to keep up a pretence of what wasn't there, gentility and prosperity on the outside, despondency and scandal behind, these houses had quite a comfortable look. There was a refreshing frankness about their poverty. Here one was free—.

The bedroom was overcrowded with two grown-up beds side by side—she was now to sleep in one of them—and two child's beds. But the window looked on to the street. The drawing room was small, but could be made charming, she could see that already. And they would have a fire in the stove here every day all through the winter, as the rooms were so arranged that all the others could be warmed from this one. The dining room was long and narrow; there was only just room for the old kitchen table in the middle, with four of the small drawing-room chairs round it. Papa's desk could just stand along one wall by the window, and at the other end of the room mamma had put one of the old bookcases, but now the shelves would be filled with things from the sideboard. It looked pretty and cheerful.

From a portfolio that Ingvild dropped on the floor a number of little watercolors fell out—some of those her mother had done when she went to the school of art. Ingvild found a box of drawing-pins and stuck them up on the narrow wall by the door in the dining room. "Mamma—come and look!" Her mother came, shook her head, and laughed: "But, child, they're not the kind of thing to put on the walls—they're not much good." But she let them stay there, and she was not displeased.

Next morning she woke quite early, and outside she saw Blaasen with the morning sun on it, so that it shone with the pale yellow of last year's grass and the bare briers glistened. Above its top the sky was clear and blue and springlike. The sight made her so happy that it gave her heart a pang.

She had not felt so cheerful for ever so long—. And that was just what made her think of papa's death—and there was no one she had been so fond of as of him, and as she thought back over it there came such a smarting wish that she had been much kinder to him and much more faithful in keeping him company while she had him. But now it was too late, and she knew with a strange and bitter certainty that it could not have been otherwise—that there is a borderline which no one can remove between the life of those who are to die and of those who are to live. It seemed to her that she already knew so much that was evil in the world and so much that was boundlessly good that it was all beyond her—there was so much to shudder at and so much to rejoice in that for a moment she almost felt weary in advance.—The little mountain outside shining in the sun, the home that had drawn closer and was beginning to heal after its loss, the freedom which awaited her out in the fields—she was so happy in it all that she could hardly bear such happiness—.

For Discussion

1. Why did Ingvild feel that this summer vacation was a time which she enjoyed "outside all other time"? From the things that interested Ingvild, what kind of person would you say she was?

2. Why do you think the girl with the bright red hat was someone Ingvild never forgot? How was the incident a preparation for later events in the narrative? Why did the author describe the sunlight so carefully in this scene? What dramatic effect was achieved?

3. In what ways was Ingvild's life in town different from her life at the seashore? What adjectives would you choose to describe each of these periods of her life?

4. Why was that winter "one long breaking-up"? What reasons do you have for believing that a new maturity was developing in Ingvild at this time in her life? Point out specific sentences to support your answer.

5. From this selection, would you say that Sigrid Undset was justified in having Ingvild think that "she already knew so much that was evil in the world and so much that was boundlessly good that it was all beyond her"? Explain. Point out where the author showed that life is a constant intermingling of good and evil, pleasure and pain, freedom and order. Give instances of this from your own experience.

6. Discuss the meaning of the title of this selection. Would you say this piece was essentially tragic in its mood? Why or why not?

7. The chief characters in a story are "brought to life" in several ways; namely, by what they say and think, by what they do, by the way they react to situations, by what other characters say and think about them, and by the comments which the author makes about them. Which methods did the author use in bringing Ingvild to life? Give specific examples from the selection to support your answers.

8. In many of Sigrid Undset's novels, mountains are used both descriptively and symbolically. In *The Burning Bush*, one character says, "Toward the mountains we Norwegians all have a religious feeling." How is this attitude toward the mountains revealed in this selection? What is the symbolic meaning of the mountains? Point out and explain other symbols used by the author.

9. In your opinion, was Sigrid Undset's style in this selection essentially severe or lyrical? Was it restrained or highly dramatic? Refer to the author's treatment of specific passages to support your answer.

10. This story, like "War," was told from the omniscient point of view. Sigrid Undset, however, was more interested in revealing in detail the mind of her main character and the effect of events on her. Everything was told as Ingvild saw it and felt it. It is as if she herself

were telling the story, except that it is in the third person, rather than the first person. Does this limited omniscient point of view make the story more personal or less personal? Why? Would you have wanted the author to reveal the thoughts of Ingvild's mother or father? Why or why not?

For Composition

1. From what you have learned about Ingvild in this narrative, write a character sketch of her. Include her interest in things, her relationship with her family, her ideas about freedom, and her growing perception as the result of events.
2. Write a short theme based on Ingvild's observation on page 16 "Few better will come after."
3. Like Ingvild, many people have childhood memories of vacation spots spent in the country or at the seashore. Write a description that recreates such a spot you remember from your childhood. Include specific details and exact descriptions that will communicate to the reader the mood and attitudes that you associate with this summer place.

Maxim Gorky

The Green Kitten

Maxim Gorky (1868–1936) was the pseudonym of Aleksei Maksimovich Peshkov, the only major writer of pre-Revolution Russia who survived the revolution and continued to work after the Soviet system was established. A novelist, short-story writer, and playwright, he devoted himself to describing with understanding and tolerance the introspective, melancholy, and basically religious temperament of the Slavic people. Like the great Russian novelists of the nineteenth century, he sympathized with his characters, no matter how degraded they might be, and implied that they could be loved for their humanity. His chief theme was the abiding kinship among all people—that all belong to the same family. Like many Russian writers, Gorky did not spend much time working out a complicated plot. He emphasized characterization, dialogue, and mood, to reveal his bittersweet observations about human beings. (It is interesting to note that the pseudonym "Maxim Gorky" means "bitter maxim.")

"The Green Kitten" is a dramatic story about a group of prisoners caught in the dreary and monotonous routine of prison life. Their way of meeting this life has implications which indicate that most people might meet such a life in the same way.

THE round window of my chamber looked out upon the prison yard. It was very high from the ground, but by placing the table against the wall and mounting upon it, I could see everything that was going on in the court-yard. Beneath the window, under the slope of the roof, the doves had built themselves a nest, and when I set about looking out of my window down into the court below, they began cooing above my head.

I had lots of time to make the acquaintance of the inhabitants of the prison yard from my coign [1] of vantage, and I knew already that the merriest member of that grim and grey population went by the name of Zazubrina.

---

[1] **coign:** projecting corner

He was a square-set, stout little fellow, with a ruddy face and a high forehead, from beneath which his large bright, lively eyes sparkled incessantly.

His cap he wore at the back of his head, his ears stuck out on both sides of his shaven head as if in joke; he never fastened the strings of his shirt collar, he never buttoned his vest, and every movement of his muscles gave you to understand that he was a merry soul and a pronounced enemy of anger and sadness.

Always laughing, alert and noisy, he was the idol of the yard; he was always surrounded by a group of grey comrades, and he would always be laughing and regaling them with all sorts of curious pranks, brightening up their dull and sorrowful life with his hearty, genuine gaiety. . . .

On one occasion he appeared at the door of the prison quarters, ready to go for a walk with three rats whom he had dexterously harnessed as if they were horses. Sometimes his inventiveness took a cruel form. Thus, for instance, he once, somehow, glued to the wall the long hair of one of the prisoners, a mere lad, who was sitting on the floor asleep against the wall, and, when his hair had dried, suddenly awoke him. The lad quickly leaped to his feet, and clapping his slim lean hands to the back of his head, fell weeping to the ground. The prisoners laughed, and Zazubrina was satisfied. Afterwards—I saw it through the window—he fell a comforting the lad, who had left no inconsiderable tuft of hair on the wall.

Besides Zazubrina, there was yet another favorite in the prison—a plump, reddish kitten, a tiny playful little animal, pampered by everyone. Whenever they went out for a walk, the prisoners used to hunt him up and take him with them a good part of the way, passing him on from hand to hand. They would run after him, too, in the yard, and let him cling on to their hands and feet with his claws, delighting in the sportive tricks of their pet.

Whenever the kitten appeared on the scene, he diverted the general attention from Zazubrina, and the latter was by no means pleased with this preference. Zazubrina was at heart an artist, and as an artist had an inordinately good opinion of his own talents. When his public was drawn away from him by the kitten, he remained alone and sat him down in some hole or corner in the courtyard, and from thence would watch the comrades who had forgotten him just then. And I, from my window, would observe him, and felt everything with which his soul was full at such moments. It appeared to me that Zazubrina must infallibly kill the kitten at the first opportunity, and I was sorry for the merry prisoner who was thus always longing to be the center of general attention. Of all the tendencies of man, this is the most injurious, for nothing kills the soul so quickly as this longing to please people.

When you have to sit in a prison—even the life of the fungi on its walls seems interesting. You will understand therefore the interest with which I observed from my window the little tragedy going on below there, this jealousy of a kitten on the part of a man—you will understand, too, the patience with which I awaited the *dénouement*. The *dénouement* was, indeed, approaching. It happened in this wise.

On a bright, sunny day, when the prisoners were pouring out of doors into the courtyard, Zazubrina observed in a corner of the yard a pail of green paint, left behind by the painters who were painting the roof of the prison. He approached it, pondered over it, and, dipping a finger into the paint, adorned himself with a pair of green whiskers. These green whiskers on his red face drew forth a burst of laughter. A certain hobbledehoy present, wishing to appropriate Zazubrina's idea, began forthwith to paint his upper lip; but Zazubrina spoiled his fun for him by dipping his hand in the pail and adroitly besprinkling his whole physiognomy. The hobbledehoy spluttered and shook his head, Zazubrina danced around him, and the public kept on laughing, and egged on its jester with cries of encouragement.

At that very moment the red kitten suddenly appeared in the yard. Leisurely he entered the courtyard, gracefully lifting his paws, trotting along with tail erect, and evidently without the slightest fear of coming to grief beneath the feet of the crowd frantically careering round Zazubrina and the bespattered hobbledehoy, who was violently rubbing away with the palm of his hand the mass of oil and verdigris which covered his face.

"My brothers!" someone suddenly exclaimed, "pussy is coming."

"Pussy! Ah, the little rogue!"

"What ho, ginger! Puss, puss, puss!"

They caught up the cat and he was passed from hand to hand; everybody caressed him.

"Look, there's no starving there! What a fat little tummy!"

"What a big cat he's growing!"

"And what claws he has got, the little devil!"

"Let him go! Let him play as he likes!"

"Well, I'll give him a back! Play away, puss!"

Zazubrina was deserted. He stood alone, wiping the green paint off his whiskers with his fingers, and watched the kitten leaping on to the backs and shoulders of the prisoners. Whenever he displayed a wish to sit still on any particular shoulder or back, the men would wriggle about and shake him off, and then he would set off leaping and bounding again from one shoulder to the next. This diverted them all exceedingly, and the laughter was incessant.

"Come, my friends! let us paint the cat!" resounded the voice of Zazubrina. It sounded just as if Zazubrina, in proposing this pastime, at the same time begged them to consent to it.

There was a commotion among the crowd of prisoners.

"But it will be the death of him," cried one.

"Paint the poor beast—what a thing to say!"

"What! paint a live animal, Zazubrina! You deserve a hiding!"

"I call it a devilish good joke," cried a little, broad-shouldered man with a fiery-red beard, enthusiastically.

Zazubrina already held the kitten in his hands, and went with it towards the pail of paint, and then Zazubrina began singing:

> "Look, my brothers! look at that!
> See me paint the ginger cat!
> Paint him well, and paint him green,
> And then we'll dance upon the scene."

There was a burst of laughter, and holding their sides, the prisoners made a way in their midst, and I saw quite plainly how Zazubrina, seizing the kitten by the tail, flung it into the pail, and then fell a singing and dancing:

> "Stop that mewing! cease to squall!
> Would you your godfather maul?"

Peals of laughter!

"Oh, crooked-bellied Judas!" piped one squeaky voice.

"Alas, Batyushka!" [2] groaned another.

They were stifled, suffocated with laughter. Laughter twisted the bodies of these people, bent them double, vibrated and gurgled in

[2] **Batyushka**: little father

the air—a mighty, devil-may-care laughter, growing louder continually, and reaching the very confines of hysteria. Smiling faces, in white kerchiefs, looked down from the windows of the women's quarters into the yard. The Inspector, squeezing his back to the wall, poked out his brawny body, and, holding it with both hands, discharged his thick, bass, overpowering laugh in regular salvoes.

The joke scattered the folks in all directions around the pail. Performing astounding antics with his legs, Zazubrina danced with all his might, singing by way of accompaniment:

> "Ah, life is a merry thing,
> As the grey cat knew, I ween;
> And her son, the ginger kitten,
> Now lives in a world all green."

"Yes, that it will, deuce take you," cried the man with the fiery-red beard.

But Zazubrina could not contain himself. Around him roared the senseless laughter of all these grey people, and Zazubrina knew that he, and he alone, was the occasion of all their laughter. In all his gestures, in every grimace of his mobile comic face, this consciousness manifestly proclaimed itself, and his whole body twitched with the enjoyment of his triumph. He had already seized the kitten by the head, and wiping from its fur the superfluous paint, with the ecstasy of the artist conscious of his victory over the mob, never ceased dancing and improvising:

> "My dear little brothers,
> In the calendar let us look,
> Here's a kitten to be christened,
> And no name for it in the book."

Everything laughed around the mob of prisoners, intoxicated by this senseless mirth. The sun laughed upon the panes of glass in the iron-grated windows. The blue sky smiled down upon the courtyard of the prison, and even its dirty old walls seemed to be smiling with the smile of beings who feel obliged to stifle all mirth, however it may run riot within them. From behind the gratings of the windows of the women's department the faces of women looked down upon the yard, they also laughed, and their teeth glistened in the sun. Everything around was transformed, as it were, threw off its dull, grey tone, so full of anguish and weariness, and awoke to merriment, impregnated with that purifying laughter which, like the sun, made the very dirt look more decent.

Placing the green kitten on the grass, little islets of which, springing up between the stones, variegated the prison-yard, Zazubrina, excited, well-nigh blown, and covered with sweat, still continued his wild dance.

But the laughter had already died away. He was overdoing it, very much overdoing it. The people were getting tired of him. Someone, here and there, still shrieked hysterically; a few continued to laugh, but already there were pauses. At last there were moments when the silence was general, save for the singing, dancing Zazubrina, and the kitten which mewed softly and piteously as it lay on the grass. It was scarcely distinguishable from the grass in color, and, no doubt, because the paint had blinded it and hampered its movements, the poor slippery, big-headed creature senselessly tottered on his trembling paws, standing still as if glued to the grass, and all the while it kept on mewing, Zazubrina commented on the movements of the kitten as follows:

> "Look ye, Christian people, look,
> The green cat seeks a private nook,
> The wholesome ginger-colored puss
> To find a place in vain makes fuss."

"Very clever, no doubt, you hound," said a red-haired lad.

The public regarded its artist with satiated eyes.

"How it mews!" observed the hobbledehoy prisoner, twisting his head in the direction of the kitten, and he looked at his comrades. They regarded the kitten in silence.

"Do you think he'll be green all his life long?" asked the lad.

"All his life long, indeed!—how long do you think he will live, then?" began a tall, grey-bearded prisoner, squatting down beside poor puss; "don't you see he's dying in the sun, his fur is all sticking to him like glue; he'll turn up his toes soon . . ."

The kitten mewed spasmodically, producing a reaction in the sentiments of the prisoners.

"Turn up his toes, eh?" said the hobbledehoy, "suppose we try to wash it off him?"

Nobody answered him. The little green lump writhed at the feet of the rough fellows, a pitiable object of utter helplessness.

"Pooh! I'm all of a muck sweat!" screamed Zazubrina, flinging himself on the ground. Nobody took the slightest notice of him.

The hobbledehoy bent over the kitten and took it up in his arms, but immediately put it on the ground again. "It's all burning hot," he explained.

Then he regarded his comrades, and sorrowfully said:

"Poor puss, look at him! We shall not have our puss much longer. What was the use of killing the poor beast, eh?"

"Wait! I think it's picking up a bit," said the red-haired man.

The shapeless green creature was still writhing on the grass; twenty pairs of eyes were following its movements, and there was not the shadow of a smile in any of them. All were serious, all were silent, all of them were as miserable to look upon as that kitten, just as if it had communicated its suffering to them and they were feeling its pangs.

"Pick up a bit, indeed!" laughed the hobbledehoy sardonically, raising his voice, "very much so! Poor puss has had his day. We all loved him. Why did we torture him so? Let someone put him out of his misery."

"And who was the cause of it all?" shrieked the red-haired prisoner savagely. "Why there he is, with his devilish joke!"

"Come," said Zazubrina soothingly, "didn't the whole lot of you agree to it?"

And he hugged himself as if he were cold.

"The whole lot of us, indeed!" sneered the hobbledehoy, "I like that. You alone are to blame!—yes, you are!"

"Don't *you* roar, pray, you bull-calf!" meekly suggested Zazubrina.

The grey-headed old man took up the kitten, and after carefully examining it, pronounced his opinion:

"If we were to dip it in kerosene we might wash the paint off."

"If you'll take my advice you'll seize it by the tail and smash it against the wall," said Zazubrina, adding, with a laugh, "that's the simplest way out of it."

"What?" roared the red-haired man, "and if I were to treat you the same way, how would *you* like it?"

"The devil," screamed the hobbledehoy, and, snatching the kitten out of the old man's hands, he set off running. The old man and a few others went after him.

Then Zazubrina remained alone in the midst of a group of people, who glowered upon him with evil and threatening eyes. They seemed to be waiting for something from him.

"Remember, I am not alone, my friends," whined Zazubrina.

"Shut up!" shrieked the red-haired man, looking at the door; "not alone! Who else is there, then?"

"Why, the whole lot of you here," piped the jester nervously.

"You hound, you!"

The red-haired man shook his clenched fist in Zazubrina's very teeth. The artist dodged back only to get a violent blow in the nape of the neck.

"My friends . . ." he implored piteously. But his friends had taken note that the two warders were a good way off, and, thronging quickly round their favorite, knocked him off his legs with a few blows. Seen from a little distance the group might easily have been taken for a party engaged in lively conversation. Surrounded and concealed by them, Zazubrina lay there at their feet. Occasionally some dull thuds were audible—they were kicking away at Zazubrina's ribs, kicking deliberately, without the least hurry, each man waiting in turn for a particularly favorable kicking spot to be revealed as his neighbor, after planting his blow, wriggled his foot out of action.

Three minutes or so passed thus. Suddenly the voice of the warder resounded in their ears:

"Now, you devils! what are you about there?"

The prisoners did not leave off the tormenting process immediately. One by one they slowly tore themselves away from Zazubrina, and as each one of them went away, he gave him a parting kick.

When they had all gone, he still remained lying on the ground. He lay on his stomach, and his shoulders were all shivering—no doubt he was weeping—and he kept on coughing and hawking. Presently, very cautiously, as if fearing to fall to pieces, he slowly began to raise himself from the ground, leaning heavily on his left arm, then bending one leg beneath him, and whining like a sick dog, sat down on the ground.

"You're pretending!" screeched the red-haired man in a threatening voice. Then Zazubrina made an effort, and quickly stood on his feet.

Then he tottered to one of the walls of the prison. One arm was pressed close to his breast, with the other he groped his way along. There he now stood, holding on to the wall with his hand, his head hanging down towards the ground. He coughed repeatedly.

I saw how dark drops were falling on to the ground; they also glistened quite plainly on the grey ground of the prison wall.

And so as not to defile with his blood the official place of detention, Zazubrina kept on doing his best to make it drip on the ground, so that not a single drop should fall on the wall.

How they did laugh and jeer at him to be sure . . .

From henceforth the kitten vanished. And Zazubrina no longer had a rival to divide with him the attention of the prisoners.

For Discussion

1. What was Zazubrina's role among the prisoners? What was revealed about his personality after he played an unkind prank on the young boy?
2. What do you think the narrator of the story meant when he observed that "nothing kills the soul so quickly as this longing to please people"? How was Zazubrina a victim of this longing? Was the narrator justified in feeling sorry for Zazubrina? Why or why not?
3. In your opinion, why was the kitten so popular with the prisoners? What might it have represented to them? Considering their fondness for the animal, explain why the prisoners allowed Zazubrina to do what he did.
4. The prisoners' laughter indicated they approved of what Zazubrina did to the cat. After approving of Zazubrina's act with great laughter, did the prisoners turn on him? What did the laughter reveal about these people and their lives? Why did they turn on the person who made them laugh? In your opinion, was their contradictory behavior believable? Why or why not?
5. Did you feel any special emotion about Zazubrina at the end of the story? Was it different from your earlier feelings about him? What purpose do you think the author had in leaving you with the final picture of Zazubrina trying not to defile the wall?
6. This is a first-person point of view story. Do you think the narrator was important to the story? Why or why not? Are there any indications as to what kind of person the narrator was?
7. Gorky described the laughter in detail because it is related to the theme of the story. What is the theme? What do you think Gorky was saying about people?
8. Atmosphere in a story is the mood created by an author through his choice of details in presenting the setting, characters, and events. Atmosphere often plays an important part in a Gorky story. What is

the atmosphere or mood of this story? Point out specific details used
by the author to create this mood.

For Composition

1. Gorky was concerned with presenting his characters in all their complexities. Write a character sketch of Zazubrina in which you outline some of his essential characteristics and contradictions.
2. The desire to please people and win their approval can sometimes lead a person to do things for which he cannot respect himself and for which others have contempt. Write a short narrative based on an actual or fictitious incident which illustrates this statement.

Miguel de Unamuno

Solitude

Miguel de Unamuno * (1864–1936) has earned himself a considerable reputation as a philosopher as well as poet, novelist, and essayist. In his many works, he emphasized that society exists for man, not man for society, and that the individual soul is unique and irreplaceable: "There cannot be any other I."

Of Catholic Basque background, Unamuno possessed a singular capacity for work. Having taken a doctor's degree in philosophy and letters, he became Professor of Greek at Salamanca, Rector of the University of Salamanca, a lecturer and writer on ancient and modern cultures, specialist in international law, and a political writer. Perhaps his finest work is *Del Sentiemiento Trágico de la Vida* (*The Tragic Sense of Life*), an autobiographical account of an adventure of the spirit that has been compared to the self-revelations of St. Augustine and Pascal.

In the following short story, the heroine, symbolically called Solitude, exemplifies Unamuno's belief in individualism and the importance of self-realization.

SOLITUDE was born of the death of her mother. Leopardi [1] sang that birth is a hazard with death:

> *"nasce l'uomo a fatica*
> *ed e rischio di morte el nascimento"*—

> ("hazard with death for the new-born,
> hazard with death for her who gives birth.")

Poor Sanctuary, Solitude's mother, had led for five years of marriage a life of shadowed and silent tragedy. Her husband was a man impenetrable and apparently without feeling. The poor woman did not know how she had ever come to marry him; she found herself bound in matrimony with this man like somebody awakening from a

---

* mē-gel' th'ā ōō nä mōō'nō
[1] **Leopardi:** Italian poet of the nineteenth century

dream. All her maiden life was lost in a misty distance, and when she thought of it she remembered herself, as she had been before her marriage, as though she were remembering somebody else.

Whether her husband loved her or hated her she could not tell. His home was to him merely a place for eating and sleeping, for all the animal side of life. He worked outside of it, he talked outside of it, he amused himself outside of it. He never raised his voice or said a harsh word to his wife. He never contradicted her. When poor Sanctuary asked him a question or sought his opinion about anything, she invariably got the same reply from him: "All right. Don't bother me. As you like."

That persistent "As you like" went to poor Sanctuary's sick heart like a sharp knife. "As you like!" the poor woman thought to herself; "that means that I'm not even worth contradicting." And then his "Don't bother me!"—that terrible "Don't bother me!" which embitters so many homes. In Sanctuary's home—in what should have been Sanctuary's home—that terrible refusal not to be bothered enshadowed everything at the hearth.

The first year that she was married Sanctuary had a son; but in the dreary desolation of her drab home she longed for a daughter. "A son," she thought, "a man! Men always have something to do outside their homes." So, when she became pregnant, she dreamed of nothing but a daughter; and her daughter must be called Solitude. The poor woman was taken gravely ill in her pangs. Her heart fluttered feebly. She realized that she would live only long enough to give birth to her daughter—to introduce her into that shadowed home. She called for her husband.

"Oh, Pedro," she said, "if it's a daughter, as I hope, you'll call her Solitude, won't you?"

"All right, all right," he replied; "time enough to think about that"; and he reflected that this day, this day of birth, he was going to miss his game of dominoes.

"But I'm going to die, Pedro; I haven't the strength to get over it."

"Nonsense!" he replied.

"It may be," Sanctuary insisted; "but if it is a daughter, you will call her Solitude, won't you?"

"All right. Don't bother me. As you like," he closed the conversation.

And she ceased to bother him forever. After she had given birth to her daughter she had only time to realize that it was a daughter; and her last words were: "Solitude, remember, Pedro—Solitude!"

The man was shocked, and would have been humbled if there had been anything of him to humble. A widower at his age, and with two small children! Who was going to look after his house now? Who was going to bring up his children—until his daughter was old enough to be able to take over the management of it? . . . Marry again? No, that he would not do. He knew now what marriage meant. If he had only known before! That was no solution. Very decidedly he would not marry again.

What he did was to send Solitude to a village to be reared away from home. He did not want the bother of an infant and the insolence of nurses. It was bad enough with the other child, little Peter, now three years old.

Solitude hardly remembered those first years of her infancy at all. Her earliest dim recollection was of that dreary, drab home, and of that hermetically sealed father of hers, that man who ate at the same table with her and whom she saw for a moment when she went to bed; and of his perfunctory, formal kisses.

Her only companionship was that of little Peter, her brother. But Peter played with her in the strictest sense of the word—that is to say, he did not play in company with her; he played with her as one plays with a toy. She, Solitude, Solita, was his plaything; and he, like the man he was going to be, was a brute. Since his fists were stronger than hers, he always had the right of it.

"You women are no good for anything. It is we men who give orders," he told her one day.

Solitude was by nature acutely receptive; she had a genius for sensitiveness. Women very often have this receptive genius; but, since it produces nothing, it languishes away without anybody noticing it. At first, crying and cut to the quick, Solitude used to go to that Sphinx of a father of hers, expecting justice; but that unswerving man received her with this cold: "All right, all right! Don't bother me! Give me a kiss, and see this doesn't happen again!"

That, he thought, settled everything, and saved him from further annoyance. The end of it was that Solitude ceased to complain to her father about her brother's brutality and bore everything in silence, leaving him in peace and sparing herself the humiliation of those perfunctory kisses.

The dreary drabness of her home grew more and more unbearable, and the shadows that it cast grew deeper. Her only relief from it was at school, where her father had made her a day-boarder, among other things in order to get her more off his hands. At school she learnt that all her companions had, or once had, mothers. One evening, at supper, she dared to bother her father with a question.

"Tell me, Father, didn't I have a mother?"

"Well, what a question!" her father replied; "of course, everybody has a mother. Why do you ask?"

"Then where is my mother, Papa?"

"She died when you were born."

"Oh, how sad!"

And then, just for once, her father abandoned his boorish taciturnity, and told her that her mother had been called Sanctuary, and sketched for her an outline of that dead woman.

"How pretty she must have been!" said the child.

"Yes," her father agreed; "yes, but not as pretty as you are." This remark that he let slip went to the bottom of one of his little idiosyncrasies. If his daughter was prettier than her mother, the fact, in his opinion, was due to himself.

"And what about you, Pedrín," Solitude, excited by this fugitive stirring of the embers of the family hearth, asked her brother; "do you remember her?"

"Now how could I remember her, when she died when I was only three years old?"

"Well, if I were in your place I should remember her," the girl replied.

"Oh, of course, you women are so clever!" cut in her would-be grown-up brother.

"No, we're not; but I think we have longer memories."

"All right, all right! Stop talking nonsense and don't bother me!"

And so ended that memorable night when Solitude learnt that she once had a mother.

It gave her so much to think about that she could almost remember for herself. She peopled her solitude with maternal dreams.

The years went on, all just the same, all drab and ashen beside that hearth where the fire had gone out. Her father seemed to grow no older, to possess no capacity for growing older. He did the same things at the same times every day, with the regularity of a machine.

But her brother began to get himself talked about until he became a byword in the town, and until finally he disappeared—whither, Solitude did not know. Father and daughter were left alone: alone, but separated; they merely ate and slept under the same roof.

At last it seemed that day had dawned in the sky of Solitude. A gallant youth, who for some time had been making eyes at her every time he saw her in the street, scraped an acquaintance with her and presented himself to her as a suitor on approval. Poor Solitude saw Life beginning to open its doors to her; and, despite some presentiments, which she tried in vain to scare away, she accepted him on this basis. It was like a spring-tide.

Solitude began to live—or, rather, she was really born for the first time. The meaning of many things which until now had had no meaning for her was revealed to her. She began to understand much that she had heard from her mistresses and companions at school, much that she had read. Everything seemed to sing inside her. But at the same time she realized all the emptiness of her home, and, if it had not been for that picture of her betrothed that was ever present to her, she would have turned into stone there to match that man of granite, her father.

For poor Solitude this betrothal was a regular dazzling of her eyes. But her father seemed to pay no attention to it, or at least to refuse to pay any attention to it. He never made the slightest allusion to it. If he met his daughter's betrothed hanging about the railings when he left home during those blissful hours when they arranged to meet, he pretended not to see him.

More than once poor Solitude intended to say something about it to her father when they were at the supper table together; but the words stuck in her throat before she could utter them. So she said nothing, and kept on saying nothing.

Solitude began to read books which her betrothed gave her. Thanks to him, she began to know something of the world. This young man did not seem to be like other men. He was caressing, gay, unreserved, ironical and sometimes even contradicted her. But about her father he never said a word.

It was her initiation into life—something to dream about at home. Solitude began, indeed, to glimpse what a real home might mean: homes such as those that her school-mates had. And this knowledge, or rather this sensing, increased her horror of the backwater in which she lived.

Then suddenly one day, when she least expected it, there came the crash. Her betrothed, who had been away for a month, wrote her a long letter, full of endearments, adorned with all kinds of trimmings and twistings, in which, amid all his protestations of affection, he made it clear that their relations must be regarded as at an end. He wound up with this terrible sentence: "Perhaps, some day, you will meet somebody who can make you happier than I could."

Solitude felt an awful shudder go through her very soul. She experienced once more all the brutality, all the indescribable brutality, of mankind—of men, of the male species. But she showed no sign, swallowing her humiliation and her pain in silence and with dry eyes. She would show no weakness in the presence of that Sphinx of a father of hers.

Why—why had her betrothed abandoned her? Had he got tired of her? Again, why? Could a man get tired of being in love? Was it possible that he should get tired? No; the truth was that he had never loved her. Solitude, who had been thirsting for affection since the day she was born, realized that this man had never really loved her. She took refuge in herself, in remembrance of her mother, in the worship of the Virgin. She did not weep. Her pain was too deep for tears; it was a pain that burned and dried up.

One night, at supper, the paternal Sphinx opened his mouth long enough to say: "Well, that seems to be the end of that!" Solitude felt as though he had plunged a sword into her heart. She got up from the table, and rushed to her own room. There, crying, "Mother, my mother!" she collapsed in a spasm of agony; and thereafter the world was a waste for her.

So two years passed, and then one morning they found her father, Don Pedro, dead in his bed. He had had a heart attack. But his daughter, now left alone in the world, did not weep for him.

Solitude was left alone—quite alone. So that her solitariness should be complete, she sold the property that her father had left her, and on the proceeds of this modest fortune she went to live far away, very far away, where nobody knew her and she knew nobody.

Solitude is that woman, today almost an old woman, that simple but dignified woman, whom you see every evening going to take the sun on the banks of the river—that mysterious little woman about whom nobody knows whence she came or who she is. She is that solitary benefactor who, doing good by stealth, relieves all those ills of others that she can relieve. She is that kind little woman from whom there sometimes escapes a bitter saying that betrays an affliction which she keeps to herself.

Nobody knows her history, and there has grown up a legend of a terrible tragedy in her life. But, as you can see for yourself, there was nothing that one could call a tragedy in her life—or, at most, merely that common, that very common tragedy, undramatic, undemonstrative, which destroys so many human lives: the tragedy of solitude.

It is recalled only that, some years ago, Solitude was sought out by a man who looked old, old before his years, bowed as though beneath the weight of vice, who a few days afterwards died in the house of that little old woman. "He was my brother!" That was all she said about him.

And now do you understand what solitude means in the soul of a woman—a woman thirsting for tenderness and hungering for a home? A man in our society has ample scope in which to escape from solitude. But a woman—unless she chooses to shut herself up in a convent—how solitary she can be among us!

That poor little woman, whom you see wandering by the river bank, without aim or object, has experienced all the weight of the brutality of the animal egotism of men. What does she think? What has she got to live for? What far-off hope keeps her going?

I have gained the acquaintanceship—I cannot say the friendship—of Solitude, and I have tried to glimpse her view of life and destiny: what one might call her philosophy. So far I have learned little or nothing about it. All that I have got for her is her story, which I have just told you.

Apart from that, I have heard nothing from her but observations which are full of common sense, but of a common sense that seems cold and ordinary. She is a woman of extraordinary range of literary culture, for she has read very widely, and she is very far-seeing. But she remains extraordinarily susceptible to offensiveness or brutality from any quarter. She leads a solitary life, alone and retired, to avoid the rude elbowings of humanity.

About us men she has a curious idea. Whenever I have succeeded in turning the conversation to the subject of men, all her answer is: "Poor little fellows!" It appears that she pities us, as though we were one of the lower order of crustaceans. But she has promised me that she will talk to me some time about men and about that great, that greatest, that supreme problem—the relationship between men and women.

"Not the sexual relationship," she said, "be clear about that; not that, but the general relationship between man and woman, whether they be mother and son, brother and sister, or merely friends, on the one hand; or husband and wife, betrothed, or lovers on the other. The important thing, the essential thing, is the general relationship— the question how a man regards a woman, whether she be his mother, his daughter, his sister, his wife, or his mistress; and how a woman regards a man, whether he be her father, her son, her brother, her husband, or her lover." I am still awaiting the day when Solitude will talk to me about this. . . .

For Discussion

1. Why was Sanctuary's marriage so painful to her? How do you explain the fact that she married Pedro at all?
2. Why do you think Sanctuary wanted her daughter to be named Solitude? Was it in any way a criticism of her husband and of men in general? Explain your answer.
3. In what ways did Solitude's brother act like her father? Why was finding out "that she once had a mother" so important to Solitude?
4. How did Solitude's engagement affect the way she saw the world? In your opinion, why did her suitor break off the engagement? Was Solitude justified in solving her problem as she did? Why or why not?
5. The narrator stated that Solitude's life was a "common tragedy." What reasons did he have for making this statement? What reasons, if any, can you give to show that Solitude's life was not wholly a tragedy?
6. This story is a severe indictment of the way some men regard women. Reread the last paragraph of the story. What did Solitude mean when she told the narrator that the "general relationship" between men and women is the important thing?
7. What would you say is the most important aspect of "Solitude"—the plot, the characters, the mood, or the theme? Give the reasons for your choice.

8. Would you say that the essential conflict in this story was between Solitude and one of the three men in her life, or between Solitude and society? Explain.
9. Was the author justified in introducing a narrator toward the end of the story, rather than at the beginning, as in "The Green Kitten"? Why or why not? What purpose did the narrator serve in this story?

For Composition

1. Write a paragraph in which you express your critical opinion of this story. Use specific details and connotative words that will effectively communicate the idea you wish to convey. When you have finished writing your paragraph, read it aloud. Is it constructed around a single idea? Has every word contributed to the idea you wanted to express?
2. Write a short version of Solitude's story either as her father or Sanctuary might tell it.

Rainer Maria Rilke

Gym Period

Rainer Maria Rilke * (1875–1926), besides being a great German poet (see page 233), was also the author of several excellent short stories, most of which were written during his youth. These stories reflect a melancholy which may, in part, be traced to his unhappy childhood and to his painful experience as an adolescent at a military school.

The Spartan training that was the core of the academy program was no worse than that at other such academies of the times, but Rilke's natural temperament and upbringing made it quite unsuitable for him. That he actually felt the horror described in "Gym Period" is evident in an account he wrote of himself much later.

"Consider," he writes in a letter to a friend, "how terribly the assault of such savage and unmerited brutalities must have echoed in the still undefiled sanctuary of a childish heart. What I suffered then can be compared with the greatest woe of the world, even though I was a child, or rather because I was one."

$\mathcal{J}HE$ Military School of St. Severin. The gymnasium. The class in their white cotton shirts stand in two rows under the big gas lights. The gym teacher, a young officer with a hard, swarthy face and contemptuous eyes, has given the order for exercises and is dividing the class into sections. "First section, horizontal bars; second section, parallel bars; third section, horses; fourth section, pole climbing. Fall out!" And the boys in their light, resined shoes scatter quickly. A few remain standing in the middle of the floor, hesitating and reluctant. They are the fourth section, the poor gymnasts, who do not enjoy playing on the equipment and are already tired after their twenty knee-bends, as well as somewhat bewildered and out of breath.

But one, Karl Gruber, ordinarily the very first on such occasions, already stands near the poles set up in a dimly lit corner of the gymnasium just beside the lockers where the coats of the boys' uniforms now hang. He has seized the nearest pole and with unusual strength

* rī′nẽr mä-rē′ä ril′k ə

41

pulls it shaking out to the spot designated for practice. Gruber does not even let go. He jumps and grabs a hold rather high up. His legs, involuntarily wound around the pole in a position for climbing such as he never achieved before, cling to the shaft. He waits for the rest of the class and seems to be considering with peculiar pleasure the astonished anger of the little Polish sergeant, who calls to him to come down. But Gruber does not obey, and Jastersky, the blond sergeant, finally shouts, "Very well. Either you come down, Gruber, or you climb the rest of the way up. Otherwise I shall report you to the lieutenant in charge."

And then Gruber begins to climb, at first frenziedly, pulling up his legs a little, his eyes raised, estimating with some alarm the incalculable section of the pole still to come. Then his movements grow slower; and as though he were relishing every fresh hold as something new and delightful, he pulls himself higher than anyone usually goes. He pays no attention to the excitement of the exasperated sergeant, but climbs and climbs, his eyes staring upward, as though he had discovered an outlet in the gymnasium roof and were straining to reach it. The eyes of his whole section follow him. And in the other sections too some notice is taken of the climber who had hardly ever been able to climb even the first third of the way without getting a cough, a red face, and a bloodshot eye.

"Bravo, Gruber!" someone calls over from the first section. Many look up then, and for a while the gym is quiet.

But at this very moment when all eyes are upon him, Gruber, high up under the roof, gestures as though to shake them off; and when he obviously does not succeed, he rivets all their glances on the iron hook above him and swishes down the slippery pole, so that everyone is still looking up, whereas he, dizzy and hot, already stands below and gazes with strangely lusterless eyes at his burning palms.

Then one or another of the boys around him asks what got into him. "Do you want to make the first section?" Gruber laughs and seems about to reply, but he thinks better of it and lowers his eyes.

And then, when the noisy tumult has begun again, he retires quietly to his locker, sits down, looks about uneasily, and after two panting breaths laughs again and tries to say something. But already he is unobserved.

Only Jerome, also in the fourth section, notices that he is bent over like someone deciphering a letter in bad light again inspecting his hands. He walks over to him presently and asks, "Did you hurt yourself?"

Gruber starts. "What?" he asks in his habitual slobbering voice.

"Let's have a look." Jerome takes his hand and turns it toward the light. A little skin is scraped from the palm. "Say, I've got something to fix it," says Jerome, who always gets sticking-plaster sent from home. "Come to my room when we get out." But it as though Gruber did not hear. He stares straight ahead into the gym as though he were seeing something indefinable, perhaps something not in the gym, perhaps outside against the window even though it is late on a dark autumn afternoon.

At this moment, the sergeant shouts in his haughty way, "Gruber!" Gruber remains as before. Only his outstretched feet slide gracelessly forward on the slippery floor. "Gruber!" roars the sergeant, and his voice breaks. Then he waits a while, and says in a quick gruff tone without looking at the boy, "Report after class. I shall see that you. . . ." And the class continues.

"Gruber," says Jerome and bends over his friend, who is leaning back farther and farther in his locker, "it was your turn to climb on the rope. Go ahead, try it. If you don't, Jastersky will fix up some kind of a story against you. You know how he is."

Gruber nods. But instead of getting up, he abruptly shuts his eyes and slips forward while Jerome is talking. As if borne by a wave, he slides slowly and silently, farther and farther—slides from his seat, and Jerome doesn't realize what is happening till Gruber's head bangs hard against the wooden seat and then droops forward. "Gruber!" he calls hoarsely. At first no one notices. Jerome stands helpless, his arms at his sides, and calls "Gruber! Gruber!" He doesn't even think to pull him up.

Then he is given a push. Someone says, "Dumbbell!" Someone else shoves him aside, and he watches them lift the motionless boy to carry him off somewhere, probably into the next room. The lieutenant in charge hurries in. In a harsh, loud voice he issues curt orders. The commands cut short the buzzing chatter. Silence. Only here and there is there any movement: swinging on the bars, gentle leaps, a belated laugh from someone who doesn't know what it's all about.

Then rapid questions. "What? What? Who? Gruber? Where?" And still more questions. Then aloud someone says, "Fainted."

And red-faced Jastersky, the sergeant, runs back of the lieutenant in charge and cries in his disagreeable voice, trembling with rage, "He's faking, lieutenant, he's faking." The lieutenant pays no attention. He looks straight ahead, gnaws his mustache so that his strong chin juts out sharper and firmer, and gives an occasional brief order. He and four pupils carrying Gruber disappear into the room.

At once, the four pupils return. A servant runs through the gym. The four get a good deal of attention and are plied with questions. "How does he look? What's the matter with him? Has he come to yet?" None of the four really knows anything. And then the lieutenant in charge calls to them that the class may continue and gives the command to Goldstein, the sergeant-major. So the exercises begin again, on the parallel and horizontal bars; and the little boys of the third section straddle the tall horse with their bowed legs.

Yet the activity is not as before. It is as though everyone were listening. Swinging on the parallel bars abruptly stops, and only small feats are performed on the horizontal bar. The voices are less confused, and the hum is fainter, as though all were uttering just one word, "Ssss. Ssss." In the meantime sly little Krix is listening at the door. The sergeant of the second section chases him away, lifting his hand to slap his bottom. Krix leaps back, catlike, his eyes bright and cunning. He has learned enough. And after a while, when no one is watching, he tells Pavlovich, "The regimental doctor's come."

Now Pavlovich's behavior is notorious. As boldly as though he were obeying an order, he goes about the gym from one section to another, saying loudly, "The regimental doctor's in there." And even the noncoms appear to be interested in the news. Glances toward the door become more and more frequent, the exercises slower and slower. A small boy with black eyes remains crouching on the horse and stares open-mouthed at the door. The strongest boys in the first class exert themselves a little, struggle against it, whirl their legs.

Pombert, the strong Tyrolean, bends his arm and contemplates his muscles, which stand out taut and strong under his shirt. His supple young limbs even make a few more turns on the bars, and suddenly the lively movement of his body is the only one in the whole gym. It is a great dazzling circle, somehow ominous in the midst of great stillness. Abruptly the little fellow brings himself to a stop, drops involuntarily to his knees, and makes a face as though he despised them all. But even his dull little eyes rest finally on the door.

Now the singing of the gas jets and the ticking of the wall clock are audible. And then the dismissal bell rattles. Today its tone is strange and peculiar. And it stops suddenly, incomplete, interrupting itself when its message is only half spoken. Sergeant-major Goldstein, however, knows his duty. He calls, "Fall in!" No one hears. No one can recall the meaning these words once had. Once? When? "Fall in!" croaks the sergeant-major angrily, and now the other noncoms cry in succession, "Fall in!" And also many of the pupils say, as if to themselves or in their sleep, "Fall in! Fall in!" But actually, all of them know there is still something to wait for.

And at this very moment the door is opening. For a second nothing happens; then Wehl, the lieutenant in charge, walks out, and his eyes are big and wrathful and his pace is decided. He marches as though he were on parade and says hoarsely, "Fall in!" With astonishing speed ranks are formed. Then no one moves. It is as though a field marshal were present. And now the command, "Attention!" A pause, and then dry and harsh, "Your friend Gruber has just died. Heart attack. Forward, march!" A pause.

And only after a little while, the voice of the pupil on duty, small and weak, "Company, column left! March!" Slow and unready, the group turns to the door. Jerome is the last. No one looks back. From the corridor chill, damp air blows against the boys. One of them suggests that it smells of carbolic acid. Pombert makes a vulgar joke about the smell. No one laughs. Suddenly Jerome feels somebody grab his arm, as though for assault. Krix is hanging on to him. "I saw him," he whispers breathlessly and squeezes Jerome's arm while an inner laughter convulses him. He can hardly go on. "He's stark naked and caved in and all stretched out. And he's got a seal on the soles of his feet. . . ."

And then he giggles shrilly, as though someone had tickled him, giggles and bites down through Jerome's sleeve.

For Discussion

1. The author gave no clear explanation for Karl Gruber's strange behavior in the gym class. What clues did he give you as to the kind of person Gruber was? What kind of life do you think he led at military school?

2. Point out specific words and phrases used by the author to characterize the young lieutenant and the sergeant. What might their attitude toward Gruber have been?

3. Keeping in mind your answers to Questions 1 and 2, describe Gruber's possible feelings on the day he climbed the pole. Why do you think he did it?

4. In what way was Jerome different from the other members of the gym class? How did the students react while they waited to hear what happened? In your opinion, was this an accurate picture of a group of boys? Give reasons to support your answer.

5. Why were the lieutenant's eyes "big and wrathful" when he made his final announcement to the class? What criticisms of him and of the school were implied by the author?

6. How did the event in the gym affect Krix? Explain the last sentence of the story. How do you think the event affected Jerome?

7. In recreating this incident from the past, Rilke used the historic present tense rather than the customary past tense. In your opinion, did this intensify the impact of the story or weaken it? Explain.

8. In this story Rilke was less interested in revealing character than in telling a dramatic incident which had critical implications. What were these implications?

9. What is the conflict in the story? Do you think Rilke ended his story with unnecessary abruptness? Explain. If you found the ending unsatisfactory, suggest one you think would have made it more satisfying.

10. Rilke brought this experience to life by using a number of vivid details with which he created the mood of the story. For example, "A small boy with black eyes remains crouching on the horse and stares open-mouthed at the door" and "From the corridor chill, damp air blows against the boys." Point out other details in the story which contribute effectively to the mood.

For Composition

1. This story was written from the omniscient point of view; that is, the author stood outside the situation and described in detail what occurred. Pretend you are Jerome, or one of the other boys in the story. Write a short composition in which you tell what your thoughts and feelings were while watching Gruber climb the pole, or while waiting to hear what happened, or after leaving the gym class.

2. Although Rilke told the story as if he were remembering it, he did not play a part in the action or comment on it in any way. Write a paragraph in which you describe your impression of the author as

revealed by the story. Wherever possible, give specific examples from the selection to support your impression.

3. Most people have vivid memories of a particularly happy or unhappy incident in which they were involved. Write a short account of such an incident in your own life. Keep in mind that the connotations of words are important in communicating the mood you wish to convey.

Romain Gary

The Search

Romain Gary (1914–   ) has become one of the most popular and esteemed French novelists since 1945, when he published his first novel, *European Education*. Born in Russia, he was brought to France as a child by his dynamic and ambitious mother, whom he later described in detail in his autobiography, *Promise at Dawn* (1961). Active as a pilot in World War II, Gary flew for the French Air Force and, after the German occupation, for the Free French Air Force. His novels have been particularly successful in England and America, and one of his best known, *The Roots of Heaven*, was made into a motion picture. Gary is a career diplomat, as well as a writer, and is now serving as the French Consul-General in Los Angeles.

The selection which follows is from Gary's realistic and ironic novel, *The Company of Men*. It is about a fifteen-year-old boy, Luc Martin, whose father has been killed by the Germans during World War II, leaving Luc adrift in post-war Paris with his pet dog, Roxane. Forced to live by his wits, Luc becomes involved with people dealing in the black market, and learns how to steal drugs and resell them. Despite his tough and cynical attitude toward people, he is searching painfully for an answer to the chaotic world in which he finds himself. One place he tries to find an answer is in American movies, which he attends constantly. In some ways, Luc Martin will remind you of Holden Caulfield, the young American hero of *The Catcher in the Rye*. The bitterness and humor in this selection reflect accurately an aspect of the post-war world in Europe and the search for new values.

$\mathcal{A}$S time went on, I did excellent business with him [the druggist]. I sold him, once, almost a hundred thousand francs' worth of sulfas when there weren't any to be had anywhere. He would welcome me in his store like an old friend.

"What are you bringing me today, young man?"

"Some penicillin."

"Well, well, well. Is it fresh?"

48

I showed him the vials. He felt them anxiously.

"You poor little wretch! Don't you know that penicillin must be kept at a certain temperature, or it isn't any good? Well, make me a special price. People are all rotten."

He had no family, no children, and I think he was revenging himself in this way against his loneliness, against his store, against the life he could have had and didn't know how to choose.

Such were my first steps, my first contacts with the city rats. I was too young to be able to distinguish good from evil when they showed themselves in such diabolical and such complicated forms. But I wasn't happy. At night, before going to sleep, I used to think a long time about what had happened to me. I was looking for some reason, some sense, some explanation. I would pet my dog, Roxane, who shared my bed. With her, I could find again the face of my childhood. Roxane was now my only link with the past, and sometimes I wanted to ask her what she thought of all this, whether or not she approved of my behavior. I felt guilty, but I didn't know why. I didn't know what were the laws of men which I was breaking. I let myself go with the world which was all around me because I didn't see any other. I did just what the city rats did, I followed their road, I adopted their habits. Actually, this didn't make me happy, but I told myself that I probably wasn't alone in this, that maybe the great law of city rats was that nobody was happy.

"It's not normal, the way we live," I said once, shyly, to Léonce.

"Of course it's not normal. It's only animals who live normally." He spat in disgust. "The dudules, you know, they're a dirty lot."

"Dudules" was a word which came up all the time in our conversation. "I saw a dudule who promised me twelve new tires for some drugs." "Don't go to Clamsy's, the boss is a dirty dudule, he works for the police." I never knew exactly what a "dudule" was. I guess it was a twisting of the word "adult" and by extension it was to mean all men in general, all humanity. The word came up constantly in our conversation, charged with an unbelievable bitterness. A hostile world was all around us, the world of the dudules, all set to destroy us. The dudules were infinitely more powerful than we were, and yet they were afraid of us and we knew it. This knowledge was a source of constant pride to us, and it woke in us a spirit of competition.

We were a minority to be feared. Our task was, above all, just to last, to get around a dangerous cape. We were fifteen, sixteen, seventeen years old, and we would have to tack into the wind until we were twenty-one to be accepted into the heart of a conspiring community. We were an advance guard. To be safe, we had to wait for the main body of troops. We had to disguise ourselves and sneak unseen up to man's estate. This was one of the rules of the game, and we understood such rules perfectly.

In order to hide ourselves better, we imitated the gestures and the dress of adults, their language and their posture; only our faces betrayed us. Léonce had got me some false documents in the name of Étienne Roger, clerk, twenty-one years old. They were beautifully forged by an old rare-stamp dealer who had specialized in this kind of work during the occupation, thus saving the lives of some hundreds of men, and who now could not keep from going on with it. He could copy perfectly any document at all, from food cards to death certificates. So he arrived at the miracle of forging a world which was already completely forged. As Vanderputte said, he was, "at heart, a man with a great hunger for authenticity."

But more and more often I would wake up at night knotted with anguish, with a terrible and vague remorse. When I would try, sitting on my bed, to remember what had pulled me out of sleep, I could see that it was my father. He had come into my room, had leaned over me, and had looked me in the eyes, as if to force me to wake up. Why had he gone? Why had he left me with empty hands? Sometimes it seemed to me that my father had not abandoned me, that he was always there, and that he used to come like this in the night to give me the key which would finally open the world to me. Then I began to wish for his return; I used to hope that some night he would stride across the forbidden frontier and tell me the password in a loud, clear voice.

But he never said anything. He would stand quietly, like a statue, his legs spread apart, leaning on his rifle, his face quiet. It was a young face, but I didn't know how old he was. I had never thought to ask him, and now it was too late. I tried to fix forever in my memory each detail about him, the shape of his shoulders, the strength of his arms and of his hands, but when I looked at him too closely, I would wake up. I tried also to remember his voice, in the hope of bringing back all the words it had said. For he must have some reason to give me, some explanation. He certainly died for something, and maybe it wasn't he who had been mistaken but those who came after him. He certainly hadn't died for Vanderputte, nor for this unintelligible world which surrounded me. He was a teacher, I used to think, he must have known what he was doing. I refused to give up and to admit that he had gone away without saying anything, taking with him the key to the world and leaving me in this fix. So then I would try with all my strength to remember the key word of the puzzle, to drag it up out of the forgetfulness into which I must have carelessly thrown it. Sometimes it seemed to me that I had it on the tip of my tongue, one try, one try more . . . But no, that wasn't the way.

Sometimes I opened my bag and looked carefully at the personal things my father had left: some pipes, a wallet with some faked papers in it, a small bound volume of the *Pensées* of Pascal. On the flyleaf of the book, my father had started to write something: "*What I am fighting for . . .*" you could read, and down below: "*Maquis of Le Véziers, November, 1943.*" Unfortunately, he hadn't finished his sentence; as it stood it made no sense to me. There were still other sentences, whole paragraphs, scrawled in the margins of the text. "*No man can change by himself. We can't change our own faces except by reflecting the changes in other people's faces.*" And on another page: "*It takes a lot of other people's love to make a traitor, many hands held out to make a treachery.*"

All this didn't mean anything to me. I examined the little book with great care to see if there might not be a secret pocket, a hiding place where my father might have slipped a message, a testament, a complete list of the mysterious things which he was fighting for. But I didn't find anything. It was an ordinary book, like any other old book, without any hiding place, without any secret. I turned it and turned it again a thousand times. I even tried to read it, but it was too complicated; it wasn't interesting. But I no longer left this book which my father's hands must have held so often; I carried it with me always. Before taking on a particularly delicate or dangerous job I would slide my hand into my pocket and would touch the book, like a lucky piece.

I continued to feel lost in my search for a road, some footprints that I could follow. I continued to ransack my memory, to recall the past, the farm at Le Véziers, the smell of cut wood, the flight of quail, the water frozen in the mornings, the visits of my father in a truck which he taught me to drive, and I hoped in a confused sort of way that one of these recovered images would someday surrender to me a forgotten detail, a hint, a trace, some words said perhaps carelessly and of which I had not then understood the importance or the meaning. I leaned over my own past the way the detective, Philip Marlowe, leaned over the dying victim in the films I saw, hoping that with his last breath he would speak the name of the murderer. But with your last breath you wouldn't want to accuse anyone. You would only want to breathe a little longer, look once more at the woods, or at the sky, at a flying bird, a face—that's certainly how one dies, that's surely how my father died.

Sometimes, however, from my diving into the past, I did bring back to the surface some lost word. I remembered, for instance, an autumn day in 1942 when my father had come to see me at the farm and several hours later they had come to warn him that a German patrol was in the village and was coming toward our house. It was noon, and the woman was cooking and the farmer had said—I still remember his voice and the anger which swelled it: "You make the soup, but you don't know who's going to eat it." Later I had asked my father, sitting in front of the rescued soup with Roxane smoking in front of the fire from all her muddy skin, "What's going to happen to me, if you are killed?" and my father answered me quietly, "You'll still have all the other men."

All the other men. For days and days I dragged this phrase around with me everywhere I went. I repeated it to myself, looking at every face I met with a new curiosity as if I had never before seen a human face. All the other men. Was it really true that no one was to be excluded from this astonishing fraternity, the company of men, in which my father seemed to have believed and which, just the same, hadn't kept him from dying? I know now that fraternity can only be given and not demanded, and that fellowship is a gift and not a bargain or an exchange. I know this now, but I didn't know it then. I believed then in wanting to live for yourself, for your own pleasure, as people say. So I continued to wander in the labyrinth and I didn't manage to pick up the piece of white bread my father had dropped to guide my steps.

But the question I had thus put myself for the first time, to know what was the sense, what was the end, what was the key to this hostile world, this quiet challenge, this anguish, left me no longer in any peace. An insidious little animal, a biter, a gnawing insect had climbed up the darkness and did not want to return below the ground. It continued to scratch, to scratch, to scratch.

Fortunately, there were always the movies. We spent all our evenings at the movies. Josette often went at two o'clock in the afternoon and came back at eleven. We would come out of them drunk, our voices a little hoarse, trying to prolong for a few more seconds, by our manner, our gestures, and our language, the astonishing life in which we had become involved. The beauty of the women and the strength of the men and the violence of the action all made the reality which caught us up again when we came out of the theaters insupportably banal.

This reality seemed to us a stage setting, a badly painted screen which you had only to slash courageously to find, behind it, the real thing, the life of the films. We collected movie posters, and I still remember one of them, my favorite, which showed Edward G. Robinson in his latest picture. I remember very well when I first saw this poster. It was on the boulevard Montmartre, about seven o'clock in the evening. I had stopped in front of a kiosk, and I was looking at the poster with humble admiration. His revolver in his fist, his eyes lost in shadows, his jaws clenched, the famous gangster had a desperate look, it's true, but he was sure of himself. Looking furtively around me, to see if anyone were watching, I clenched my jaws, bit my cigarette, wrinkled my eyes up wickedly, and tried to imitate as closely as I could the virile mask in front of me. It was only necessary to look at that man to understand that nothing could stop him. He moved through the world like a tornado, leaving behind him a gaping hole where his enemies were tangled in a bunch, clutching their stomachs, and where ridiculous policemen lifted their whistles to their lips before dying. Besides, what is more ridiculous than a man who blows a whistle with his dying breath? One day I shall be like him, I thought, and I let myself go in dream. I imagined that I was at the wheel of a powerful Buick and Robinson was behind me, a machine gun in his arms, his eyes screwed up, firing through the door at the F.B.I. car which was chasing us.

"Butch."

"Yeah."

"A cigarette."

In spite of the tragic situation in which we found ourselves, Robinson couldn't keep from showing his gold teeth in a smile. It was like his faithful partner, Lucky Martin, to ask for a cigarette at such a moment! He was right, this young Frenchman, just arrived from Europe but already cool and strong: it was better to die with a little dash, a hundred and twenty miles an hour, than to go on living a crab's life in the common basket. He stopped firing and put a cigarette between my lips.

"Yep."

A skid almost sent us into the underbrush.

"A light," I grated.

A machine-gun blast tore the cigarette out of my lips and smashed the windshield into little bits. Robinson fired for several seconds, then came back and put another cigarette in my mouth. I heard him swear suddenly, in a low voice.

"Hit?" I cried.

"Stop, Lucky, my lighter fell out."

"You're out of your mind!"

"Stop! That lighter's all I've got left of hers."

I clenched my teeth and stopped the car with my whole weight on the brakes. We jumped out on the road.

"There it is, I've found it."

One shot, only one. Robinson reeled, stayed for a second as if suspended in air like a spider at the end of his web. I dragged him behind the embankment. The great gangster's eyes were already dying, but a smile still shone on his gold teeth.

"A cigarette?"

I stuck one between his lips.

"The lighter."

I made the flame spit out and moved it close to his white lips. Robinson smiled weakly at the little flickering light. He dragged in the smoke, once, another time. He was at the end of his strength.

"Take the butt."

I took it.

"Take it to Josette. Tell her that my last breath is in that cigarette, the last breath of Public Enemy Number One. Let her finish smoking it and then, when she's thrown it away, let her forget me. Marry her. Good-by."

Oh, I had tears in my eyes, I could hardly bear it. I took Josette in my arms and I held her for a long time while the music played something, until the audience got up and the curtain came down on us.

Then I woke up in front of the poster, shook myself, turned up the collar of my coat, and went away slowly, with Roxane dragging sadly behind me.

I wasn't sure yet whether I was going to be a great actor or a famous gangster, but it was clear that the first thing to do was to get to America. There were other films besides, all of them equally marvelous.

"Have you seen *The Big Sleep?*" I asked Léonce.

"Naturally, what do you expect? It's a terrific picture. There's one scene, you've really got to see it. Humphrey Bogart is having a fight with some guy, but the guy is disarmed and Humphrey has a Colt in his hand. So, what do you suppose he does?"

"He lets him have it in the stomach," I decided.

"Not at all," Léonce said triumphantly. "He throws his loaded revolver right between himself and this guy. The other man, you can be sure, jumps for it and leans over to grab it, and Humphrey, what do you suppose he does?"

I kept quiet, my eyes round. I had no idea what Humphrey would do. It was clearly beyond me.

"He clips him with a tremendous kick right in the mouth. But it's out of this world, I swear, you've got to see it! Right in the teeth. As he deserves, the dope is on his back, his mouth a pulp. Humphrey doesn't even need to kill him, there's nothing to do but spit on him. That, my friend, that's art! No, I swear, you've got to see it, it's really marvelous."

I saw it. I stayed for two or three shows and I studied the great artist's kick in its tiniest details. I came out of there with wicked eyes and I walked like someone in a dream, stopping from time to time to make tremendous kicks at imaginary mouths. Roxane looked at me with some anxiety. I lowered my nose, drew myself into my raincoat as into a shell, and kept on walking the streets, a cigarette butt hanging sadly from my lips.

For Discussion

1. Who were the "city rats" with whom Luc Martin came in contact? What did they reveal about people's attitude toward each other? What was Luc's reaction to these people?

2. What did the teen-agers in post-war Paris think of the world in which they lived? Do you see any relation between these boys and the juvenile delinquents of today? Explain.

3. Luc's memory of his father was his one clue to another kind of life, but it was a clue which he couldn't understand. From the brief notations his father wrote and from the recollections the boy had of his father, what kind of person would you say the father was? How did the father's attitude toward the world differ from that of the people around Luc?

4. In Luc's search for a meaning to life, he tried to find the answer in American gangster movies. What made the reality of these films more attractive to him than the reality of everyday life? How did the philosophy toward life expressed in these films differ from the philosophy of Luc's father?

5. Luc's daydream is a take-off on hundreds of gangster movies. What are some of the typical clichés in this daydream? In what way is this daydream a bad (and funny) mingling of toughness and sentimentality? What did Luc achieve through this daydream?

6. Do you think Luc's desire to imitate Humphrey Bogart was an attempt to cover up the feeling of fright he felt? Explain.

7. Reread the last sentence of this selection. Why do you think Luc felt sad and lonely after coming out of the movie? What point do you think the author is making?

8. Explain the meaning of the boy's observation on page 52: "I know now that fraternity can only be given and not demanded, and that fellowship is a gift and not a bargain or an exchange." How did Luc's viewpoint at that time differ from the one expressed in this statement?

9. There is a marked difference in mood between the two parts of this selection. What are these two moods? Do you think that the author has presented two aspects of Luc which are inconsistent, or which explain each other? Give reasons for your opinion.

10. Luc Martin is very different from Karl Gruber in "Gym Period," but both boys found themselves in a hostile world which they could not understand. Compare and contrast the ways in which they tried to deal with this problem. Do you think both made a mistake in different ways? Why or why not?

For Composition

1. Read James Thurber's famous short story, "The Secret Life of Walter Mitty." Write a short comparison of this story and the second half of "The Search" by Romain Gray. How are Walter Mitty and Luc Martin alike? How are they different?
2. Write a critical paper in which you express your views on the way movies and television dramas are misused today by people of all ages. In what ways is this misuse the fault of the movies or TV programs? In what ways is this misuse the fault of the people watching?

Giovanni Guareschi

The Treasure

Giovanni Guareschi* (1908–1968) has become one of the most popular
Italian writers since the appearance of his book, *The Little World of Don
Camillo*, in 1946. The delightful adventures of this lovable parish priest
and his adversary, Peppone, the leftist Mayor of his village, proved so
successful that Guareschi has since written some two hundred more episodes in the life of Don Camillo, which have appeared in several volumes, including *Don Camillo and His Flock*, *Don Camillo's Dilemma*,
and *Don Camillo Takes the Devil by the Tail*. These warm and humorous stories have satirical undertones, pointing up the weaknesses of man,
as all satire does, but in a manner that is gentle and without bitterness.
The two episodes from *The Little World of Don Camillo* which follow,
are filled with a lively faith in men of good will and God's infinite patience with His creatures.

*J*HE little world of Don Camillo is to be found somewhere in the
valley of the Po River. It is almost any village on that stretch of
plain in Northern Italy. There, between the Po and the Apennines,
the climate is always the same. The landscape never changes and, in
country like this, you can stop along any road for a moment and look
at a farmhouse sitting in the midst of maize and hemp—and immediately a story is born.

Why do I tell you this instead of getting on with my story? Because
I want you to understand that, in the Little World between the river
and the mountains, many things can happen that cannot happen anywhere else. Here, the deep, eternal breathing of the river freshens the
air, for both the living and the dead, and even the dogs, have souls.
If you keep this in mind, you will easily come to know the village
priest, Don Camillo, and his adversary Peppone, the Communist
Mayor. You will not be surprised that Christ watches the goings-on
from a big cross in the village church and not infrequently talks, and
that one man beats the other over the head, but fairly—that is, with-

* jō vä′nē gwär es′kē

out hatred—and that in the end the two enemies find they agree about essentials.

And one final word of explanation before I begin my story. If there is a priest anywhere who feels offended by my treatment of Don Camillo, he is welcome to break the biggest candle available over my head. And if there is a Communist who feels offended by Peppone, he is welcome to break a hammer and sickle on my back. But if there is anyone who is offended by the conversations of Christ, I can't help it; for the one who speaks in this story is not Christ but my Christ—that is, the voice of my conscience.

One day Smilzo came to the rectory. He was a young ex-partisan who had been Peppone's orderly during the fighting in the mountains and now worked as a messenger at the Town Hall. He was the bearer of a handsome letter, printed on handmade paper with the Party heading in Gothic lettering, which read:

"Your honor is invited to grace with his presence a ceremony of a social nature which will take place tomorrow at ten o'clock A.M. *in the Plaza of Liberty. The Secretary of the Section, Comrade Bottazzi, Mayor, Guiseppe."*

Don Camillo looked severely at Smilzo. "Tell Comrade Peppone Mayor Guiseppe that I have no wish to go and listen to the usual imbecilities against reaction and the capitalists. I already know them by heart."

"No," explained Smilzo, "there won't be any political speeches. This is for patriotism and social activities. If you refuse, it means that you don't understand democracy."

Don Camillo nodded his head slowly. "If that's it," he said, "then I have nothing more to say."

"Good. And the Mayor says you are to come in uniform and to bring all your paraphernalia."

"Paraphernalia?"

"Yes—a pail of holy water and all that stuff; there is something to be blessed."

Smilzo got away with talking this way to Don Camillo precisely because he was Smilzo, that is, the lean one. He was so skinny and quick that during the fighting in the mountains he had been known to slip between the bullets. Therefore, by the time the heavy book Don Camillo hurled at him reached the spot where his head had been,

Smilzo was already on his bike pedaling away for all he was worth.

Don Camillo got up, rescued the book and went to the church to let off steam. When he reached the altar he said, "Lord, I must find out what those people are planning to do tomorrow. I never heard of anything so mysterious. What is the meaning of all those preparations? All those branches that they are sticking into the ground round the meadow between the drugstore and Baghetti's house? What kind of deviltry can they be up to?"

"My son, if it were deviltry, first of all they wouldn't be doing it in the open and secondly they wouldn't be sending for you to bless it. Be patient until tomorrow."

That evening Don Camillo went to have a look around but saw nothing but branches and decorations surrounding the meadow, and nobody seemed to know anything.

When he set out next morning, followed by two acolytes, his knees were trembling. He felt that something was not as it should be, that there was treachery in the air.

An hour later he returned, shattered and with a temperature.

"What happened?" asked Christ from the altar.

"Enough to make one's hair stand on end," stammered Don Camillo. "A terrible thing. A band, Garibaldi's hymn, a speech from Peppone, and the laying of the first stone of 'The People's Palace'! And I had to bless the stone while Peppone chuckled with joy. And the ruffian asked me to say a few words, and I had to make a suitable little address because, although it is a Party affair, that dog dressed it up as a social undertaking."

Don Camillo paced back and forth in the empty church. Then he came to a standstill in front of Christ. "A mere trifle," he exclaimed. "An assembly hall, reading room, library, gymnasium, dispensary, and theater. A skyscraper of two floors with ground for sports and bowling. And the whole lot for the miserable sum of ten million lire."

"Not bad, given the high cost of building today," observed Christ.

Don Camillo sank down in a pew. "Lord," he moaned, "why have You done this to me?"

"Don Camillo, you are unreasonable."

"No, I'm not unreasonable. For ten years I have been praying to You on my knees to find me a little money so that I could build a library, an assembly hall for the young people, a playground for the children with a merry-go-round and swings and possibly a little swimming pool. For ten years I have humbled myself to bloated land-owners when I would have preferred smacking them between the eyes every time I saw them. I must have organized two hundred bazaars and knocked at easily two thousand doors and I have nothing at all to show for it. Then this excommunicate dog comes along, and behold ten million lire drop into his pockets from Heaven."

Christ shook His head. "They didn't fall from Heaven," He replied. "He found them underground. I had nothing to do with it, Don Camillo. It is entirely due to his own personal initiative."

Don Camillo spread out his arms. "Then the obvious deduction is that I am a poor fool.'"

He went off to stamp up and down his study in the rectory, roaring with fury. He had to exclude the possibility that Peppone had got those ten million by holding people up on the roads or by robbing a bank.

He thought of the days of the liberation when Peppone came down from the mountains and it seemed as if the proletarian revolution might break out at any moment. "Peppone must have threatened those cowards of gentry and squeezed their money out of them," he said to himself. Then he remembered that in those days there had been no landowners in the neighborhood, but that there had been a detachment of the British Army which arrived simultaneously with Peppone and his men. The British moved into the landowners' houses, replacing the Germans who had stripped them of everything of any value. Therefore, Peppone couldn't have got the ten million by looting.

Maybe the money came from Russia? He burst out laughing; was it likely that the Russians should give a thought to Peppone?

At last he returned to the church. "Lord," he begged, from the foot of the altar, "won't You tell me where Peppone found the money?"

"Don Camillo," replied Christ with a smile, "do you take Me for a private detective? Why ask God to tell you the truth, when you have only to seek it within yourself? Look for it, Don Camillo, and meanwhile, in order to distract your mind, why not make a trip to the city?"

The following evening, when he got back from his excursion to the city, Don Camillo went before Christ in a condition of extreme agitation.

"What has upset you, Don Camillo?"

"Something quite mad," exclaimed Don Camillo breathlessly. "I have met a dead man! Face to face in the street!"

"Don Camillo, calm yourself and reflect. Usually the dead whom one meets face to face in the street are alive."

"This one cannot be!" shouted Don Camillo. "This one is as dead as mutton, and I know it because I myself carried him to the cemetery."

"If that is the case," Christ replied, "then I have nothing more to say. You must have seen a ghost."

Don Camillo shrugged his shoulders. "Of course not! Ghosts don't exist except in the minds of hysterical women!"

"And therefore?"

"Well . . ." muttered Don Camillo.

Don Camillo collected his thoughts. The deceased had been a thin young man who lived in a nearby village, and Don Camillo had seen him from time to time before the war. He had come down from the mountains with Peppone and his men and had been wounded in the head. Peppone put him up in the house which had been the German headquarters and which that day became the headquarters of the British Command. Peppone had his office in the room next to the invalid. Don Camillo remembered it all clearly: the villa was surrounded by sentries three deep and not a fly could leave it, because the British were still fighting nearby and were particularly careful of their own skins.

All this had happened one morning, and on the same evening the young man died. Peppone sent for Don Camillo toward midnight, but by the time he got there the young man was already in his coffin. The British didn't want the body in the house and so, at about noon, Peppone and his most trusted men carried out the coffin, covered with the Italian flag. A detachment of British soldiers had kindly volunteered to supply military honors.

Don Camillo recalled that the ceremony had been most moving. The whole village had walked behind the coffin which had been placed on a gun carriage. He himself had officiated, and his sermon before the body was lowered into the grave had people actually weeping. Peppone in the front row had sobbed.

"I certainly know how to express myself, when I put my mind to it!" said Don Camillo to himself complacently, recalling the episode. Then he took up his train of thought. "And in spite of all that, I could swear that the young man I met today in the city was the same one I followed to the grave."

He sighed. "Such is life!"

The following day, Don Camillo paid a visit to Peppone at his workshop where he found him lying on his back underneath a car.

"Good morning, Comrade Mayor. I want to tell you that for the past two days I have been thinking over your description of your 'People's Palace'!"

"And what do you think of it?" jeered Peppone.

"Magnificent! It has made me decide to start work on that scheme of a little place with a bathing-pool, garden, sports ground, theater, et cetera, which, as you know, I have planned for the past ten years. I expect to lay the foundation stone next Sunday. It would give me great pleasure if you, as Mayor, would attend the ceremony."

"Willingly—courtesy for courtesy."

"Meanwhile, you might try to trim down the plans for your own place a bit. It looks too big for my taste."

Peppone stared at him in amazement. "Don Camillo, are you crazy?"

"No more than when I conducted a funeral and made a patriotic address over a coffin that can't have been securely closed, because only yesterday I met the corpse walking about in the city."

Peppone sneered, "What are you trying to insinuate?"

"Nothing. Merely that the coffin to which the British presented arms was full of what you found in the cellars of that villa where the German Command had hidden it. And that the dead man was alive and hidden in the attic."

"A-a-h!" howled Peppone, "the same old story! An attempt to malign the partisan movement!"

"Leave the partisans out of it. They don't interest me!"

And he walked away while Peppone stood muttering vague threats.

That same evening, Don Camillo was reading the paper and waiting for Peppone. He arrived accompanied by Brusco and two other prominent supporters—the same men who had acted as pall-bearers.

"You," said Peppone, "can drop your insinuations. It was all of it stuff looted by the Germans: silver, cameras, instruments, gold, et cetera. If we hadn't taken it, the British would have. We took the only possible means of getting it out of the place. I have witnesses and receipts: nobody has touched so much as a lira. Ten million was taken and ten million will be spent for the people."

Brusco, who was hot tempered, began to shout that it was God's truth and that he, if necessary, knew well enough how to deal with certain people.

"So do I," Don Camillo replied calmly. He dropped the newspaper which he had been holding in front of him, and it was easy to see that under his right armpit he held the famous Tommy gun that once belonged to Peppone.

Brusco turned pale but Peppone held up his hands. "Don Camillo—there is no need to quarrel."

"I agree," replied Don Camillo. "In fact, I agree all the way around. Ten million was acquired and ten million will be spent for the people. Seven on your People's Palace and three on my Recreation Center for the people's children. *Suffer little children to come unto Me.* I ask only what is my due."

The four consulted together for a moment in undertones. Then Peppone spoke: "If you didn't have that damnable thing in your hands, I'd tell you that your suggestion is the filthiest blackmail in the world."

On the following Sunday, Peppone, together with all the village Council, assisted at the laying of the first stone of Don Camillo's Recreation Center. Peppone also made a short speech. However, he was able to whisper in Don Camillo's ear:

"It might be better to tie this stone around your neck and throw you in the Po."

That evening, Don Camillo went to report to Christ. "Well, what do You think about it?" he said after he had described the events of the day.

"Exactly what Peppone said. That if you didn't have that damnable thing in your hands, I should say that it was the filthiest blackmail in the world."

"But I have nothing at all in my hands except the check that Peppone has just given me."

"Precisely," whispered Christ. "And with that three million you are going to do so many beautiful things, Don Camillo, that I haven't the heart to scold you."

Don Camillo genuflected and went off to bed to dream of a

garden full of children—a garden with a merry-go-round and a swing, and on the swing sat Peppone's youngest son, Libero Camillo Lenin, chirping joyfully like a fledgling.

For Discussion

1. Why was Don Camillo so angry at Peppone for beginning the construction of "The People's Palace"? What did Don Camillo's reactions reveal about him as a person? What other qualities did he reveal in this story? Point out specific sentences or passages to support your answer.

2. Explain how Don Camillo figured out the mystery about the "ghost" he had seen. What did he do with his information? Do you think his methods for getting what he wanted were justified? Why or why not?

3. What was Christ's attitude toward Don Camillo? Did He in any subtle way help Don Camillo? How? Do you think Christ really thought that what Don Camillo had done was "blackmail"? Why or why not?

4. How would you describe the attitude of the author toward Don Camillo and Peppone? What sentence in the introduction to the story is a clue to his attitude?

Raw Material

ONE afternoon Don Camillo, who for the past week had been in a chronic state of agitation and done nothing but rush around, was returning from a visit to a neighboring village. When he reached his own parish, he had to get off his bicycle because some men had appeared since his departure and were digging a ditch right across the road.

"We are putting in a new drain," a workman explained, "by the Mayor's orders."

Don Camillo went straight to the Town Hall and when he found Peppone, he lost his temper. "Are we all going off our nuts?" he exclaimed. "Here you are, digging this filthy ditch. Don't you know that this is Friday?"

"Well!" replied Peppone with astonishment. "And is it forbidden to dig a ditch on a Friday?"

Don Camillo roared: "But don't you realize that it's less than two days to Sunday?"

Peppone looked worried. He rang a bell and Smilzo came in. "Hey, Smilzo," said Peppone. "The reverendo says that since today is Friday, it's less than two days to Sunday. What do you think?"

Smilzo pondered seriously. Then he pulled out a pencil and made calculations on a piece of paper. "Why," he said presently, "taking into consideration that it is now four o'clock in the afternoon and therefore within eight hours of midnight, it will actually be Sunday within thirty-two hours from the present time."

Don Camillo watched all these maneuvers and by now was almost frothing at the mouth. "I understand!" he shouted. "This is a put-up job to boycott the Bishop's visit."

"Reverendo," replied Peppone, "where is the connection between our local sewage and the Bishop's visit? And also, may I ask what Bishop and why he should be coming here?"

"To the devil with your black soul!" bawled Don Camillo. "That ditch must be filled in at once, or else the Bishop will be unable to pass on Sunday!"

Peppone's face looked completely blank. "Unable to pass? But then how did you pass? There are a couple of planks across the ditch, if I am not mistaken."

"But the Bishop is coming by car," exclaimed Don Camillo. "We can't ask a bishop to get out of his car and walk!"

"You must forgive me, I didn't know that bishops were unable to walk," retorted Peppone. "If that is so then it is quite another matter. Smilzo, call the city and tell them to send us a crane immediately. We'll put it near the ditch and as soon as the Bishop's car arrives the crane can grapple onto it and lift it over the ditch. Understand?"

"Perfectly, chief. And what color crane should I ask for?"

"Tell them chromium or nickel-plated; it will look better."

In such circumstances even a man who lacked Don Camillo's armor-plated fists might have been tempted to come to blows. But it was precisely in such cases as these that Don Camillo, on the contrary, became entirely composed. His arguments to himself was as follows: "If this fellow sets out so deliberately to provoke me, it is because he hopes that I will lose my temper. Therefore, if I give him one on the jaw I am simply playing his game. As a fact, I should not be striking Peppone, but a Mayor in the exercise of his functions, and that would make an infernal scandal and create an atmosphere not only hostile to me personally but also to the Bishop."

"Never mind," he said quietly, "even bishops can walk."

Speaking in church that evening, he implored his congregation to remain calm, to concentrate on asking God to shed light upon the mind of their Mayor so that he would not ruin the impending ceremony by compelling the faithful to pass one at a time over a couple of insecure boards. And they must also pray God to prevent this improvised bridge from breaking under the undue strain and thus turning a day of rejoicing into one of mourning.

This Machiavellian sermon had its calculated effect upon all the women of the congregation who, on leaving the church, collected in front of Peppone's house and carried on to such an extent that at last Peppone came to a window and shouted that the ditch would be filled in.

And so all was well, but on Sunday morning the village streets were adorned with large printed posters:

"*Comrades! Alleging as a pretext of offense the initiation of work of public utility, the reactionaries have staged an unseemly agitation that has offended our democratic instincts. On Sunday our borough is to receive a visit from the representative of a foreign power, the same in fact who has been indirectly, the cause of the aforementioned agitation. Bearing in mind your just resentment and indignation, we are anxious to avoid, on Sunday, any demonstration which might complicate our relations with strangers. We therefore categorically exhort you to keep your reception of this representative of a foreign power within the limits of a dignified indifference.*

"*Hurrah for the Democratic Republic! Hurrah for the Proletariat! Hurrah for Russia!*"

The streets were further enlivened by a throng of Party members who, it was easy to understand, had been specially mobilized with orders to parade the streets with "*dignified indifference*," wearing red handkerchiefs or red ties.

Don Camillo, very pale around the gills, went into the church for a moment and was about to hurry away when he heard Christ calling him. "Don Camillo, why are you in such a hurry?"

"I have to go and receive the Bishop along the road," Don Camillo explained. "It is some distance, and then there are so many people about wearing red handkerchiefs that if the Bishop does not see me immediately he will think that he has come to Stalingrad."

"And are these wearers of red handkerchiefs foreigners or of another religion?"

"No, they are the usual rascals that You see before You from time to time, here in the church."

"Then if that is the case, Don Camillo, it would be better for you to take off that contraption that you have strapped on under your cassock and to put it back in the closet." Don Camillo removed the Tommy gun and went to put it away in the sacristy.

"You can leave it there until I tell you to take it out again," commanded Christ and Don Camillo shrugged his shoulders.

"If I have to wait until You tell me to use a Tommy gun, we'll really be in the soup!" he exclaimed. "You aren't likely ever to give the word, and I must confess that in many cases the Old Testament . . ."

"Reactionary!" smiled Christ. "And while you are wasting time chattering, your poor old defenseless Bishop is the prey of savage Russian reds!"

This was a fact: the poor old defenseless Bishop was indeed in the hands of the agitators. From early morning, the faithful had flocked to both sides of the main road, forming two long and impressive walls of enthusiasm, but a few minutes before the Bishop's car was sighted, Peppone, warned by a rocket fired by his outpost to signal the approach of the enemy, gave the order to advance and by a lightning maneuver the red forces rushed forward half a mile, so that upon his arrival the Bishop found the entire road a mass of men wearing red handkerchiefs. People wandered to and fro and clustered into gossiping groups, displaying a "dignified indifference" toward the difficulties of the Bishop's driver who had to go at a snail's pace, clearing a passage by continuous use of his horn.

The Bishop, a bent and white-haired man whose voice when he spoke seemed to come not from his lips but from another century, immediately understood the *"dignified indifference"* and, telling his driver to stop the car, made an abortive movement to open the door. It appeared that he lacked the necessary strength. Brusco, who was standing nearby, fell into the trap, and when he realized his mistake because of the kick Peppone had landed on his shin, it was too late and he had already opened the door.

"Thank you, my son," said the Bishop. "I think it would be better if I walked to the village."

"But it is some distance," muttered Smilzo, also receiving a kick on the shin.

"Never mind," replied the Bishop, laughing, "I wouldn't want to disturb your political meeting."

"It is not a political meeting," explained Peppone gloomily. "These are only workers quietly discussing their own affairs. You'd better stay in your car."

But by now the Bishop was standing in the road, and Brusco had earned another kick because, realizing that he was unsteady on his feet, he had offered the support of his arm.

"Thank you, thank you so much, my son," said the Bishop, and he set out, having made a sign to his secretary not to accompany him, as he wished to go alone.

And thus it was at the head of the entire red horde that he reached the zone occupied by Don Camillo's forces. And at the Bishop's side were Peppone, his headquarters staff, and all his most devoted henchmen because, as Peppone pointed out, the slightest gesture of discourtesy shown by any hot-headed fool to the representative of a foreign power would give the reactionaries the opportunities of their lives.

"The order remains and will remain unchanged," stated Peppone. "*Dignified indifference.*"

The instant Don Camillo sighted the Bishop, he rushed toward him. "Excellency," he exclaimed, with great agitation. "Forgive me, but it was not my fault! I was awaiting you with all the faithful, but at the last moment . . ."

"Don't worry," smiled the Bishop. "The fault has been entirely my own. I took it into my head to leave the car and take a walk. All Bishops as they get old become a little crazy!"

The faithful applauded, the bands struck up and the Bishop looked about him with obvious enjoyment. "What a lovely village!" he said as he walked on. "Really lovely, and so beautifully neat and clean. You must have an excellent local administration."

"We do what we can for the good of the people," replied Brusco, receiving his third kick from Peppone.

The Bishop, on reaching the Square, noticed the large new edifice and was interested. "And what is that handsome building?"

"The People's Palace," replied Peppone proudly.

"But it is really magnificent!" exclaimed the Bishop.

"Would you care to go through it?" said Peppone while a terrific kick on the shins made him wince. That particular kick had come from Don Camillo.

The Bishop's secretary, a lean young man with spectacles perched upon a big nose, had caught up with the procession and now hurried forward to warn him that this was an unsuitable departure from routine, but the Bishop had already entered the building. And they showed him everything: the gymnasium, the reading-room, the writing-room, and when they reached the library he went up to the book shelves and studied the titles of the books. Before the bookcase labeled "Political," which was filled with propagandist books and pamphlets, he said nothing but only sighed, and Peppone, who was close to him, noticed that sigh.

"Nobody ever reads them," whispered Peppone.

He spared his visitor the inspection of the offices, but could not resist the temptation to show off the tea-room that was the object of his special pride, and thus the Bishop, on his way out, was confronted by the enormous portrait of the man with the big mustache and the small eyes.

"You know how it is in politics," said Peppone in a confidential voice. "And then, believe me, he isn't really such a bad egg."

"May God in His Mercy shed light upon his mind also," replied the Bishop quietly.

Throughout all this, Don Camillo's position was precarious. While he was indignant at the presumption upon the Bishop's kindness that inflicted on him an inspection of the People's Palace, which was a structure that surely cried to God for vengeance, on the other hand he was proud that the Bishop should know how progressive and up-to-date the village was. Moreover, he was not displeased that the Bishop should realize the strength of the local leftist organization, since it could only enhance the merits of his own Recreation Center in the Bishop's eyes.

When the inspection was at an end, Don Camillo approached the Bishop. "It seems a pity, Excellency," he said, so loudly that Peppone could not fail to hear him; "it seems a pity that our Mayor has not shown you the arsenal. It is believed to be the most fully supplied of the entire province."

Peppone was about to retort, but the Bishop forestalled him. "Surely not as well supplied as your own," he replied, laughing.

"That's no lie!" exclaimed Smilzo.

"He even has an S.S. mortar buried somewhere," added Brusco.

The Bishop turned toward Peppone's staff. "You wanted him back," he said, "and now you can keep him. I warned you that he was dangerous."

"He doesn't scare us," said Peppone with a grin.

"Keep an eye on him all the same," the Bishop advised him.

Don Camillo shook his head. "You will always have your joke, Excellency," he exclaimed. "But you have no idea what these people are like!"

On his way out of the People's Palace, the Bishop passed the bulletin-board, saw the poster and paused to read it.

"Ah," he remarked, "you are expecting a visit from the representative of a foreign power! And who may that be, Don Camillo?"

"I know very little about politics," replied Don Camillo. "We must ask the gentleman who is responsible for the poster. Mr. Mayor, His Excellency wishes to know who is the representative of a foreign power who is mentioned in your manifesto?"

"Oh," said Peppone, after a moment's hesitation. "The usual American."

"I understand," replied the Bishop. "One of those Americans who are looking for oil in these parts. Am I right?"

"Yes," said Peppone. "It's a downright scandal—any oil there may be, belongs to the people."

"I quite agree," said the Bishop with the utmost gravity. "But I think you were wise to tell your men to limit their reactions to a 'dignified indifference.' We would be foolish to quarrel with America, don't you agree?"

Peppone shrugged. "Excellency," he said, "you know how it is: one puts up with as much as one can and then comes the last straw!"

When the Bishop arrived in front of the church, he found all the local children from Don Camillo's Recreation Center in a neat formation, singing a song of welcome. Then an immense bouquet of flowers was presented to the Bishop by a small child with such beautiful curls and clothes that all the women nearly went out of their minds. There was complete silence while the infant, without pause and in a voice as clear and pure as a little spring of water, recited a poem in the Bishop's honor. After which everyone applauded the child, exclaiming that he was adorable.

Peppone went up to Don Camillo. "Dastard!" he hissed in his ear. "You take advantage of a child's innocence to make me ridiculous before everybody! I'll break every bone in your body. And as for that brat, I'll show him where he gets off. I'll chuck him in the river!"

"Good hunting!" replied Don Camillo. "Since he's your own son you can do what you want with him."

And it really was shocking, because Peppone carried the poor child off to the river like a bundle, and made him recite the poem in honor of the Bishop three times in a row.

For Discussion

1. Contrast Don Camillo's and Christ's attitude toward "the wearers of red handkerchiefs."
2. How did the Bishop show his cleverness on meeting the "dignified indifference" of Peppone's supporters? In what way were Don Camillo and Peppone in competition for the Bishop's attention?
3. What unexpected aspect of Peppone was revealed as he escorted the Bishop through "The People's Palace"? How do you explain this aspect of the Mayor?
4. Point out lines which showed the Bishop's sense of humor and tolerance during his visit. In your opinion, what was the Bishop's attitude toward Don Camillo and Peppone?
5. How did Don Camillo humiliate Peppone? Who do you think won out in this humorous tussle over the Bishop? Explain.
6. Point out instances of irony in this selection. Do you think Guareschi is criticizing a particular group of men or mankind as a whole? Explain.
7. Perhaps the most startling and delightful aspect of these two stories is Don Camillo's "conversations with Christ," who represents Don Camillo's conscience. Describe Christ as He is presented by the author. How is He like and different from Christ as He is customarily portrayed?
8. Describe the character of the Italian people as they are revealed by the author in these two stories. Do you think that Guareschi's satirical tone is harsh or gentle? Give examples from these two selections to support your answer.

For Composition

1. Don Camillo is hardly a model priest, yet he is extremely likable. Write a character sketch of him which reveals why this is so.
2. Rivalry between people has existed since the beginning of civilization. Write a short narrative in which you recount an incident from your own experience based on rivalry that may have been bitter or friendly. Tell what the outcome was.

Thomas Mann

Railway Accident

Thomas Mann (1875–1955), influenced by Schopenhauer, Nietzsche, and later, by Goethe, wrote novels and short stories which deal with dilemmas and conflicts in modern European society. One of his leading themes is the struggle of the artist in a decaying, bourgeois world, and the situation that results when the romantic, represented by the literary artist, is forced to live in the same world as the realist, or the businessman. It is Mann's ability to recreate a whole era, through plot and character, that has earned him his reputation as one of the finest novelists of the century. *The Magic Mountain*, which pictures the decay of modern society, is an excellent example of this.

Mann achieved fame with the publication of his first novel, *Buddenbrook*, in 1901, which deals with the conflicts in a middle-class German family. He was awarded the Nobel Prize for Literature in 1929. With the rise of Nazism, Mann left Germany in 1933 and lived first in Switzerland and then in the United States. His later works of fiction revealed his growing conviction that the artist cannot live detached from society but must involve himself in the problems of his time.

"Railway Accident" is one of Mann's early stories, which he saw as "an incidental sketch, humorous in conception." It shows the author's preoccupation with class distinctions in Germany before World War I, and what can happen to these distinctions in a moment of crisis. Mann also reveals his view of how a writer can react when face to face with a personal crisis.

TELL you a story? But I don't know any. Well, yes, after all, here is something I might tell.

Once, two years ago now it is, I was in a railway accident; all the details are clear in my memory.

It was not really a first-class one—no wholesale telescoping or "heaps of unidentifiable dead"—not that sort of thing. Still, it was a proper accident, with all the trimmings, and on top of that it was at night. Not everybody has been through one, so I will describe it the best I can.

I was on my way to Dresden, whither I had been invited by some
friends of letters: it was a literary and artistic pilgrimage, in short,
such as, from time to time, I undertake not unwillingly. You make
appearances, you attend functions, you show yourself to admiring
crowds—not for nothing is one a subject of William II. And certainly Dresden is beautiful, especially the Zwinger; and afterwards
I intended to go for ten days or a fortnight to the White Hart to
rest, and if, thanks to the treatments, the spirit should come upon
me, I might do a little work as well. To this end I had put my manuscript at the bottom of my trunk, together with my notes—a good
stout bundle done up in brown paper and tied with string in the
Bavarian colors. I like to travel in comfort, especially when my
expenses are paid. So I patronized the sleeping-cars, reserving a place
days ahead in a first-class compartment. All was in order; nevertheless
I was excited, as I always am on such occasions, for a journey is still
an adventure to me, and where traveling is concerned I shall never
manage to feel properly blasé. I perfectly well know that the night
train for Dresden leaves the central station at Munich regularly every
evening, and every morning is in Dresden. But when I am traveling
with it, and linking my momentous destiny to its own, the matter
assumes importance. I cannot rid myself of the notion that it is
making a special trip today, just on my account, and the unreason-
ing and mistaken conviction sets up in me a deep and speechless
unrest, which does not subside until all the formalities of departure
are behind me—the packing, the drive in the loaded cab to the station,
the arrival there, and the registration of luggage—and I can feel myself finally and securely bestowed. Then, indeed, a pleasing relaxa-
tion takes place, the mind turns to fresh concerns, the unknown
unfolds itself beyond the expanse of window-pane, and I am con-
sumed with joyful anticipations.

And so on this occasion. I had tipped my porter so liberally that
he pulled his cap and gave me a pleasant journey; and I stood at the
corridor window of my sleeping-car, smoking my evening cigar and
watching the bustle on the platform. There were whistlings and
rumblings, hurryings and farewells, and the singsong of newspaper
and refreshment vendors, and over all the great electric moons
glowed through the mist of the October evening. Two stout fellows
pulled a hand-cart of large trunks along the platform to the baggage
car in front of the train. I easily identified, by certain unmistakable

features, my own trunk; one among many it lay, and at the bottom of it reposed my precious package. "There," thought I, "no need to worry; it is in good hands. Look at that guard with the leather cartridge-belt, the prodigious sergeant-major's moustache, and the inhospitable eye. Watch him rebuking the old woman in the thread-bare black cape—for two pins she would have got into a second-class carriage. He is security, he is authority, he is our parent, he is the State. He is strict, not to say gruff, you would not care to mingle with him; but reliability is writ large upon his brow, and in his care your trunk reposes as in the bosom of Abraham."

A man was strolling up and down the platform in spats and a yellow autumn coat, with a dog on a leash. Never have I seen a handsomer dog: a small, stocky bull, smooth-coated, muscular, with black spots; as well groomed and amusing as the dogs one sees in circuses, who make the audience laugh by dashing round and round the ring with all the energy of their small bodies. This dog had a silver collar, with a plaited leather leash. But all this was not surprising, considering his master, the gentleman in spats, who had beyond a doubt the noblest origins. He wore a monocle, which accentuated without dis-torting his general air; the defiant perch of his moustache bore out the proud and stubborn expression of his chin and the corners of his mouth. He addressed a question to the martial guard, who knew perfectly well with whom he was dealing and answered hand to cap. My gentleman strolled on, gratified with the impression he had made. He strutted in his spats, his gaze was cold, he regarded men and affairs with penetrating eye. Certainly he was far above feeling journey-proud; travel by train was no novelty to him. He was at home in life, without fear of authority or regulations; he was an authority him-self—in short, a nob.[1] I could not look at him enough. When he thought the time had come, he got into the train (the guard had just turned his back). He came along the corridor behind me, bumped into me, and did not apologize. What a man! But that was nothing to what followed. Without turning a hair he took his dog with him into the sleeping-compartment! Surely it was forbidden to do that. When should I presume to take a dog with me into a sleeping-compartment? But he did it, on the strength of his prescriptive rights as a nob, and shut the door behind him.

There came a whistle outside, the locomotive whistled in response,

[1] **nob:** British slang for a person of wealth or social distinction

gently the train began to move. I stayed awhile by the window watching the hand-waving and the shifting lights. . . . I retired inside the carriage.

The sleeping-car was not very full, a compartment next to mine was empty and had not been got ready for the night; I decided to make myself comfortable there for an hour's peaceful reading. I fetched my book and settled in. The sofa had a silky salmon-pink covering, an ash-tray stood on the folding table, the light burned bright. I read and smoked.

The sleeping-car attendant entered in pursuance of his duties and asked for my ticket for the night. I delivered it into his grimy hands. He was polite but entirely official, did not even vouchsafe me a good-night as from one human being to another, but went out at once and knocked on the door of the next compartment. He would better have left it alone, for my gentleman of the spats was inside; and perhaps because he did not wish anyone to discover his dog, but possibly because he had really gone to bed, he got furious at anyone daring to disturb him. Above the rumbling of the train I heard his immediate and elemental burst of rage. "What do you want?" he roared. "Leave me alone, you swine." He said "swine." It was a lordly epithet, the epithet of a cavalry officer—it did my heart good to hear it. But the sleeping-car attendant must have resorted to diplomacy—of course he had to have the man's ticket—for just as I stepped into the corridor to get a better view the door of the compartment abruptly opened a little way and the ticket flew out into the attendant's face; yes, it was flung with violence straight in his face. He picked it up with both hands, and though he had got the corner of it in one eye, so that the tears came, he thanked the man, saluting and clicking his heels together. Quite overcome, I returned to my book.

I considered whether there was anything against my smoking another cigar and concluded that there was little or nothing. So I did it, rolling onward and reading; I felt full of contentment and good ideas. Time passed, it was ten o'clock, half past ten, all my fellow-travelers had gone to bed, at last I decided to follow them. I got up and went into my own compartment. A real little bedroom, most luxurious, with stamped leather wall hangings, clothes-hooks, a nickel-plated wash-basin. The lower berth was snowily prepared, the covers invitingly turned back. Oh, triumph of modern times! I thought. One lies in this bed as though at home, it rocks a little all night, and the result is that next morning one is in Dresden. I took my suitcase out of the rack to get ready for bed; I was holding it above my head, with my arms stretched up.

It was at this moment that the railway accident occurred. I remember it like yesterday.

We gave a jerk—but jerk is a poor word for it. It was a jerk of deliberately foul intent, a jerk with a horrid reverberating crash, and so violent that my suitcase leaped out of my hands I knew not whither, while I was flung forcibly with my shoulder against the wall. I had no time to stop and think. But now followed a frightful rocking of the carriage, and while that went on, one had plenty of leisure to be frightened. A railway carriage rocks going over switches or on sharp curves, that we know; but this rocking would not let me stand up, I was thrown from one wall to the other as the carriage careened. I had only one simple thought, but I thought it with concentration, exclusively, I thought: "Something is the matter, something is the matter, something is *very much* the matter!" Just in those words. But later I thought: "Stop, stop, stop!" For I knew that it would be a great help if only the train could be brought to a halt. And lo, at this my unuttered but fervent behest, the train did stop.

Up to now a deathlike stillness had reigned in the carriage, but at this point terror found tongue. Shrill feminine screams mingled with deeper masculine cries of alarm. Next door someone was shouting "Help!" No doubt about it, this was the very same voice which, just previously, had uttered the lordly epithet—the voice of the man in spats, his very voice, though distorted by fear. "Help!" it cried; and just as I stepped into the corridor, where the passengers were collecting, he burst out of his compartment in a silk sleeping-suit and halted, looking wildly round him. "Great God!" he exclaimed, "Almighty God!" and then, as though to abase himself utterly, perhaps in hope to avert destruction, he added in a deprecating tone: "*Dear God!*" But suddenly he thought of something else, of trying to help himself. He threw himself upon the case on the wall where an axe and saw are kept for emergencies, and broke the glass with his fist. But finding that he could not release the tools at once, he abandoned them, buffeted his way through the crowd of passengers, so that the half-dressed women screamed afresh, and leaped out of the carriage.

All that was the work of a moment only. And then for the first time I began to feel the shock: in a certain weakness of the spine, a passing inability to swallow. The sleeping-car attendant, red-eyed, grimy-handed, had just come up; we all pressed round him; the women, with bare arms and shoulders, stood wringing their hands.

The train, he explained, had been derailed, we had run off the track. That, as it afterwards turned out, was not true. But behold, the man in his excitement had become voluble, he abandoned his official neutrality; events had loosened his tongue and he spoke to us in confidence, about his wife. "I told her today, I did, 'Wife,' I said, 'I feel in my bones somethin's goin' to happen.'" And sure enough, hadn't something happened? We all felt how right he had been. The carriage had begun to fill with smoke, a thick smudge; nobody knew where it came from, but we all thought it best to get out into the night.

That could only be done by quite a big jump from the footboard onto the line, for there was no platform of course, and besides our carriage was canted a good deal towards the opposite side. But the ladies—they had hastily covered their nakedness—jumped in desperation and soon we were all standing there between the lines.

It was nearly dark, but from where we were we could see that no damage had been done at the rear of the train, though all the carriages stood at a slant. But further forward—fifteen or twenty paces further forward! Not for nothing had the jerk we felt made such a horrid crash. There lay a waste of wreckage; we could see the margins of it, with the little lights of the guards' lanterns flickering across and to and fro.

Excited people came towards us, bringing reports of the situation. We were close by a small station not far beyond Regensburg, and as the result of a defective point our express had run onto the wrong line, had crashed at full speed into a stationary freight train, hurling it out of the station, annihilating its rear carriages, and itself sustaining serious damage. The great express engine from Maffei's in Munich lay smashed up and done for. Price seventy thousand marks. And in the forward coaches, themselves lying almost on one side, many of the seats were telescoped. No, thank goodness, there were no lives lost. There was talk of an old woman having been "taken out," but nobody had seen her. At least, people had been thrown in all directions, children buried under luggage, the shock had been great. The baggage car was demolished. Demolished—the baggage car? Demolished.

There I stood.

A bareheaded official came running along the track. The station-master. He issued wild and tearful commands to the passengers, to make them behave themselves and get back into the coaches. But nobody took any notice of him, he had no cap and no self-control. Poor wretch! Probably the responsibility was his. Perhaps this was the end of his career, the wreck of his prospects. I could not ask him about the baggage car—it would have been tactless.

Another official came up—he *limped* up. I recognized him by the sergeant-major's moustache: it was the stern and vigilant guard of the early evening—our Father, the State. He limped along, bent over with his hand on his knee, thinking about nothing else. "Oh, dear!" he said, "oh, dear, oh dear me!" I asked him what was the matter. "I got stuck, sir, jammed me in the chest, I made my escape through the roof." This "made my escape through the roof" sounded like a newspaper report. Certainly the man would not have used the phrase in everyday life; he had experienced not so much an accident as a newspaper account of it—but what was that to me? He was in no state to give me news of my manuscript. So I accosted a young man who came up bustling and self-important from the waste of wreckage, and asked him about the heavy luggage.

"Well, sir, nobody can say anything as to that"—his tone implied that I ought to be grateful to have escaped unhurt. "Everything is all over the place. Women's shoes—" he said with a sweeping gesture to indicate the devastation, and wrinkled his nose. "When they start the clearing operations we shall see. . . . Women's shoes. . . ."

There I stood. All alone I stood there in the night and searched my heart. Clearing operations. Clearing operations were to be under-taken with my manuscript. Probably it was destroyed, then, torn up, demolished. My honeycomb, my spider-web, my nest, my earth, my pride and pain, my all, the best of me—what should I do if it were gone? I had no copy of what had been welded and forged, of what already was a living, speaking thing—to say nothing of my notes and drafts, all that I had saved and stored up and overheard and sweated over for years—my squirrel's hoard. What should I do? I inquired of my own soul and I knew that I should begin over again from the beginning. Yes ,with animal patience, with the tenacity of a primitive creature the curious and complex produce of whose little ingenuity and industry has been destroyed; after a moment of helpless bewilderment I should set to work again—and perhaps this time it would come easier!

But meanwhile a fire brigade had come up, their torches cast a red light over the wreck; when I went forward and looked for the baggage car, behold it was almost intact, the luggage quite unharmed. All the things that lay strewn about came out of the freight train: among the rest a quantity of balls of string—a perfect sea of string covered the ground far and wide.

A load was lifted from my heart. I mingled with the people who stood talking and fraternizing in misfortune—also showing off and being important. So much seemed clear, that the engine-driver had acted with great presence of mind. He had averted a great catastrophe by pulling the emergency brake at the last moment. Otherwise, it was said, there would have been a general smash and the whole train would have gone over the steep embankment on the left. Oh, praiseworthy engine-driver! He was not about, nobody had seen him, but his fame spread down the whole length of the train and we all lauded him in his absence. "That chap," said one man, and pointed with one hand somewhere off into the night, "that chap saved our lives." We all agreed.

But our train was standing on a track where it did not belong, and it behooved those in charge to guard it from behind so that another one did not run into it. Firemen perched on the rear carriage with torches of flaming pitch, and the excited young man who had given me such a fright with his "women's shoes" seized upon a torch too and began signalling with it, though no train was anywhere in sight.

Slowly and by degrees something like order was produced, the State our Father regained poise and presence. Steps had been taken, wires sent, presently a breakdown train from Regensburg steamed cautiously into the station and great gas flares with reflectors were set up about the wreck. We passengers were now turned off and told to go into the little station building to wait for our new conveyance. Laden with our hand luggage, some of the party with bandaged heads, we passed through a lane of inquisitive natives into the tiny waiting-room, where we herded together as best we could. And inside of an hour we were all stowed higgledy-piggledy into a special train.

I had my first-class ticket—my journey being paid for—but it availed me nothing, for everybody wanted to ride first and my carriage was more crowded than the others. But just as I found me a little niche, whom do I see diagonally opposite to me, huddled in the corner? My hero, the gentleman with the spats and the vocabulary of a cavalry officer. He did not have his dog, it had been taken away from him in defiance of his rights as a nob and now sat howling in a gloomy prison just behind the engine. His master, like myself, held a yellow ticket which was no good to him, and he was grumbling, he was trying to make head against this communistic levelling of rank in the face of general misfortune. But another man answered him in a virtuous tone: "You ought to be thankful that you can sit down." And with a sour smile my gentleman resigned himself to the crazy situation.

And now who got in, supported by two firemen? A wee little old grandmother in a tattered black cape, the very same who in Munich would for two pins have got into a second-class carriage. "Is this the first class?" she kept asking. And when we made room and assured her that it was, she sank down with a "God be praised!" onto the plush cushions as though only now was she safe and sound.

By Hof it was already five o'clock and light. There we breakfasted; an express train picked me up and deposited me with my belongings, three hours late, in Dresden.

Well, that was the railway accident I went through. I suppose it had to happen once; but whatever mathematicians may say, I feel that I now have every chance of escaping another.

For Discussion

1. In what spirit did the narrator set out on his journey? How did he feel about his first-class accommodations? What did these feelings tell you about the kind of person he was?
2. Why did the narrator feel secure just because of the way the guard looked? In view of what occurred later, why was this ironic? What do you think Mann might be implying about Germany or any nation?
3. Describe the attitude of the man in the spats. Why was the way he treated the sleeping-car attendant so offensive? What comment on German society does Mann seem to be making?
4. Why was the railway accident a crisis for the narrator? What did this event reveal to him about himself?
5. What effect did the accident have on the passengers? How did it affect the status of the man in the spats? What was the significance of the

little old lady with the black cape getting into the first-class compartment?

6. State in one sentence what you consider the theme of "Railway Accident." Is it related to the theme of any other story you have read in this book? Explain.

7. Mann frequently uses an ironical tone in describing the people and their reactions to what occurred. Point out instances of this ironical tone.

8. You have read several stories in this book which are told from the first-person point of view. Why do you think Mann chose a writer to tell this story, rather than the man in the spats or one of the other passengers? How would the story have differed in tone, in emphasis on details, and in theme if the accident had been narrated by the old woman with the black cape? Explain.

For Composition

1. Write a character sketch of the sleeping-car attendant or of another character.

2. Imagine you are the sleeping-car attendant. Using the first-person point of view, retell the incident between you and the man in the spats. In your account, reveal what went on in your mind as you attempted to collect the gentleman's ticket.

3. Pretend you are a newspaper reporter. Write an account of the railway accident. Include an interview with one of the passengers.

4. Write a composition in which you express your feelings about travel by describing a specific instance from your personal experience.

Leonid Andreyev

Laughter

Leonid Andreyev (1871–1919), short-story writer and playwright, was, like Maxim Gorky, one of the most popular Russian literary figures in the early part of this century. When he began writing he used a realistic style but his works became more and more symbolic, even mystical. This emphasis on symbolism is to be found in most of his plays, notably *He Who Gets Slapped*, which has enjoyed considerable success in America. His short stories are essentially pessimistic. One of his most famous *novellas* (long short stories), "The Red Death," is a fierce anti-war tract. Its message is that death and annihilation are the only realities. Another, "The Seven That Were Hanged," is a powerful psychological study of the reactions of a group of men awaiting execution. Disillusionment is present in almost all of Andreyev's writings. His heroes are lonely individuals, living in a cruel world that mocks them. "Laughter," in which this idea is presented, is one of his most effective symbolic stories.

1

AT six-thirty I was certain that she would come, and I was desperately happy. My coat was fastened only by the top button and fluttered in the cold wind; but I felt no cold. My head was proudly thrown back and my student's cap was cocked on the back of my head; my eyes with respect to the men they met were expressive of patronage and boldness, with respect to the women, of a seductive tenderness. Although she had been my only love for four whole days, I was so young, and my heart was so rich in love, that I could not remain perfectly indifferent to other women. My steps were quick, bold and free.

At six-forty-five my coat was fastened by two buttons, and I looked only at the women, no longer with a seductive tenderness, but rather with disgust. I only wanted *one* woman—the others might go to the Devil; they only confused me, and, with their seeming resemblance to Her, gave to my movements an uncertain and jerky indecision.

At six-fifty-five I felt warm.

At six-fifty-eight I felt cold.

As it struck seven I was convinced that she would not come.

By eight-thirty I presented the appearance of the most pitiful creature in the world. My coat was fastened with all its buttons, collar turned up, cap tilted over my nose, which was blue with cold; my hair was over my forehead, my moustache and eyelashes were whitening with rime, and my teeth gently chattered. From my shambling gait and bowed back, I might have been taken for a fairly hale old man returning from a party at the almshouse.

And She was the cause of all this—She! Oh, the Dev—! No, I won't. Perhaps She couldn't get away, or She's ill, or dead. She's dead!—and I swore.

2

"Eugenia Nikolaevna will be there tonight," one of my companions, a student, remarked to me, without the slightest *arrière pensée*.[1] He could not know that I had waited for her in the frost from seven to half-past eight.

"Indeed," I replied, as if in deep thought, but within my soul there leapt out, Oh, the Dev—! "There" meant at the Polozovs' evening party. Now the Polozovs were people with whom I was not upon visiting terms. But this evening I would be there.

"You fellows!" I shouted cheerfully. "Today is Christmas Day, when everybody enjoys himself. Let's do so too."

"But how?" one of them mournfully replied.

"And, where?" continued another.

"We'll dress up and go around to all the evening parties," I decided.

And these insensate individuals actually became cheerful. They shouted, leapt, and sang. They thanked me for my suggestion, and counted up the amount of "the ready" available. In the course of half an hour we had collected all the lonely, disconsolate students in town, and when we had recruited a cheerful dozen or so of leaping devils, we repaired to a hairdresser's—he was also a costumier—and let in there the cold, and youth, and laughter.

I wanted something somber and handsome, with a shade of elegant sadness; so I requested, " Give me the dress of a Spanish grandee."

[1] *arrière pensée:* hindsight (French)

Apparently this grandee had been very tall, for I was altogether swallowed up in his dress, and felt as absolutely alone as though I had been in a wide, empty hall. Getting out of this costume, I asked for something else.

"Would you like to be a clown? Motley with bells?"

"A clown, indeed!" I exclaimed with contempt.

"Well, then, a bandit. Such a hat and dagger!"

Oh! dagger! Yes, that would suit my purpose. But unfortunately the bandit whose clothes they gave me had scarcely grown to full stature. Most probably he had been a corrupt youth of eight years. His little hat would not cover the back of my head, and I had to be dragged out of his velvet breeches as out of a trap. A page's dress would not do: It was all spotted like the pard. The monk's cowl was all in holes.

"Look sharp; it's late," said my companions, who were already dressed, trying to hurry me up.

There was but one costume left—that of a distinguished Chinese man. "Give me the Chinese man's," I said with a wave of my hand. And they gave it to me. It was the Devil knows what! I am not speaking of the costume itself. I pass over in silence those idiotic, flowered boots, which were too short for me, and reached only half-way to my knees; but in the remaining, by far the most essential part stuck out like two incomprehensible adjuncts on either side of my feet. I say nothing of the pink rag which covered my head like a wig, and was tied by threads to my ears, so that they protruded and stood up like a bat's. But the mask!

It was, if one may use the expression, a face *in the abstract*. It had nose, eyes, and mouth all right enough, and all in the proper places; but there was nothing human about it. A human being could not look so placid—even in his coffin. It was expressive neither of sorrow, nor cheerfulness, nor surprise—it expressed absolutely nothing! It looked at you squarely, and placidly—and an uncontrollable laughter overwhelmed you. My companions rolled about on the sofas, sank impotently down on the chairs, and gesticulated.

"It will be the most original mask of the evening," they declared.

I was ready to weep; but no sooner did I glance in the mirror than I too was convulsed with laughter. Yes, it will be a most original mask!

"In no circumstances are we to take off our masks," said my companions on the way. "We'll give our word."

"Honor bright!"

3

Positively it was the most original mask. People followed me in crowds, turned me about, jostled me, pinched me. But when, harried, I turned on my persecutors in anger—uncontrollable laughter seized them. Wherever I went, a roaring cloud of laughter encompassed and pressed on me; it moved together with me, and I could not escape from this circle of mad mirth. Sometimes it seized even myself, and I shouted, sang, and danced till everything seemed to go around before me, as if I was drunk. But how remote everything was from me! And how solitary I was under that mask! At last they left me in peace. With anger and fear, with malice and tenderness intermingling, I looked at her.

"It's I."

Her long eyelashes were lifted slowly in surprise, and a whole sheaf of black rays flashed upon me, and a laugh, resonant, joyous, bright as the spring sunshine—a laugh answered me.

"Yes, it's I; I, I say," I insisted with a smile. "Why didn't you come this evening?"

But she only laughed, laughed joyously.

"I suffered so much; I felt so hurt," I said, imploring an answer.

But she only laughed. The black sheen of her eyes was extinguished, and still more brightly her smile lit up. It was the sun indeed, but burning, pitiless, cruel.

"What's the matter with you?"

"Is it really you?" she said, restraining herself. "How comical you are!"

My shoulders were bowed, and my head hung down—such despair was there in my pose. And while she, with the expiring afterglow of the smile upon her face, looked at the happy, young couples that hurried by us, I said, "It's not nice to laugh. Don't you feel that there's a living, suffering face behind my ridiculous mask—and can't you see that it was only for the opportunity it gave me of seeing you that I put it on? You gave me reason to hope for your love, and then so quickly, so cruelly deprived me of it. Why didn't you come?"

With a protest on her tender, smiling lips, she turned sharply to

me, and a cruel laugh utterly overwhelmed her. Choking, almost
weeping, covering her face with a fragrant lace handkerchief, she
brought out with difficulty, "Look at yourself in the mirror behind
you. Oh, how droll you are!"

Contracting my brows, clenching my teeth with pain, with a face
grown cold, from which all the blood had fled, I looked at the mirror.
There gazed back at me an idiotically placid, stolidly complacent, in-
humanly immovable face. And I burst into an uncontrollable fit
of laughter. And with the laughter not yet subsided, but already with
the trembling of rising anger, with the madness of despair, I said—
no, almost shouted, "You shouldn't laugh!"

And when she was quiet again, I went on speaking in a whisper of
my love. I had never spoken so well, for I had never loved so strongly.
I spoke of the tortures of expectation, of the venomous tears of mad
jealously and grief, of my own soul, which was all love. And I saw how
her drooping eyelashes cast thick, dark shadows over her blanched
cheeks. I saw how across their dull pallor the fire, bursting into flame,
threw a red reflection, and how her whole pliant body involuntarily
bent towards me.

She was dressed as the Goddess of Night, and was all mysterious,
clad in a black, mist-like face, which twinkled with stars of brilliants.
She was as beautiful as a forgotten dream of far-off childhood. As
I spoke, my eyes filled with tears, and my heart beat with gladness.
And I perceived, I perceived at last, how a tender, piteous smile
parted her lips, and her eyelashes were lifted all a-tremble. Slowly,
timorously, but with infinite confidence, she turned her head towards
me and . . .

And such a shriek of laughter I had never heard!

"No, no, I can't," she almost groaned, and throwing back her head,
she burst into a resonant cascade of laughter.

Oh, if but for a moment I could have had a human face! I bit my
lips, tears rolled down over my heated face; but it—that idiotic mask,
on which everything was in its right place, nose, eyes, and lips—looked
with a complacency stolidly horrible in its absurdity. And when I
went out, swaying on my flowered feet, it was a long time before I
got out of reach of that ringing laugh. It was as though a silvery
stream of water were falling from an immense height, and breaking in cheerful song upon the hard rock.

4

Scattered over the whole sleeping street, and rousing the stillness of the night with our lusty, excited voices, we walked home.

A companion said to me, "You've had a colossal success. I never saw people laugh so—Hey! what are you up to? Why are you tearing your mask? I say, you fellows, he's gone mad! Look, he's tearing his costume to pieces! By Heaven! he's actually crying."

For Discussion

1. From the way the narrator reacted in section 1, what kind of person would you say he was? What mood did Andreyev establish in this section? Point out specific details to support your answer.
2. The author's attitude toward the world and toward the relationships between people is implied throughout the story. In section 2, what attitude toward the world and the individual's place in it was implied in the situation of the narrator and the other "lonely, disconsolate students"? What was revealed about the narrator's relationship with people in the way he thought about his friends? Was he, or was he not, justified in referring to them as "insensate individuals"? Explain.
3. The fact that the narrator and his friends had to "dress up" before they could go out into the world to meet people has a symbolic, as well as a literal, meaning; that is, the "dressing up" stands for a general or abstract idea. What is the symbolic meaning of the students' having to "dress up"?
4. The central symbol in the story is the mask the narrator wore. What does it represent? Why did the mask evoke such laughter? What symbolic meaning do you see in the laughter? What effect did the people's laughter have on the narrator? Why do you think the narrator joined others in laughing at his mask?
5. At any point in the narrator's conversation with the girl, he might have removed his mask. What would this have meant symbolically? Why didn't he remove the mask? Was it that he *wouldn't* or that he *couldn't* remove it? Explain. What do you think Andreyev is saying about the relationship between people?
6. From the description of the girl at the party, what reasons do you have for believing that she is a symbolic, as well as a literal, character? What does she represent?
7. The contrast between the narrator's mask and his real face is both dramatic and ironical. Why? Point out other examples of irony both

in the action of the story and in what the narrator says about the
action.
8. Andreyev divided his story into four sections. Do you think this made
it a better story? Why or why not?

For Composition

1. At one point in the story, the narrator says, "And how solitary I was
under that mask!" In a short composition, explain what this symbolizes.
What does it say about the way people live today? List the reasons a
person might have for not removing his "mask."
2. Andreyev implied that there is a sad triumph in achieving individuality
through isolating oneself from other people. Write a paragraph in
which you present another way of achieving individuality which you
consider more satisfactory.
3. Write a critical paper in which you compare and contrast the styles
of Andreyev and Thomas Mann. In what ways are their stories different? In what ways are they similar?

Franz Kafka

The Hunter Gracchus

Franz Kafka (1883–1924) was born in Prague, Bohemia, which is now a part of Czechoslovakia, and lived most of his life in that city. The world Kafka writes about is at once real and dreamlike. He sees man haunted by a sense of guilt and accused by anonymous powers who show themselves only in the form of official documents, bureaucratic red tape, and machines. In addition to this, Kafka's characters can never find out what it is they are being accused of, and they are constantly burdened by a sense of fear, anxiety, and frustration. In presenting this nightmarish world, Kafka uses a clear, realistic prose style which makes these strange, dreamlike events seem like actual, everyday occurrences. His strange view of the world is to be seen most notably in his novels, *The Trial* and *The Castle*, and in stories, such as "The Hunter Gracchus."

"The Hunter Gracchus" may first be enjoyed on a literal level, simply as a supernatural story. On the other hand, it may puzzle the reader until he realizes that it is an allegory about man's search for personal salvation in which the author expresses, in allegorical terms, one of his favorite themes: man is caught up by forces over which he has no control.

TWO boys were sitting on the harbor wall playing with dice. A man was reading a newspaper on the steps of the monument, resting in the shadow of a hero who was flourishing his sword on high. A girl was filling her bucket at the fountain. A fruitseller was lying beside his scales, staring out to sea. Through the vacant window and door openings of a café one could see two men quite at the back drinking their wine. The proprietor was sitting at a table in front and dozing. A bark was silently making for the little harbor, as if borne by invisible means over the water. A man in a blue blouse climbed ashore and drew the rope through a ring. Behind the boatman two other men in dark coats with silver buttons carried a bier, on which, beneath a great flower-patterned tasselled silk cloth, a man was apparently lying.

Nobody on the quay troubled about the newcomers; even when they lowered the bier to wait for the boatman, who was still occupied with his rope, nobody went nearer, nobody asked them a question, nobody accorded them an inquisitive glance.

The pilot was still further detained by a woman who, a child at her breast, now appeared with loosened hair on the deck of the boat. Then he advanced and indicated a yellowish two-storied house that rose abruptly on the left beside the sea; the bearers took up their burden and bore it to the low but gracefully pillared door. A little boy opened a window just in time to see the party vanishing into the house, then hastily shut the window again. The door too was now shut; it was of black oak, and very strongly made. A flock of doves which had been flying round the belfry alighted in the street before the house. As if their food were stored within, they assembled in front of the door. One of them flew up to the first story and pecked at the windowpane. They were bright-hued, well-tended, beautiful birds. The woman on the boat flung grain to them in a wide sweep; they ate it up and flew across to the woman.

A man in a top hat tied with a band of crepe now descended one of the narrow and very steep lanes that led to the harbor. He glanced round vigilantly, everything seemed to displease him, his mouth twisted at the sight of some offal in a corner. Fruit skins were lying on the steps of the monument; he swept them off in passing with his stick. He rapped at the house door, at the same time taking his top hat from his head with his black-gloved hand. The door was opened at once, and some fifty little boys appeared in two rows in the long entry-hall, and bowed to him.

The boatman descended the stairs, greeted the gentleman in black, conducted him up to the first story led him round the bright and elegant loggia which encircled the courtyard, and both of them entered, while the boys pressed after them at a respectful distance, a cool spacious room looking towards the back, from whose window no habitation, but only a bare, blackish grey rocky wall was to be seen. The bearers were busied in setting up and lighting several long candles at the head of the bier, yet these did not give light, but only scared away the shadows which had been immobile till then, and made them flicker over the walls. The cloth covering the bier had been thrown back. Lying on it was a man with wildly matted hair, who looked somewhat like a hunter. He lay without motion and, it seemed, without breathing, his eyes closed; yet only his trappings indicated that this man was probably dead.

The gentleman stepped up to the bier, laid his hand on the brow of the man lying upon it, then kneeled down and prayed. The boatman made a sign to the bearers to leave the room; they went out, drove away the boys who had gathered outside, and shut the door. But even that did not seem to satisfy the gentleman, he glanced at the boatman; the boatman understood, and vanished through a side door into the next room. At once the man on the bier opened his eyes, turned his face painfully towards the gentleman, and said: "Who are you?" Without any mark of surprise the gentleman rose from his kneeling posture and answered. "The Burgomaster of Riva."

The man on the bier nodded, indicated a chair with a feeble movement of his arm, and said, after the Burgomaster had accepted his invitation: "I knew that, of course, Burgomaster, but in the first moments of returning consciousness I always forget, everything goes round before my eyes, and it is best to ask about anything even if I know. You too probably know that I am the hunter Gracchus."

"Certainly," said the Burgomaster. "Your arrival was announced to me during the night. We had been asleep for a good while. Then towards midnight my wife cried: 'Salvatore'—that's my name—'look at that dove at the window.' It was really a dove, but as big as a cock. It flew over me and said in my ear: 'Tomorrow the dead hunter Gracchus is coming; receive him in the name of the city.' "

The hunter nodded and licked his lips with the tip of his tongue: "Yes, the doves flew here before me. But do you believe, Burgomaster, that I shall remain in Riva?"

"I cannot say that yet," replied the Burgomaster. "Are you dead?"

"Yes," said the hunter, "as you see. Many years ago, yes, it must be a great many years ago, I fell from a precipice in the Black Forest —that is in Germany—when I was hunting a chamois. Since then I have been dead."

"But you are alive too," said the Burgomaster.

"In a certain sense," said the hunter, "in a certain sense I am alive too. My death ship lost its way; a wrong turn of the wheel, a moment's absence of mind on the pilot's part, a longing to turn aside towards my lovely native country, I cannot tell what it was; I only know this, that I remained on earth and that ever since my ship has sailed earthly waters. So I, who asked for nothing better than to live among my mountains, travel after my death through all the lands of the earth."

"And you have no part in the other world?" asked the Burgomaster, knitting his brow.

"I am forever," replied the hunter, "on the great stair that leads up to it. On that infinitely wide and spacious stair I clamber about, sometimes up, sometimes down, sometimes on the right, sometimes on the left, always in motion. The hunter has been turned into a butterfly. Do not laugh."

"I am not laughing," said the Burgomaster in self-defence.

"That is very good of you," said the hunter. "I am always in motion. But when I make a supreme flight and see the gate actually shining before me I awaken presently on my old ship, still stranded forlornly in some earthly sea or other. The fundamental error of my one-time death grins at me as I lie in my cabin. Julia, the wife of the pilot, knocks at the door and brings me on my bier the morning drink of the land whose coasts we chance to be passing. I lie on a wooden pallet, I wear—it cannot be a pleasure to look at me—a filthy winding sheet, my hair and beard, black tinged with grey, have grown together inextricably, my limbs are covered with a great flower-patterned woman's shawl with long fringes. A sacramental candle stands at my head and lights me. On the wall opposite me is a little picture, evidently of a Bushman who is aiming his spear at me and taking cover as best he can behind a beautifully painted shield. On shipboard one is often a prey to stupid imaginations, but that is the stupidest of them all. Otherwise my wooden case is quite empty. Through a hole in the side wall come in the warm airs of the southern night, and I hear the water slapping against the old boat.

"I have lain here ever since the time when, as the hunter Gracchus living in the Black Forest, I followed a chamois and fell from a precipice. Everything happened in good order. I pursued, I fell, bled to death in a ravine, died, and this ship should have conveyed me to the next world. I can still remember how gladly I stretched myself out on this pallet for the first time. Never did the mountains listen to such songs from me as these shadowy walls did then.

"I had been glad to live and I was glad to die. Before I stepped aboard, I joyfully flung away my wretched load of ammunition, my knapsack, my hunting rifle that I had always been proud to carry, and I slipped into my winding sheet like a girl into her marriage dress. I lay and waited. Then came the mishap."

"A terrible fate," said the Burgomaster, raising his hand defensively. "And you bear no blame for it?"

"None," said the hunter. "I was a hunter; was there any sin in that? I followed my calling as a hunter in the Black Forest, where there were still wolves in those days. I lay in ambush, shot, hit my mark, flayed the skins from my victims: was there any sin in that? My labors were blessed. 'The great hunter of the Black Forest' was the name I was given. Was there any sin in that?"

"I am not called upon to decide that," said the Burgomaster, "but to me also there seems to be no sin in such things. But, then whose is the guilt?"

"The boatman's," said the hunter. "Nobody will read what I say here, no one will come to help me; even if all the people were commanded to help me, every door and window would remain shut, everybody would take to bed and draw the bedclothes over his head, the whole earth would become an inn for the night. And there is sense in that, for nobody knows of me, and if anyone knew he would not know where I could be found, and if he knew where I could be found, he would not know how to deal with me, he would not know how to help me. The thought of helping me is an illness that has to be cured by taking to one's bed.

"I know that, and so I do not shout to summon help, even though at moments—when I lose control over myself, as I have done just now, for instance—I think seriously of it. But to drive out such thoughts I need only look round me and verify where I am, and—I can safely assert—have been for hundreds of years."

"Extraordinary," said the Burgomaster, "extraordinary.—And now do you think of staying here in Riva with us?"

"I think not," said the hunter with a smile, and, to excuse himself, he laid his hand on the Burgomaster's knee. "I am here, more than that I do not know, further than that I cannot go. My ship has no rudder, and it is driven by the wind that blows in the undermost regions of death."

For Discussion

1. Describe briefly the fate of the hunter. In your opinion, was he in any way to blame for his fate? Could anyone help him? Explain.
2. The hunter was both dead and alive. What do you think is the mean-

ing of this life-in-death? Do you see a symbolic meaning in the fact that the hunter had to be constantly in motion? Explain the last paragraph of the story.

3. In his notebook, Kafka wrote: "The state in which we find ourselves is sinful, quite independently of guilt." Explain this statement in relation to "The Hunter Gracchus." What do you think is the meaning of the story?

4. Kafka began with a realistic description of the scene on the quay. What clue in the first paragraph gave you a hint of the supernatural element in the story? Point out details throughout the story which conveyed a feeling of strangeness, as in a dream.

5. Kafka used many symbols in this allegory; for example, in the opening sentence, the two boys playing with dice. What symbolic meaning do you see in the dice game? Point out and explain other symbols, such as the doves and the boatman. Why might Kafka have chosen a hunter as his main character?

6. As in many modern stories, the conflict in "The Hunter Gracchus" is not resolved. What is the conflict? Why isn't it resolved? How does this fit in with Kafka's view of life? Do you agree or disagree with this? Why?

For Composition

1. In his novel, *The Trial*, Kafka wrote that "only our concept of time makes it possible for us to speak of the Day of Judgment by that name; in reality, it is a summary court in perpetual motion." Do you think there is, as Kafka implied, an "ethical court" within us, constantly judging us? Write a composition in which you present your reasons for agreeing or disagreeing with Kafka. Use specific examples from your own experience.

2. "The Hunter Gracchus" and "The Rime of the Ancient Mariner" have much in common. Reread Coleridge's poem. In a carefully organized paper, point out similarities between these two works.

3. In "The Hunter Gracchus," as in most of his writings, Kafka expressed the frustration he saw in man's attempt to live in a disordered world. Do you see the world as essentially frustrating man or as assisting him in his purposes? Write a paper in which you give reasons or examples to support your answer.

4. In his *The Divine Mileu*, Father Teilhard de Chardin writes that "in each soul, God loves and partly saves the whole world which that soul sums up in an incommunicable and particular way." Write a paper in which you develop this thought of the individual soul's positive reponse to his own life as ordained by Providence.

Roger Martin du Gard

The Operation

Roger Martin du Gard (1881–1958), one of the most esteemed modern French novelists, was awarded the Nobel Prize for Literature in 1937. His first successful novel, *Jean Barois*, was published in France in 1913. It was not translated into English, however, until 1949, after the great success of his major ten-volume novel, *The World of the Thibaults*, which he wrote between 1922 and 1940, and which appeared in English in 1939–1940. Because of his objectivity, his stark realism, and his exactness, Martin du Gard has been called the Flaubert of the twentieth century.

The World of the Thibaults is the story of two generations of a bourgeois family in the early years of the twentieth century. The selection that follows from the book is about Antoine Thibault, the eldest son, a doctor, and a man of action. In it you will see Martin du Gard's careful use of realistic details to create true-to-life characters and an incident of dramatic impact.

*W*HEN the taxi pulled up near the Tuileries in front of the house in the Rue d'Alger where the Chasles lived, Antoine had pieced together, from the concierge's flustered explanations, an outline of the accident. The victim was a little girl who used to meet "M. Jules" each evening on his way back. Had she tried to cross the Rue de Rivoli on this occasion, as M. Jules was late in coming home? A delivery tri-car had knocked her down and passed over her body. A crowd had gathered and a newspaper vender who was present had recognized the child by her plaited hair, and furnished her address. She had been carried unconscious to the flat.

M. Chasle, crouching in a corner of the taxi, shed no tears, but each new detail drew from him a racking sob, half muffled by the hand he pressed against his mouth.

A crowd still lingered round the doorway. They made way for M. Chasle, who had to be helped up the stairs as far as the top landing by his two companions. A door stood open at the end of a corridor, down which M. Chasle made his way on stumbling feet. The concierge stood back to let Antoine pass, and touched him on the arm.

"My wife, who's got a head on her shoulders, ran off to fetch the young doctor who dines at the restaurant next door. I hope she found him there."

Antoine nodded approval and followed M. Chasle. They crossed a sort of anteroom, redolent of musty cupboards, then two low rooms with tiled floors; the light was dim and the atmosphere stifling despite the open windows giving on a courtyard. In the further room Antoine had to edge round a circular table where a meal for four was laid on a strip of dingy oilcloth. M. Chasle opened a door and, entering a brightly lit room, stumbled forward with a piteous cry:

"Dédette! Dédette!"

"Now, Jules!" a raucous voice protested.

The first thing Antoine noticed was the lamp which a woman in a pink dressing gown was lifting with both hands; her ruddy hair, her throat and forehead were flooded with the lamplight. Then he observed the bed on which the light fell, and shadowy forms bending above it. Dregs of the sunset, filtering through the window, merged in the halo of the lamp, and the room was bathed in a half-light where all things took the semblance of a dream. Antoine helped M. Chasle to a chair and approached the bed. A young man wearing a pince-nez, with his hat still on, was bending forward and slitting up with a pair of scissors the blood-stained garments of the little girl. Her face, ringed with matted hair, lay buried in the bolster. An old woman on her knees was helping the doctor.

"Is she alive?" Antoine asked.

The doctor turned, looked at him, and hesitated; then mopped his forehead.

"Yes." His tone lacked assurance.

"I was with M. Chasle when he was sent for," Antoine explained, "and I've brought my first-aid kit. I'm Dr. Thibault," he added in a whisper, "house-physician at the Children's Hospital."

The young doctor rose and was about to make way for Antoine.

"Carry on! Carry on!" Antoine drew back a step. "Pulse?"

"Almost imperceptible," the doctor replied, intent once more on his task.

Antoine raised his eyes toward the red-haired young woman, saw the anxiety in her face, and made a suggestion.

"Wouldn't it be best to telephone for an ambulance and have your child taken at once to my hospital?"

"No!" an imperious voice answered him.

Then Antoine descried an old woman standing at the head of the bed—was it the child's grandmother?—and scanning him intently with eyes limpid as water, a peasant's eyes. Her pointed nose and resolute features were half submerged in a vast sea of fat that heaved in billowy folds upon her neck.

"I know we look like paupers," she continued in a resigned tone, "but, believe me, even folk like us would rather die at home in our own beds. Dédette shan't go to the hospital."

"But why not, Madame?" Antoine protested.

She straightened up her back, thrust out her chin, and sadly but sternly rebuked him.

"We prefer not," was all she said.

Antoine tried to catch the eye of the younger woman, but she was busy brushing off the flies that obstinately settled on her glowing cheeks, and seemed of no opinion. He decided to appeal to M. Chasle. The old fellow had fallen on his knees in front of the chair to which Antoine had led him; his head was buried on his folded arms as though to shut out all sights from his eyes, and, from his tears, all sounds. The old lady, who was keenly watching Antoine's movements, guessed his intention and forestalled him.

"Isn't that so, Jules?"

M. Chasle started.

"Yes, Mother."

She looked at him approvingly and her voice grew mothering.

"Don't stay there, Jules. You'd be much better in your room."

A pallid forehead rose into view, eyes tremulous behind their spectacles; then, without a protest, the poor old fellow stood up and tiptoed from the room.

Antoine bit his lips. Meanwhile, pending an occasion further to insist, he took off his coat and rolled up his sleeves above the elbows. Then he knelt at the bedside. He seldom took thought without at the same time beginning to take action—such was his incapacity for long deliberation on any issue raised, and such his keenness to be up and doing. The avoidance of mistakes counted less with him than bold decision and prompt activity. Thought, as he used it, was merely the lever that set an act in motion—premature though it might be.

Aided by the doctor and the old woman's trembling hands, he had soon stripped off the child's clothing; pale, almost grey, her body lay beneath their eyes in its frail nakedness. The impact of the car must have been very violent, for she was covered with bruises, and a black streak crossed her thigh transversely from hip to knee.

"It's the right leg," Antoine's colleague observed. Her right foot was twisted, bent inwards, and the whole leg was spattered with blood and deformed, shorter than the other one.

"Fracture of the femur?" suggested the doctor.

Antoine did not answer. He was thinking. "That's not all," he said to himself; "the shock is too great for that. But what can it be?" He tapped her knee-cap, then ran his fingers slowly up her thigh; suddenly there spurted through an almost imperceptible lesion on the inner side of the thigh, some inches above the knee, a jet of blood.

"That's it," he said.

"The femoral artery!" the other exclaimed.

Antoine rose quickly to his feet. The need to make, unaided, a decision gave him a new access of energy and, as ever when others were present, his sense of power intensified. A surgeon? he speculated. No, we'd never get her alive to the hospital. Then who? I? Why not? And, anyhow, there's no alternative.

"Will you try a ligature?" asked the doctor, piqued by Antoine's silence.

But Antoine did not heed his question. It must be done, he was thinking, and without a moment's delay; it may be too late already, who knows? He threw a quick glance round him. A ligature. What can be used? Let's see. The red-headed girl hasn't a belt; no loops on the curtains. Something elastic. Ah, I have it! In a twinkling he had thrown off his waistcoat and unfastened his braces. Snapping them with a jerk, he knelt down again, made with them a tourniquet, and clamped it tightly round the child's groin.

"Good! Two minutes' breathing-time," he said as he rose. Sweat was pouring down his cheeks. He knew that every eye was fixed on him. "Only an immediate operation," he said decisively, "can save her life. Let's try!"

The others moved away at once from the bed—even the woman with the lamp, even the young doctor, whose face had paled.

Antoine clenched his teeth, his eyes narrowed and grew hard, he seemed to peer into himself. Must keep calm, he mused. A table? That round table I saw, coming in.

"Bring the lamp!" he cried to the young woman, then turned to the doctor. "You there—come with me!" He strode quickly into the next room. Good, he said to himself; here's our operating theater. With a quick gesture he cleared the table, stacked the plates in a pile. "That's for my lamp." Like a general in charge of a campaign, he allotted each thing its place. "Now for our little patient." He went back to the bedroom. The doctor and the young woman hung on his every gesture and followed close behind him. Addressing the doctor, he pointed to the child:

"I'll carry her. She's light as a feather. Hold up her leg, you."

As he slipped his arms under the child's back and carried her to the table, she moaned faintly. He took the lamp from the red-haired woman and, removing the shade, stood it on the pile of plates. As he surveyed the scene, a thought came suddenly and went: "I'm a wonderful fellow!" The lamp gleamed like a brazier, reddening the ambient shadow, where only the young woman's glowing cheeks and the doctor's pince-nez showed up as highlights; its rays fell harshly on the little body, which twitched spasmodically. The swarming flies seemed worked up to a frenzy by the oncoming storm. Heat and anxiety brought beads of sweat to Antoine's brow. Would she live through it? he wondered, but some dark force he did not analyse buoyed up his faith; never had he felt so sure of himself.

He seized his bag and, taking out a bottle of chloroform and some gauze, handed the former to the doctor.

"Open it somewhere. On the sideboard. Take off the sewing-machine. Get everything out."

As he turned, holding the bottle, he noticed two dim figures in the dark doorway, the two old women like statues posted there. One, M. Chasle's mother, had great, staring eyes, an owl's eyes; the other was pressing her breast with her clasped hands.

"Go away!" he commanded. They retreated some steps into the shadows of the bedroom, but he pointed to the other end of the flat. "No. Out of the room. That way." They obeyed, crossed the room, vanished without a word.

"Not you!" he cried angrily to the red-haired woman, who was about to follow them.

She turned on her heel and, for a moment, he took stock of her. She had a handsome, rather fleshy face, touched with a certain dignity, it seemed, by grief; an air of calm maturity that pleased him. Poor woman! he could not help thinking. . . . But I need her!

"You're the child's mother?" he asked.

"No." She shook her head.

"All the better."

As he spoke he had been soaking the gauze and now he swiftly stretched it over the child's nose. "Stand there, and keep this." He handed her the bottle. "When I give the signal, you'll pour some more of it on."

The air grew heavy with the reek of chloroform. The little girl groaned, drew a deep breath or two, grew still.

A last look round. The field was clear; the rest lay with the surgeon's skill. Now that the crucial moment had come, Antoine's anxieties vanished as if by magic. He went to the sideboard where the doctor, holding the bag, was laying on a napkin the last of its contents. "Let's see," he murmured, as though to gain a few seconds' respite. "There's the instrument box; good. The scalpel, the artery-forceps. A packet of gauze, cotton-wool, that'll do. Alcohol. Caffeine. Tincture of iodine. And so forth. . . . All's ready. Let's begin." And yet again there came to him that sense of buoyancy, of boundless confidence, of vital energies tautened to breaking-point, and, crowning all, a proud awareness of being lifted high above his workaday self.

Raising his head, he looked his junior for a moment in the eyes. "Have you the nerve?" his eyes seemed to inquire. "It's going to be a tough job. Now for it!"

The young man did not flinch. And now he hung on Antoine's gestures with servile assiduity. Well he knew that in this operation lay their only hope, but never would he have dared to take the risk, alone. With Antoine, however, nothing seemed impossible.

He's not so bad, this young chap, thought Antoine. Lucky for me! Let's see. A basin? No matter—this will do as well. Grasping the bottle of iodine he sluiced his arms up to the elbow with the liquid.

"Your turn!" He passed the bottle to the doctor, who was feverishly polishing the lenses of his pince-nez.

A vivid lightning flash, closely followed by a deafening clap of thunder, lit up the window.

"A bit previous, the applause," Antoine said to himself. "I hadn't even taken up my lancet. The young woman didn't turn a hair. It'll cool things down; good for our nerves. Must be pretty nearly a hundred degrees in this room."

He had laid out a series of compresses round the injured limb, delimiting the operative field. Now he turned towards the young woman.

"A whiff of chloroform. That'll do. Right!"

She obeys orders, he mused, like a soldier under fire. Women! Then, fixing his eyes on the swollen little thigh, he swallowed his saliva and raised the scalpel.

"Here goes!"

With one neat stroke he cut the skin.

"Swab!" he commanded the doctor bending beside him. "What a thin child!" he said to himself. "Well, we'll be there all the sooner. Hallo, there's little Dédette starting snoring! Good! Better be quick about it. Now for the retractors."

"Now, you," he said aloud, and the other let fall the blood-stained swabs of cotton-wool and, grasping the retractors, held the wound open.

Antoine paused a moment. "Good!" he murmured. "My probe? Here it is. In Hunter's canal. The classical ligation; all's well. Zip! Another flash! Must have landed pretty near. On the Louvre. Perhaps on the 'gentlemen at Saint-Roch.' " He felt quite calm—no more anxiety for the child, none for death's imminence—and cheerfully repeated under his breath: "The ligature of the femoral artery in Hunter's canal."

Zip! There goes another! Hardly any rain, either. It's stifling. Artery injured at the site of the fracture; the end of the bone tore it open. Simple as anything. Still she hadn't much blood to spare. He glanced at the little girl's face. Hallo! Better hurry up. Simple as anything—but could be fatal, too. A forceps; right! Another; that will do. Zip! These flashes are getting a bore; cheap effect! I've only plaited silk; must make the best of it. Breaking a tube, he pulled out the skein and made a ligature beside each forceps. Splendid! Almost finished now. The collateral circulation will be quite enough, especially at that age. I'm really wonderful! Can I have missed my vocation? I've all the makings of a surgeon, sure enough; a great surgeon. In the silent interval between two thunder-claps dying into the distance, the sharp metallic click of scissors snipping the loose ends of the silk was audi-

ble. Yes; quickness of eye, coolness, energy, dexterity. Suddenly he
picked up his ears and his cheeks paled.

"The devil!" he muttered under his breath.

The child had ceased to breathe.

Brushing aside the woman, he tore away the gauze from the unconscious child's face and pressed his ear above her heart. Doctor and
young woman waited in suspense, their eyes fixed on Antoine.

"No!" he murmured. "She's breathing still."

He took the child's wrist, but her pulse was so rapid that he did
not attempt to count it. "Ouf!" He drew a deep breath, the lines of
anxiety deepened on his forehead. The two others felt his gaze pass
across their faces, but he did not see them.

He rapped out a brief command.

"You, doctor, remove the forceps, put on a dressing, and then undo
the tourniquet. Quickly. You, Madame, get me some note paper—no,
you needn't; I've my notebook." He wiped his hands feverishly with
a wad of cotton-wool. "What's the time? Not nine yet. The pharmacist's open. You'll have to hurry."

She stood before him, waiting; her tentative gesture—to wrap the
dressing gown more closely round her body—told him of her reluc-
tance at going thus, half dressed, into the streets, and for the fraction
of a second a picture of the opulent form under the garment held his
imagination. He scribbled a prescription, signed it. "A two-pint ampoule. As quickly as you can."

"And if—?" she stammered.

"If the pharmacist's shut, ring, and keep on hammering on the
door till they open. Be quick!"

She was gone. He followed her with his eyes to make sure she was
running, then addressed the doctor.

"We'll try the saline. Not subcutaneously; that's hopeless now.
Intravenously. Our last hope." He took two small phials from the
sideboard.

"You've removed the tourniquet? Right. Give her an injection of
camphor to begin with, then the caffeine—only half of it for her, poor
kid! Only, be quick about it!"

He went back to the child and took her thin wrist between his
fingers; now he could feel nothing more than a vague, restless fluttering. "It's got past counting," he said to himself. And suddenly a feeling of impotence, of sheer despair, swept over him.

"Damn it!" he broke out. "To think it went off perfectly—and it was all no use!"

The child's face became more livid with every second. She was dying. Antoine observed, beside the parted lips, two slender strands of curling hair, lighter than gossamer, that rose and fell; anyhow, she was breathing still.

He watched the doctor giving the injections. Neat with his fingers, he thought, considering his short sight. But we can't save her. Vexation rather than grief possessed him. He had the callousness common to doctors, for whom the sufferings of others count only as so much new experience, or profit, or professional advantage; men to whose fortunes death and pain are frequent ministers.

But then he thought he heard a banging door and ran towards the sound. It was the young woman coming back with quick, lithe steps, trying to conceal her breathlessness. He snatched the parcel from her hands.

"Bring some hot water." He did not even pause to thank her.

"Boiled?"

"No. To warm the solution. Be quick!"

He had hardly opened the parcel when she returned, bringing a steaming saucepan.

"Good! Excellent!" he murmured, but did not look towards her.

No time to lose. In a few seconds he had nipped off the tips of the ampoule and slipped on the rubber tubing. A Swiss barometer in carved wood hung on the wall. With one hand he unhooked it, while with the other he hung the ampoule on the nail. Then he took the saucepan of hot water, hesitated for a fraction of a second, and looped the rubber tubing round the bottom of it. That'll heat the saline as it flows through, he said to himself. Smart idea, that! He glanced towards the other doctor to see if he had noticed what he had done. At last he came back to the child, lifted her inert arm, and sponged it with iodine. Then, with a stroke of his scalpel, he laid bare the vein, slipped his probe beneath it and inserted the needle.

"It's flowing in all right," he cried. "Take her pulse. I'll stay where I am."

The ten minutes that followed seemed an eternity. No one moved or spoke.

Streaming with sweat, breathing rapidly, with knitted brows, Antoine waited, his gaze riveted on the needle. After a while he glanced up at the ampoule.

"How much gone?"

"Nearly a pint."

"The pulse?"

The doctor silently shook his head.

Five more minutes passed, five minutes more of sickening suspense. Antoine looked up again.

"How much left?"

"Just over half a pint."

"And the pulse?"

The doctor hesitated.

"I'm not sure. I almost think . . . it's beginning to come back a little."

"Can you count it?"

A pause.

"No."

If only the pulse came back! sighed Antoine. He would have given ten years of his own life to restore life to this little corpse. Wonder what age she is. Seven? And, if I save her, she'll fall a victim to consumption within the next ten years, living in this hovel. But shall I save her? It's touch and go; her life hangs on a thread. Still—damn it!—I've done all I could. The saline's flowing well. But it's too late. There's nothing more to be done, nothing else to try. We can only wait. . . . That red-haired girl did her bit. A good-looker. She's not the child's mother; who can she be then? Chasle never breathed a word about all these people. Not his daughter, I imagine. Can't make head or tail of it! And that old woman, putting on airs. . . . Anyhow, they made themselves scarce, good riddance! Curious how one suddenly gets them in hand. They all knew the sort of man they had to deal with. The strong hand of a masterful man. But it was up to me to bring it off. Shall I now? No, she lost too much blood on the way here. No signs of improvement so far, worse luck! Oh, damn it all!

His gaze fell on the child's pale lips and the two strands of golden hair, rising and falling still. The breathing struck him as a little better. Was he mistaken? Half a minute passed. Her chest seemed to flutter with a faint sigh which slowly died into the air, as though a fragment of her life were passing with it. For a moment Antoine stared at her in perplexity. No, she was breathing still. Nothing to be done but to wait, and keep on waiting.

A minute later she sighed again, more plainly now.

"How much left?"

"The ampoule's almost empty."

"And the pulse? Coming back?"

"Yes."

Antoine drew a deep breath.

"Can you count it?"

The doctor took out his watch, settled his pince-nez, and, after a minute's silence, announced:

"A hundred and forty. A hundred and fifty, perhaps."

"Better than nothing!" The exclamation was involuntary, for Antoine was straining every nerve to withstand the flood of huge relief that surged across his mind. Yet it was not imagination; the improvement was not to be gainsaid. Her breathing was steadier. It was all he could do to stay where he was; he had a childish longing to sing or whistle. *Better than nothing tra-la-la*—he tried to fit the words to the tune that had been haunting him all day. *In my heart tra-la-la. In my heart sleeps* . . . Sleeps—sleeps *what?* Got it. *The pale moonlight.*

> In my heart sleeps the pale moonlight
> Of a lovely summer night . . .

The cloud of doubt lifted, gave place to radiant joy.

"The child's saved," he murmured. "She's *got to be* saved!"

> . . . a lovely summer night!

"The ampoule's empty," the doctor announced.

"Capital!"

Just then the child, whom his eyes had never left, gave a slight shudder. Antoine turned almost gaily to the young woman, who, leaning against the sideboard, had been watching the scene with steady eyes for the past quarter of an hour.

"Well, Madame!" he cried with affected gruffness. "Gone to sleep, have we? And how about the hot-water bottle?" He almost smiled at her amazement. "But, my dear lady, nothing could be more obvious. A bottle, piping hot, to warm her little toes!"

A flash of joy lit up her eyes as she hastened from the room.

Then Antoine, with redoubled care and gentleness, bent down and drew out the needle, and with the tips of his fingers applied a compress to the tiny wound. He ran his fingers along the arm from which the hand still hung limp.

"Another injection of camphor, old man, just to make sure; and then we'll have played our last card. Shouldn't wonder," he added under his breath, "if we've pulled it off." Once more that sense of power that was half joy elated him.

The woman came back carrying a jar in her arms. She hesitated, then, as he said nothing, came and stood by the child's feet.

"Not like that!" said Antoine, with the same brusque cheerfulness. "You'll burn her. Give it here. Just imagine my having to show you how to wrap up a hot-water bottle!"

Smiling now, he snatched up a rolled napkin that caught his eye and, flinging the ring onto the sideboard, wrapped the jar in it and pressed it to the child's feet. The red-haired woman watched him, taken aback by the boyish smile that made his face seem so much younger.

"Then she's—saved?" she ventured to ask.

He dared not affirm it as yet.

"I'll tell you in an hour's time." His voice was gruff, but she took his meaning and cast on him a bold, admiring look.

For the third time Antoine asked himself what this handsome girl could be doing in the Chasle household. Then he pointed to the door.

"What about the others?"

A smile hovered on her lips.

"They're waiting."

"Hearten them up a bit. Tell them to go to bed. You too, Madame, you'd better take some rest."

"Oh, as far as I'm concerned . . ." she murmured, turning to go.

"Let's get the child back to bed," Antoine suggested to his colleague. "The same way as before. Hold up her leg. Take the bolster away; we'd better keep her head down. The next thing is to rig up some sort of a gadget. . . . That napkin, please, and the string from the parcel. Some sort of extension, you see. Slip the string between the rails; handy things these iron bedsteads. Now for a weight. Anything will do. How about this saucepan? No, the flat-iron there will be better. We've all we need here. Yes, hand it over. Tomorrow we'll improve on it. Meanwhile it will do if we stretch the leg a bit, don't you think so?"

The young doctor did not reply. He gazed at Antoine with spell-bound awe—the look that Martha may have given the Saviour when Lazarus rose from the tomb. His lips worked and he stammered timidly:

"May I . . . shall I arrange your instruments?" The faltered words breathed such a zeal for service and for devotion that Antoine thrilled with the exultation of an acknowledged chief. They were alone. Antoine went up to the younger man and looked him in the eyes.

"You've been splendid, my dear fellow."

The young man gasped. Antoine, who felt even more embarrassed than his colleague, gave him no time to put in a word.

"Now you'd better be off home; it's late. There's no need for two of us here." He hesitated. "We may take it that she's saved, I think. That's my opinion. However, for safety's sake, I'll stay here for the night, if you'll permit me." The doctor made a vague gesture. "If you permit me, I repeat. For I don't forget that she's your patient. Obviously. I only gave a hand, as there was nothing else for it. That's so, eh? But from tomorrow on I leave her in your hands. They're competent hands and I have no anxiety." As he spoke he led the doctor towards the door. "Will you look in again towards noon? I'll come back when I'm done at the hospital and we will decide on the treatment to follow."

"Sir, it's . . . it's been a privilege for me to . . . to . . ."

Never before had Antoine been "sirred" by a colleague, never before been treated with such deference. It went to his head, like generous wine, and unthinkingly he held out both hands towards the young man. But in the nick of time he regained his self-control.

"You've got a wrong impression," he said in a subdued tone. "I'm only a learner, a novice—like you. Like so many others. Like everyone. Groping our way. We do our best—and that's all there is to it!"

For Discussion

1. What was the first obstacle Dr. Antoine Thibault met in trying to take care of the injured little girl, Dédette? What did this situation reveal about the relationship between M. Chasle and his mother?

2. What important decision did Antoine have to make? In what way were the young woman and the other doctor of use to him?

3. What did you learn about Antoine during the operation? How, for example, did he react to emergencies? In what way did his thoughts reveal a mingling of humility and vanity?

4. How did Antoine react when things took a turn for the worse? What did the author mean when he said, "Vexation rather than grief possessed him"? Point out a passage which revealed his tenderness for the child.

5. How would you describe Antoine's attitude toward the other young doctor at the end of the story? Was it one of generosity? Was it one of patronage? Was it one of conceit masked as modesty? Was it a mingling of attitudes? Explain.

6. You have learned that in fiction there are two kinds of conflicts: inner conflict and outer conflict. In this story, which is predominant? What is the essential conflict?

7. "The Operation" is very different from "The Hunter Gracchus." Kafka emphasizes the strangeness of reality, though he uses ordinary details. Martin du Gard emphasizes the ordinary aspect of reality, but he is aware that strangeness exists in the everyday. Reread the paragraph on page 98, beginning "The first thing Antoine noticed . . ." Point out the mingling of the strange and the everyday in this paragraph.

8. Martin du Gard carefully arranges realistic details to set the scene for his story. He describes the room, the heat, and the people, all of which contribute to the atmosphere of the story. Point out details which you feel are particularly effective in creating this atmosphere.

For Composition

1. In this selection, Martin du Gard is critical of doctors, though obviously admiring of their skill. He says of Antoine, "He had the callousness common to doctors, for whom the sufferings of others count only as so much new experience, or profit, or professional advantage. . . ." Write a composition in which you express your opinion of this statement. You might describe an incident from your own experience to support your viewpoint.

2. One of the things that makes Antoine a believable character is that he is neither all good nor all bad. He has mixed motives and feelings like all human beings. Write a character sketch of someone you know well, in which you try to present a true-to-life picture of that person by describing some of his contradictory ways of mind and behavior. The person you choose to describe might even be yourself.

Albert Camus

The Guest

Perhaps more than any other contemporary writer, Albert Camus *
(1913–1960) spoke of and for modern man. Upon receiving the Nobel
Prize for Literature in 1957, he expressed his philosophy of life this way:
"Probably every generation sees itself as charged with the remaking of
the world. Mine, however, knows that it will not remake the world. But
its task is perhaps even greater, for it consists in keeping the world from
destroying itself. . . . My generation has had to re-establish, both within
and without itself, a little of what constitutes the dignity of life and
death." His senseless death in an automobile collision at the age of
forty-six stunned the literary world, in which he was an outstanding
figure. Lamenting this unnatural end to so shining and hopeful a career,
the writer François Mauriac noted that "a whole generation became aware
of itself and of its problems through Camus."

Camus was, in his own words, born "halfway between misery and the
sun." Shaped by the poverty and injustice that characterized his youth
in his native Algeria, Camus moved from the near-nihilism of Existen-
tialism to a revival of faith in life. The bleak, sensuous beauty of the
North African deserts nourished his love for life, his rejection of death.
To be sure, the modern awareness of human alienation, of the meaninglessness, absurdity, and futility of life constituted significant themes in
his work. But ultimately, as a writer and as a human being, Camus rejected despair in favor of a free life. "I Rebel, therefore, we are," he wrote
in his 1951 essay, The Rebel. Above all, he prized the virtue he defined
as the "will to live without refusing anything in life. . . ."

This final affirmation of life in the face of despair and absurdity was,
for Camus, a product of a free and conscious effort of the will. His novels,
including The Stranger, The Plague, and The Fall; his collection of
short stories, Exile and the Kingdom; and his essays, of which The
Myth of Sisyphus is perhaps the best known, all testify to his concern
with problems of the will and human freedom: Does man really have
the power to choose freely? he wondered, and what meaning and consequences do his choices have for himself and his world? As a French
Resistance fighter during World War II, as the memorable journalist of

* ál ber' ká mü'

111

the Resistance paper, *Combat*, as an outspoken critic of tyranny wherever he found it, Camus deliberately chose to achieve, defend, and ultimately share his personal freedom: "Each and every man," he wrote, "on the foundation of his own sufferings and joys, builds for all."

THE schoolmaster was watching the two men climb toward him. One was on horseback, the other on foot. They had not yet tackled the abrupt rise leading to the schoolhouse built on the hillside. They were toiling onward, making slow progress in the snow, among the stones, on the vast expanse of the high, deserted plateau. From time to time the horse stumbled. Without hearing anything yet, he could see the breath issuing from the horse's nostrils. One of the men, at least, knew the region. They were following the trail although it had disappeared days ago under a layer of dirty white snow. The schoolmaster calculated that it would take them half an hour to get onto the hill. It was cold; he went back into the school to get a sweater.

He crossed the empty, frigid classroom. On the blackboard the four rivers of France, drawn with four different colored chalks, had been flowing toward their estuaries for the past three days. Snow had suddenly fallen in mid-October after eight months of drought without the transition of rain, and the twenty pupils, more or less, who lived in the villages scattered over the plateau had stopped coming. With fair weather they would return. Daru now heated only the single room that was his lodging, adjoining the classroom and giving also onto the plateau to the east. Like the class windows, his window looked to the south too. On that side the school was a few kilometers from the point where the plateau began to slope toward the south. In clear weather could be seen the purple mass of the mountain range where the gap opened onto the desert.

Somewhat warmed, Daru returned to the window from which he had first seen the two men. They were no longer visible. Hence they must have tackled the rise. The sky was not so dark, for the snow had stopped falling during the night. The morning had opened with a dirty light which had scarcely become brighter as the ceiling of clouds lifted. At two in the afternoon it seemed as if the day were merely beginning. But still this was better than those three days when the thick snow was falling amidst unbroken darkness with little gusts of wind that rattled the double door of the classroom. Then Daru had spent long hours in his room, leaving it only to go to the shed and feed the chickens or get some coal. Fortunately the delivery truck from Tadjid, the nearest village to the north, had brought his supplies two days before the blizzard. It would return in forty-eight hours.

Besides, he had enough to resist a siege, for the little room was cluttered with bags of wheat that the administration left as a stock to distribute to those of his pupils whose families had suffered from the drought. Actually they had all been victims because they were all poor. Every day Daru would distribute a ration to the children. They had missed it, he knew, during these bad days. Possibly one of the fathers or big brothers would come this afternoon and he could supply them with grain. It was just a matter of carrying them over to the next harvest. Now shiploads of wheat were arriving from France and the worst was over. But it would be hard to forget that poverty, that army of ragged ghosts wandering in the sunlight, the plateaus burned to a cinder month after month, the earth shriveled up little by little, literally scorched, every stone bursting into dust under one's foot. The sheep had died then by thousands and even a few men, here and there, sometimes without anyone's knowing.

In contrast with such poverty, he who lived almost like a monk in his remote schoolhouse, nonetheless satisfied with the little he had and with the rough life, had felt like a lord with his whitewashed walls, his narrow couch, his unpainted shelves, his well, and his weekly provision of water and food. And suddenly this snow, without warning, without the foretaste of rain. This is the way the region was, cruel to live in, even without men—who didn't help matters either. But Daru had been born here. Everywhere else, he felt exiled.

He stepped out onto the terrace in front of the schoolhouse. The two men were now halfway up the slope. He recognized the horseman as Balducci, the old gendarme [1] he had known for a long time. Balducci was holding on the end of a rope an Arab who was walking behind him with hands bound and head lowered. The gendarme waved a greeting to which Daru did not reply, lost as he was in contemplation of the Arab dressed in a faded blue jellaba,[2] his feet in

[1] **gendarme:** a policeman, particularly in France
[2] **jellaba:** a full loose woolen cloak with a hood, sleeves, and skirt worn by men, especially in North Africa and Arabic countries

sandals but covered with socks of heavy raw wool, his head sur-
mounted by a narrow, short *chèche*.[3] They were approaching. Balducci was holding back his horse in order not to hurt the Arab, and
the group was advancing slowly.

Within earshot, Balducci shouted: "One hour to do the three
kilometers from El Ameur!" Daru did not answer. Short and square
in his thick sweater, he watched them climb. Not once had the Arab
raised his head. "Hello," said Daru when they got up onto the terrace. "Come in and warm up." Balducci painfully got down from
his horse without letting go the rope. From under his bristling mustache he smiled at the schoolmaster. His little dark eyes, deep-set
under a tanned forehead, and his mouth surrounded with wrinkles
made him look attentive and studious. Daru took the bridle, led the
horse to the shed, and came back to the two men, who were now
waiting for him in the school. He led them into his room. "I am
going to heat up the classroom," he said. "We'll be more comfortable
there." When he entered the room again, Balducci was on the couch.
He had undone the rope tying him to the Arab, who had squatted
near the stove. His hands still bound, the *chèche* pushed back on his
head, he was looking toward the window. At first Daru noticed only
his huge lips, fat, smooth, almost Negroid; yet his nose was straight,
his eyes were dark and full of fever. The *chèche* revealed an obstinate
forehead and, under the weathered skin now rather discolored by the
cold, the whole face had a restless and rebellious look that struck
Daru when the Arab, turning his face toward him, looked him
straight in the eyes. "Go into the other room," said the schoolmaster,
"and I'll make you some mint tea." "Thanks," Balducci said. "What
a chore! How I long for retirement." And addressing his prisoner in
Arabic: "Come on, you." The Arab got up and, slowly, holding his
bound wrists in front of him, went into the classroom.

With the tea, Daru brought a chair. But Balducci was already en-
throned on the nearest pupil's desk and the Arab had squatted against
the teacher's platform facing the stove, which stood between the
desk and the window. When he held out the glass of tea to the
prisoner, Daru hesitated at the sight of his bound hands. "He might
perhaps be untied." "Sure," said Balducci. "That was for the trip."
He started to get to his feet. But Daru, setting the glass on the floor,

[3] *chèche:* a scarf worn by French troops in North Africa

had knelt beside the Arab. Without saying anything, the Arab watched him with his feverish eyes. Once his hands were free, he rubbed his swollen wrists against each other, took the glass of tea, and sucked up the burning liquid in swift little sips.

"Good," said Daru. "And where are you headed?"

Balducci withdrew his mustache from the tea. "Here, son."

"Odd pupils! And you're spending the night?"

"No. I'm going back to El Ameur. And you will deliver this fellow to Tinguit. He is expected at police headquarters."

Balducci was looking at Daru with a friendly little smile.

"What's this story?" asked the schoolmaster. "Are you pulling my leg?"

"No, son. Those are the orders."

"The orders? I'm not . . ." Daru hesitated, not wanting to hurt the old Corsican. "I mean, that's not my job."

"What! What's the meaning of that? In wartime people do all kinds of jobs."

"Then I'll wait for the declaration of war!"

Balducci nodded.

"O.K. But the orders exist and they concern you too. Things are brewing, it appears. There is talk of a forthcoming revolt.[4] We are mobilized, in a way."

Daru still had his obstinate look.

"Listen, son," Balducci said. "I like you and you must understand. There's only a dozen of us at El Ameur to patrol throughout the whole territory of a small department and I must get back in a hurry. I was told to hand this guy over to you and return without delay. He couldn't be kept there. His village was beginning to stir; they wanted to take him back. You must take him to Tinguit tomorrow before the day is over. Twenty kilometers shouldn't faze a husky fellow like you. After that, all will be over. You'll come back to your pupils and your comfortable life."

Behind the wall the horse could be heard snorting and pawing the earth. Daru was looking out the window. Decidedly, the weather was clearing and the light was increasing over the snowy plateau. When all the snow was melted, the sun would take over again and

[4] **forthcoming revolt:** The stabilty of French control of Algeria was constantly threatened with revolt by Algerian nationalists and patriots. In 1962, De Gaulle signed a treaty granting Algeria its independence.

once more would burn the fields of stone. For days, still, the unchanging sky would shed its dry light on the solitary expanse where nothing had any connection with man.

"After all," he said, turning around toward Balducci, "what did he do?" And, before the gendarme had opened his mouth, he asked: "Does he speak French?"

"No, not a word. We had been looking for him for a month, but they were hiding him. He killed his cousin."

"Is he against us?"

"I don't think so. But you can never be sure."

"Why did he kill?"

"A family squabble, I think. One owed the other grain, it seems. It's not at all clear. In short, he killed his cousin with a billhook.[5] You know, like a sheep, *kreezk!*"

Balducci made the gesture of drawing a blade across his throat and the Arab, his attention attracted, watched him with a sort of anxiety. Daru felt a sudden wrath against the man, against all men with their rotten spite, their tireless hates, their blood lust.

But the kettle was singing on the stove. He served Balducci more tea, hesitated, then served the Arab again, who, a second time, drank avidly. His raised arms made the jellaba fall open and the schoolmaster saw his thin, muscular chest.

"Thanks, kid," Balducci said. "And now, I'm off."

He got up and went toward the Arab, taking a small rope from his pocket.

"What are you doing?" Daru asked dryly.

Balducci, disconcerted, showed him the rope.

"Don't bother."

The old gendarme hesitated. "It's up to you. Of course, you are armed?"

"I have my shotgun."

"Where?"

"In the trunk."

"You ought to have it near your bed."

"Why? I have nothing to fear."

"You're crazy, son. If there's an uprising, no one is safe, we're all in the same boat."

"I'll defend myself. I'll have time to see them coming."

[5] **billhook:** a hooked tool used for cutting or pruning

Balducci began to laugh, then suddenly the mustache covered the white teeth.

"You'll have time? O.K. That's just what I was saying. You have always been a little cracked. That's why I like you, my son was like that."

At the same time he took out his revolver and put it on the desk.

"Keep it; I don't need two weapons from here to El Ameur."

The revolver shone against the black paint of the table. When the gendarme turned toward him, the schoolmaster caught the smell of leather and horseflesh.

"Listen, Balducci," Daru said suddenly, "every bit of this disgusts me, and first of all your fellow here. But I won't hand him over. Fight, yes, if I have to. But not that."

The old gendarme stood in front of him and looked at him severely.

"You're being a fool," he said slowly. "I don't like it either. You don't get used to putting a rope on a man even after years of it, and you're even ashamed—yes, ashamed. But you can't let them have their way."

"I won't hand him over," Daru said again.

"It's an order, son, and I repeat it."

"That's right. Repeat to them what I've said to you: I won't hand him over."

Balducci made a visible effort to reflect. He looked at the Arab and at Daru. At last he decided.

"No, I won't tell them anything. If you want to drop us, go ahead; I'll not denounce you. I have an order to deliver the prisoner and I'm doing so. And now you'll just sign this paper for me."

"There's no need. I'll not deny that you left him with me."

"Don't be mean with me. I know you'll tell the truth. You're from hereabouts and you are a man. But you must sign, that's the rule."

Daru opened his drawer, took out a little square bottle of purple ink, the red wooden penholder with the "sergeant-major" pen he used for making models of penmanship, and signed. The gendarme carefully folded the paper and put it into his wallet. Then he moved toward the door.

"I'll see you off," Daru said.

"No," said Balducci. "There's no use being polite. You insulted me."

He looked at the Arab, motionless in the same spot, sniffed peevishly, and turned away toward the door. "Good-by, son," he said. The door shut behind him. Balducci appeared suddenly outside the window and then disappeared. His footsteps were muffled by the snow. The horse stirred on the other side of the wall and several chickens fluttered in fright. A moment later Balducci reappeared outside the window leading the horse by the bridle. He walked toward the little rise without turning around and disappeared from sight with the horse following him. A big stone could be heard bouncing down. Daru walked back toward the prisoner, who, without stirring, never took his eyes off him. "Wait," the schoolmaster said in Arabic and went toward the bedroom. As he was going through the door, he had a second thought, went to the desk, took the revolver, and stuck it in his pocket. Then, without looking back, he went into his room.

For some time he lay on his couch watching the sky gradually close over, listening to the silence. It was this silence that had seemed painful to him during the first days here, after the war. He had requested a post in the little town at the base of the foothills separating the upper plateaus from the desert. There, rocky walls, green and black to the north, pink and lavender to the south, marked the frontier of eternal summer. He had been named to a post farther north, on the plateau itself. In the beginning, the solitude and the silence had been hard for him on these wastelands peopled only by stones. Occasionally, furrows suggested cultivation, but they had been dug to uncover a certain kind of stone good for building. The only plowing here was to harvest rocks. Elsewhere a thin layer of soil accumulated in the hollows would be scraped out to enrich paltry village gardens. This is the way it was: bare rock covered three quarters of the region. Towns sprang up, flourished, then disappeared; men came by, loved one another or fought bitterly, then died. No one in this desert, neither he nor his guest, mattered. And yet, outside this desert neither of them, Daru knew, could have really lived.

When he got up, no noise came from the classroom. He was amazed at the unmixed joy he derived from the mere thought that the Arab might have fled and that he would be alone with no decision to make. But the prisoner was there. He had merely stretched out between the stove and the desk. With eyes open, he was staring at the ceiling. In that position, his thick lips were particularly noticeable, giving him a pouting look. "Come," said Daru. The Arab got up and followed him. In the bedroom, the schoolmaster pointed to a chair near the table under the window. The Arab sat down without taking his eyes off Daru.

"Are you hungry?"

"Yes," the prisoner said.

Daru set the table for two. He took flour and oil, shaped a cake in a frying-pan, and lighted the little stove that functioned on bottled gas. While the cake was cooking, he went out to the shed to get cheese, eggs, dates, and condensed milk. When the cake was done he set it on the window sill to cool, heated some condensed milk diluted with water, and beat up the eggs into an omelette. In one of his motions he knocked against the revolver stuck in his right pocket. He set the bowl down, went into the classroom, and put the revolver in his desk drawer. When he came back to the room, night was falling. He put on the light and served the Arab. "Eat," he said. The Arab took a piece of the cake, lifted it eagerly to his mouth, and stopped short.

"And you?" he asked.

"After you. I'll eat too."

The thick lips opened slightly. The Arab hesitated, then bit into the cake determinedly.

The meal over, the Arab looked at the schoolmaster. "Are you the judge?"

"No, I'm simply keeping you until tomorrow."

"Why do you eat with me?"

"I'm hungry."

The Arab fell silent. Daru got up and went out. He brought back a folding bed from the shed, set it up between the table and the stove, perpendicular to his own bed. From a large suitcase which, upright in a corner, served as a shelf for papers, he took two blankets and arranged them on the camp bed. Then he stopped, felt useless, and sat down on his bed. There was nothing more to do or to get ready. He had to look at this man. He looked at him, therefore, trying to imagine his face bursting with rage. He couldn't do so. He could see nothing but the dark yet shining eyes and the animal mouth.

"Why did you kill him?" he asked in a voice whose hostile tone surprised him.

The Arab looked away.

"He ran away. I ran after him."

He raised his eyes to Daru again and they were full of a sort of woeful interrogation. "Now what will they do to me?"

"Are you afraid?"

He stiffened, turning his eyes away.

"Are you sorry?"

The Arab stared at him openmouthed. Obviously he did not understand. Daru's annoyance was growing. At the same time he felt awkward and self-conscious with his big body wedged between the two beds.

"Lie down there," he said impatiently. "That's your bed."

The Arab didn't move. He called to Daru:

"Tell me!"

The schoolmaster looked at him.

"Is the gendarme coming back tomorrow?"

"I don't know."

"Are you coming with us?"

"I don't know. Why?"

The prisoner got up and stretched out on top of the blankets, his feet toward the window. The light from the electric bulb shone straight into his eyes and he closed them at once.

"Why?" Daru repeated, standing beside the bed.

The Arab opened his eyes under the blinding light and looked at him, trying not to blink.

"Come with us," he said.

In the middle of the night, Daru was still not asleep. He had gone to bed after undressing completely; he generally slept naked. But when he suddenly realized that he had nothing on, he hesitated. He felt vulnerable and the temptation came to him to put his clothes back on. Then he shrugged his shoulders; after all, he wasn't a child and, if need be, he could break his adversary in two. From his bed he could observe him, lying on his back, still motionless with his eyes closed under the harsh light. When Daru turned out the light, the darkness seemed to coagulate all of a sudden. Little by little, the night came back to life in the window where the starless sky was stirring gently. The schoolmaster soon made out the body lying at his feet. The Arab still did not move, but his eyes seemed open. A faint wind was prowling around the schoolhouse. Perhaps it would drive away the clouds and the sun would reappear.

During the night the wind increased. The hens fluttered a little and then were silent. The Arab turned over on his side with his back to Daru, who thought he heard him moan. Then he listened for his guest's breathing, become heavier and more regular. He listened to that breath so close to him and mused without being able to go to sleep. In this room where he had been sleeping alone for a year, this presence bothered him. But it bothered him also by imposing on him a sort of brotherhood he knew well but refused to accept in the present circumstances. Men who share the same rooms, soldiers or prisoners, develop a strange alliance as if, having cast off their armor with their clothing, they fraternized every evening, over and above their differences, in the ancient community of dream and fatigue. But Daru shook himself; he didn't like such musings, and it was essential to sleep.

A little later, however, when the Arab stirred slightly, the schoolmaster was still not asleep. When the prisoner made a second move, he stiffened, on the alert. The Arab was lifting himself slowly on his arms with almost the motion of a sleepwalker. Seated upright in bed, he waited motionless without turning his head toward Daru, as if he were listening attentively. Daru did not stir; it had just occurred to him that the revolver was still in the drawer of his desk. It was better to act at once. Yet he continued to observe the prisoner, who, with the same slithery motion, put his feet on the ground, waited again, then began to stand up slowly. Daru was about to call out to him when the Arab began to walk, in a quite natural but extraordinarily silent way. He was heading toward the door at the end of the room that opened into the shed. He lifted the latch with precaution and went out, pushing the door behind him but without shutting it. Daru had not stirred. "He is running away," he merely thought. "Good riddance!" Yet he listened attentively. The hens were not fluttering; the guest must be on the plateau. A faint sound of water reached him, and he didn't know what it was until the Arab again stood framed in the doorway, closed the door carefully, and came back to bed without a sound. Then Daru turned his back on him and fell asleep. Still later he seemed, from the depths of his sleep, to hear furtive steps around the schoolhouse. "I'm dreaming! I'm dreaming!" he repeated to himself. And he went on sleeping.

When he awoke, the sky was clear; the loose window let in a cold, pure air. The Arab was asleep, hunched up under the blankets now, his mouth open, utterly relaxed. But when Daru shook him, he started dreadfully, staring at Daru with wild eyes as if he had never seen him and such a frightened expression that the schoolmaster stepped back. "Don't be afraid. It's me. You must eat." The Arab nodded his head and said yes. Calm had returned to his face, but his expression was vacant and listless.

The coffee was ready. They drank it seated together on the folding bed as they munched their pieces of the cake. Then Daru led the Arab under the shed and showed him the faucet where he washed. He went back into the room, folded the blankets and the bed, made his own bed and put the room in order. Then he went through the classroom and out onto the terrace. The sun was already rising in the blue sky; a soft, bright light was bathing the deserted plateau. On the ridge the snow was melting in spots. The stones were about to reappear. Crouched on the edge of the plateau, the schoolmaster looked at the deserted expanse. He thought of Balducci. He had hurt him, for he had sent him off in a way as if he didn't want to be associated with him. He could still hear the gendarme's farewell and, without knowing why, he felt strangely empty and vulnerable. At that moment, from the other side of the schoolhouse, the prisoner coughed. Daru listened to him almost despite himself and then, furious, threw a pebble that whistled through the air before sinking into the snow. That man's stupid crime revolted him, but to hand him over was contrary to honor. Merely thinking of it made him smart with humiliation. And he cursed at one and the same time his own people who had sent him this Arab and the Arab too who had dared to kill and not managed to get away. Daru got up, walked in a circle on the terrace, waited motionless, and then went back into the schoolhouse.

The Arab, leaning over the cement floor of the shed, was washing his teeth with two fingers. Daru looked at him and said: "Come." He went back into the room ahead of the prisoner. He slipped a hunting-jacket on over his sweater and put on walking-shoes. Standing, he waited until the Arab had put on his *chèche* and sandals. They went into the classroom and the schoolmaster pointed to the exit, saying: "Go ahead." The fellow didn't budge. "I'm coming," said Daru. The Arab went out. Daru went back into the room and made a package of pieces of rusk, dates, and sugar. In the classroom, before going out, he hesitated a second in front of his desk, then crossed the threshold and locked the door. "That's the way," he said. He started toward the east, followed by the prisoner. But, a short distance from the school-house, he thought he heard a slight sound behind them. He retraced his steps and examined the surroundings of the house; there was no one there. The Arab watched him without seeming to understand. "Come on," said Daru.

They walked for an hour and rested beside a sharp peak of lime-stone. The snow was melting faster and faster and the sun was drinking up the puddles at once, rapidly cleaning the plateau, which gradually dried and vibrated like the air itself. When they resumed walking, the ground rang under their feet. From time to time a bird rent the space in front of them with a joyful cry. Daru breathed in deeply the fresh morning light. He felt a sort of rapture before the vast familiar expanse, now almost entirely yellow under its dome of blue sky. They walked an hour more, descending toward the south. They reached a level height made up of crumbly rocks. From there on, the plateau sloped down, eastward, toward a low plain where there were a few spindly trees and, to the south, toward outcroppings of rock that gave the land-scape a chaotic look.

Daru surveyed the two directions. There was nothing but the sky on the horizon. Not a man could be seen. He turned toward the Arab, who was looking at him blankly. Daru held out the package to him. "Take it," he said. "There are dates, bread, and sugar. You can hold out for two days. Here are a thousand francs too." The Arab took the package and the money but kept his full hands at chest level as if he didn't know what to do with what was being given him. "Now look," the schoolmaster said as he pointed in the direction of the east, "there's the way to Tinguit. You have a two-hour walk. At Tinguit you'll find the administration and the police. They are expecting you." The Arab looked toward the east, still holding the package and the money against his chest. Daru took his elbow and turned him rather roughly toward the south. At the foot of the height on which they stood could be seen a faint path. "That's the trail across the plateau. In a day's walk from here you'll find pasturelands and the first nomads. They'll take you in and shelter you according to their law." The Arab had now turned toward Daru and a sort of panic was visible in his expression. "Listen," he said. Daru shook his head: "No, be quiet. Now I'm leaving you." He turned his back on him, took two long steps in the direction of the school, looked hesitantly at the motion-less Arab, and started off again. For a few minutes he heard nothing but his own step resounding on the cold ground and did not turn his head. A moment later, however, he turned around. The Arab was still there on the edge of the hill, his arms hanging now, and he was looking at the schoolmaster. Daru felt something rise in his throat. But he swore with impatience, waved vaguely, and started off again. He had already gone some distance when he again stopped and looked. There was no longer anyone on the hill.

Daru hesitated. The sun was now rather high in the sky and was beginning to beat down on his head. The schoolmaster retraced his steps, at first somewhat uncertainly, then with decision. When he reached the little hill, he was bathed in sweat. He climbed it as fast as he could and stopped, out of breath, at the top. The rock-fields to the south stood out sharply against the blue sky, but on the plain to the east a steamy heat was already rising. And in that slight haze, Daru, with heavy heart, made out the Arab walking slowly on the road to prison.

A little later, standing before the window of the classroom, the schoolmaster was watching the clear light bathing the whole surface of the plateau, but he hardly saw it. Behind him on the blackboard, among the winding French rivers, sprawled the clumsily chalked-up words he had just read: "You handed over our brother. You will pay for this." Daru looked at the sky, the plateau, and, beyond, the invisible lands stretching all the way to the sea. In this vast landscape he had loved so much, he was alone.

For Discussion

1. How did Daru react at first to Balducci and the Arab prisoner? What statements indicated that Daru began to feel he had certain things in common with, or began to identify with, the Arab prisoner? Describe Daru's feelings of "brotherhood" toward the Arab. Why did "such musings" (page 121) upset Daru?

2. Describe in detail the setting of "The Guest." How does the setting influence or affect the characters and their actions?

3. What thoughts come to your mind when you think of the word "guest"? In your opinion, what is the significance of the story's title? Why wouldn't a title such as "The Prisoner" be more fitting?

4. What elements of meaninglessness (absurdity), rather than maliciousness and evil, characterized the Arab's crime? Was Daru simply infuriated with the Arab for having committed murder, or

did Daru seem to feel that the act had a greater significance? If you choose the latter alternative, tell what that "greater significance" was.

5. Consult the Glossary of Literary Terms for the definition of "irony." Explain the irony of the Arab's question, "Are you the judge?" How was Daru's answer also ironical? Was Daru eventually forced into acting as a "judge"? Was the Arab also forced into this role? Explain.

6. What were the decisions that Daru and the Arab had to make? What were the consequences of their decisions? Why do you think they made these particular choices? Would you say that they were able to choose freely? If, in your opinion, they did not really have a free choice, what circumstances (both internal or personal and external or social) prevented them from acting freely?

7. Discuss the significance of the words written on the blackboard: "You handed over our brother. You will pay for this." Who do you think wrote them? Considering the way Daru felt about the Arab, why are these lines ironical? In what ways do you think Daru will "pay for this"?

8. Why do you think Daru felt alone at this point? What did his feelings of isolation indicate about the way he viewed his own actions?

For Composition

1. The term "alienation" may be applied to "The Guest." Define this word and apply it to the relationship between Daru and the Arab, between both of them and society, and between each of them and his inner, personal self. Have you ever felt alienated from other people or even from yourself? Discuss.

2. Have you ever been forced into making a decision in which you felt that you really had no choice? Describe the incident and your emotional reactions in detail.

3. Find the lines in which Daru discussed "honor." Did he act in accordance with his conception of this virtue? Explain. How does your idea of honor compare with Daru's? If you were faced with Daru's decision, how might you have acted? How might you have reacted if you were confronted with the Arab's "choice"?

NONFICTION

*Y*OU will realize, as you read this section of the book, that European writers, like those in America and England, can, and do, write about every conceivable subject. The nonfiction selections that follow range from a humorous account of London streets and English people by a Czech to a serious analysis of Shakespeare's plays by a Russian; from a philosophical essay by a Frenchman to a thrilling personal reminiscence by a Norwegian. As you read, another point that will become apparent is that there is no style in common among European writers. Each has his own style; that is, the particular way he uses words to convey what he has seen and thought.

Just before reading these selections it might be well to review some of the points concerning nonfiction writing that will increase your appreciation of what these writers have done.

The nonfiction writer works in the field of facts and ideas about people, places, and things. Even when the author treats them in a colorful way, he is expected to tell the truth as he knows it and sees it. An author may propose theories or arrive at conclusions with which you do not agree. Nevertheless, you should be able to assume he is sincere in his convictions and honest in his expression of them.

Facts can sometimes be dull things. There would, for example, be little to hold your interest in statements about the kinds of birds in Spain or the import taxes of European countries. But it is the function of the nonfiction writer to use these facts to get his particular message over to you. He must present them in such a way that you are pleased and interested as you acquire this new information, or are instructed in the how, or why, of the subject under discussion.

Sometimes the nonfiction writer will change your opinion about something. At other times, the nonfiction writer will try to get you to do something. There are many ways he may do it. The choice is his. He may use description, narration, exposition, or argumentation. He may use one or several of these things at the same time. He may be serious or humorous. The only thing he may not be is dull.

In this volume you will see how present-day European writers have treated similar subjects. It will give you some idea of the kind of thinking and feeling that is going on in Europe today; an idea of the characteristics and distinguishing attitudes—the *ethos*, as it is called—of today's European writers.

The nonfiction writer can choose any one of many ways to achieve his purpose—to get the reader to know, feel, or do something. He can do it by writing a personal reminiscence, an autobiography or biography, a formal or informal essay. There are examples of each of these forms of nonfiction in this volume, and a good last question when you finish this section of the book could be "Which is which?"

One important difference that you will notice between European writers and American and English writers is that European writers are less concerned with amusing or diverting the reader than with convincing him of something or instructing him. You will not, for example, find many essays like G. K. Chesterton's "On Running After One's Hat" or Phyllis McGinley's "A Lost Privilege" among the nonfiction work of a European writer. This does not mean that he isn't aware that he must sustain the interest of the reader. He is still concerned with expressing his ideas and feelings in the most effective way and with making experiences, places, people—even himself—come to life for the reader. He does, in fact, use many of the methods and techniques of fiction writers to create tone and mood, dramatic tension, and even suspense. He will not exaggerate or distort facts, but he may, and often does, interpret the facts for the reader.

Thor Heyerdahl

At the Mercy of the Breakers

Thor Heyerdahl (1914–   ), the Norwegian anthropologist and writer, is best known for his book, *Kon-Tiki*, the stirring account of the expedition he led across the Pacific Ocean on a raft in 1947. This book has been translated into twenty-four languages.

Some years ago when Heyerdahl was in the South Pacific, he saw unusual art relics and heard strange legends of ancestors who had crossed the seas with their chief, Tiki. These remnants reminded him of cultures in Peru, and he wondered whether the Polynesians might have come from there. He knew that it was considered unlikely that the ancient Polynesians could have voyaged from Peru to Tahiti aboard a raft but his theory seemed reasonable to him. To test it, Heyerdahl asked five men to go with him, guaranteeing "nothing but a free trip to Peru and the South Seas and back" and good use for their technical abilities. They built a primitive raft of bamboo and balsa logs and floated from Peru across the Pacific toward Tahiti. Heyerdahl believed that if he could reach Polynesia from Peru by raft, the first settlers could also have accomplished such a journey.

$\mathcal{W}$E were drifting straight toward the ominous Takume and Raroia reefs, which together blocked up forty to fifty miles of the sea ahead of us. We made desperate efforts to steer clear, to the north of these dangerous reefs, and things seemed to be going well till one night the watch came hurrying in and called us all out.

The wind had changed. We were heading straight for the Takume reef. It had begun to rain, and there was no visibility at all. The reef could not be far off.

In the middle of night we held a council of war. It was a question of saving our lives now. To get past on the north side was now hopeless; we must try to get through on the south side instead. We trimmed the sail, laid the oar over, and began a dangerous piece of sailing with the uncertain north wind behind us. If the east wind

128

came back before we had passed the whole façade of the fifty-mile-long reefs, we should be hurled in among the breakers, at their mercy.

We agreed on all that should be done if shipwreck was imminent. We would stay on board the *Kon-Tiki* at all costs. We would not climb up the mast, from which we should be shaken down like rotten fruit, but would cling tight to the stays of the mast when the seas poured over us. We laid the rubber raft loose on the deck and made fast to it a small watertight radio transmitter, a small quantity of provisions, water bottles, and medical stores. This would be washed ashore independently of us if we ourselves should get over the reef safe but empty-handed. In the stern of the *Kon-Tiki* we made fast a long rope with a float which also would be washed ashore, so that we could try to pull in the raft if she were stranded out on the reef. And so we crept into bed and left the watch to the helmsman out in the rain.

As long as the north wind held, we glided slowly but surely down along the façade of the coral reefs which lay in ambush below the horizon. But then one afternoon the wind died away, and when it returned it had gone round into the east. According to Erik's position we were already so far down that we now had some hope of steering clear of the southernmost point of the Raroia reef. We would try to get round it and into shelter before going on to other reefs beyond it.

When night came, we had been a hundred days at sea.

Late in the night I woke, feeling restless and uneasy. There was something unusual in the movement of the waves. The *Kon-Tiki's* motion was a little different from what it usually was in such conditions. We had become sensitive to changes in the rhythm of the logs. I thought at once of suction from a coast, which was drawing near, and was continually out on deck and up the mast. Nothing but sea was visible. But I could get no quiet sleep. Time passed.

At dawn, just before six, Torstein came hurrying down from the masthead. He could see a whole line of small palm-clad islands far ahead. Before doing anything else we laid the oar over to southward as far as we could. What Torstein had seen must be the small coral islands which lay strewn like pearls on a string behind the Raroia reef. A northward current must have caught us.

At half-past seven palm-clad islets had appeared in a row all along the horizon to westward. The southernmost lay roughly ahead of our bow, and thence there were islands and clumps of palms all along the horizon on our starboard side till they disappeared as dots away to northward. The nearest were four or five sea miles away.

A survey from the masthead showed that, even if our bow pointed toward the bottom island in the chain, our drift sideways was so great that we were not advancing in the direction in which our bow pointed. We were drifting diagonally right in toward the reef. With fixed centerboards we should still have had some hope of steering clear. But sharks were following close astern, so that it was impossible to dive under the raft and tighten up the loose centerboards with fresh guy ropes.

We saw that we had now only a few hours more on board the *Kon-Tiki*. They must be used in preparation for our inevitable wreck on the coral reef. Every man learned what he had to do when the moment came; each one of us knew where his own limited sphere of responsibility lay, so that we should not fly round treading on one another's toes when the time came and seconds counted. The *Kon-Tiki* pitched up and down, up and down, as the wind forced us in. There was no doubt that here was the turmoil of the waves created by the reef—some waves advancing while others were hurled back after beating vainly against the surrounding wall.

We were still under full sail in the hope of even now being able to steer clear. As we gradually drifted nearer, half sideways, we saw from the mast how the whole string of palm-clad isles was connected with a coral reef, part above and part under water, which lay like a mole where the sea was white with foam and leaped high into the air. The Raroia atoll is oval in shape and has a diameter of twenty-five miles, not counting the adjoining reefs of Takume. The whole of its longer side faces the sea to eastward, where we came pitching in. The reef itself, which runs in one line from horizon to horizon, is only a few hundred yards clear, and behind it idyllic islets lie in a string round the still lagoon inside.

It was with mixed feelings that we saw the blue Pacific being ruthlessly torn up and hurled into the air all along the horizon ahead of us. I knew what awaited us; I had visited the Tuamotu group before and had stood safe on land looking out over the immense spectacle in the east, where the surf from the open Pacific broke in over the reef. New reefs and islands kept on gradually appearing to southward. We must be lying off the middle of the façade of the coral wall.

On board the *Kon-Tiki* all preparations for the end of the voyage were being made. Everything of value was carried into the cabin and lashed fast. Documents and papers were packed into watertight bags, along with films and other things which would not stand a dip in the sea. The whole bamboo cabin was covered with canvas, and especially strong ropes were lashed across it. When we saw that all hope was gone, we opened up the bamboo deck and cut off with machete knives all the ropes which held the centerboards down. It was a hard job to get the centerboards drawn up, because they were all thickly covered with stout barnacles. With the centerboards up the draught of our vessel was no deeper than to the bottom of the timber logs, and we would therefore be more easily washed in over the reef. With no centerboards and with the sail down, the raft lay completely sideways on and was entirely at the mercy of wind and sea.

We tied the longest rope we had to the homemade anchor and made it fast to the step of the port mast, so that the *Kon-Tiki* would go into the surf stern first when the anchor was thrown overboard. The anchor itself consisted of empty water cans filled with used radio batteries and heavy scrap, and solid mangrove-wood sticks projected from it, set crosswise.

Order number one, which came first and last, was: Hold on to the raft! Whatever happened, we must hang on tight on board and let the nine great logs take the pressure from the reef. We ourselves had more than enough to do to withstand the weight of the water. If we jumped overboard, we should become helpless victims of the suction which would fling us in and out over the sharp corals. The rubber raft would capsize in the steep seas, or, heavily loaded with us in it, it would be torn to ribbons against the reef. But the wooden logs would sooner or later be cast ashore, and we with them, if we only managed to hold fast.

Next, all hands were told to put on their shoes for the first time in a hundred days and to have their life belts ready. The last precaution, however, was not of much value, for if a man fell overboard he would be battered to death, not drowned. We had time, too, to put our passports and such few dollars as we had left into our pockets. But it was not lack of time that was troubling us.

Those were anxious hours in which we lay drifting helplessly sideways, step after step, in toward the reef. It was noticeably quiet on board; we all crept in and out from cabin to bamboo deck, silent or laconic, and carried on with our jobs. Our serious faces showed that no one was in doubt as to what awaited us, and the absence of nervousness showed that we had all gradually acquired an unshakable confidence in the raft. If it had brought us across the sea, it would also manage to bring us ashore alive.

Inside the cabin there was a complete chaos of provision cartons and cargo, lashed fast. Torstein had barely found room for himself in the radio corner, where he had got the shortwave transmitter working. We were now over 4,000 sea miles from our old base at Callao, where the Peruvian Naval War School had maintained regular contact with us, and still farther from Hal and Frank and the other radio amateurs in the United States. But, as chance willed, we had on the previous day got in touch with a capable radio "ham" who had a set on Rarotonga in the Cook Islands, and the operators, quite contrary to all our usual practice, had arranged for an extra contact with him early in the morning. All the time we were drifting closer and closer in to the reef, Torstein was sitting tapping his key and calling Rarotonga.

Entries in the *Kon-Tiki's* log ran:

—8:15: *We are slowly approaching land. We can now make out with the naked eye the separate palm trees inside on the starboard side.*

—8:45: *The wind has veered into a still more unfavorable quarter for us, so we have no hope of getting clear. No nervousness on board, but hectic preparations on deck. There is something lying on the reef ahead of us which looks like the wreck of a sailing vessel, but it may be only a heap of driftwood.*

—9:45: *The wind is taking us straight toward the last island but one we see behind the reef. We can now see the whole coral reef clearly; here it is built up like a white and red speckled wall which barely sticks up out of the water as a belt in front of all the islands. All along the reef white foaming surf is flung up toward the sky. Bengt is just serving up a good hot meal, the last before the great action!*

It is a wreck lying in there on the reef. We are so close now that we can see right across the shining lagoon behind the reef and see the outlines of other islands on the other side of the lagoon.

As this was written, the dull drone of the surf came near again;

it came from the whole reef and filled the air like thrilling rolls of the drum, heralding the exciting last act of the *Kon-Tiki*.

—9:50: *Very close now. Drifting along the reef. Only a hundred yards or so away. Torstein is talking to the man on Rarotonga. All clear. Must pack up log now. All in good spirits; it looks bad, but we shall make it!*

A few minutes later the anchor rushed overboard and caught hold of the bottom, so that the *Kon-Tiki* swung around and turned her stern inward toward the breakers. It held us for a few valuable minutes, while Torstein sat hammering like mad on the key. He had got Rarotonga now. The breakers thundered in the air and the sea rose and fell furiously. All hands were at work on deck, and now Torstein got his message through. He said we were drifting toward the Raroia reef. He asked Rarotonga to listen in on the same wave length every hour. If we were silent for more than thirty-six hours, Rarotonga must let the Norwegian Embassy in Washington know. Torstein's last words were:

"O.K. Fifty yards left. Here we go. Good-by."

Then he closed down the station, Knut sealed up the papers, and both crawled out on deck as fast as they could to join the rest of us, for it was clear now that the anchor was giving way.

The swell grew heavier and heavier, with deep troughs between the waves, and we felt the raft being swung up and down, up and down, higher and higher.

Again the order was shouted: "Hold on, never mind about the cargo, hold on!"

We were now so near the waterfall inside that we no longer heard the steady continuous roar from all along the reef. We now heard only a separate boom each time the nearest breaker crashed down on the rocks.

All hands stood in readiness, each clinging fast to the rope he thought the most secure. Only Erik crept into the cabin at the last moment; there was one part of the program he had not yet carried out—he had not found his shoes!

No one stood aft, for it was there the shock from the reef would come. Nor were the two firm stays which ran from the masthead down to the stern safe. For if the mast fell they would be left hanging overboard, over the reef. Herman, Bengt, and Torstein had climbed up on some boxes which were lashed fast forward of the cabin wall, and, while Herman clung on to the guy ropes from the ridge of the roof, the other two held on to the ropes from the masthead by which the sail at other times was hauled up. Knut and I chose the stay running from the bow up to the masthead, for, if mast and cabin and everything else went overboard, we thought the rope from the bow would nevertheless remain lying inboard, as we were now head on to the seas.

When we realized that the seas had got hold of us, the anchor rope was cut and we were off. A sea rose straight up under us, and we felt the *Kon-Tiki* being lifted up in the air. The great moment had come; we were riding on the wave back at breathless speed, our ramshackle craft creaking and groaning as she quivered under us. The excitement made one's blood boil. I remember that, having no other inspiration, I waved my arm and bellowed "Hurrah!" at the top of my lungs; it afforded a certain relief and could do no harm anyway. The others certainly thought I had gone mad, but they all beamed and grinned enthusiastically. On we ran with the seas rushing in behind us; this was the *Kon-Tiki's* baptism of fire. All must and would go well.

But our elation was soon dampened. A new sea rose high up astern of us like a glittering, green glass wall. As we sank down it came rolling after us, and, in the same second in which I saw it high above me, I felt a violent blow and was submerged under floods of water. I felt the suction through my whole body with such great power that I had to strain every single muscle in my frame and think of one thing only—hold on, hold on! I think that in such a desperate situation the arms will be torn off before the brain consents to let go, evident as the outcome is. Then I felt that the mountain of water was passing on and relaxing its devilish grip of my body. When the whole mountain had rushed on, with an ear-splitting roaring and crashing, I saw Knut again hanging on beside me, doubled up into a ball. Seen from behind, the great sea was almost flat and gray. As it rushed on, it swept over the ridge of the cabin roof which projected from the water, and there hung the three others, pressed against the cabin roof as the water passed over them.

We were still afloat.

In an instant I renewed my hold, with arms and legs bent round the strong rope. Knut let himself down and with a tiger's leap joined

the others on the boxes, where the cabin took the strain. I heard
reassuring exclamations from them, but at the same time I saw a
new green wall rise up and come towering toward us. I shouted a
warning and made myself as small and hard as I could where I hung.
In an instant hell was over us again, and the *Kon-Tiki* disappeared
completely under the masses of water. The sea tugged and pulled
with all the force it could bring to bear at the poor little bundles
of human bodies. The second sea rushed over us, to be followed by
a third like it.

Then I heard a triumphant shout from Knut, who was now
hanging on to the rope ladder:

"Look at the raft—she's holding!"

After three seas only the double mast and the cabin had been
knocked a bit crooked. Again we had a feeling of triumph over the
elements, and the elation of victory gave us new strength.

Then I saw the next sea come towering up, higher than all the
rest, and again I bellowed a warning aft to the others as I climbed up
the stay, as high as I could get in a hurry, and hung on fast. Then
I myself disappeared sideways into the midst of the green wall which
towered high over us. The others, who were farther aft and saw me
disappear first, estimated the height of the wall of water at twenty-
five feet, while the foaming crest passed by fifteen feet above the part
of the glassy wall into which I had vanished. Then the great wave
reached them, and we had all one single thought—hold on, hold on,
hold, hold, hold!

We must have hit the reef that time. I myself felt only the strain
on the stay, which seemed to bend and slacken jerkily. But whether
the bumps came from above or below I could not tell, hanging there.
The whole submersion lasted only seconds, but it demanded more
endurance than we usually have in our bodies. There is greater
strength in the human mechanism than that of the muscles alone.
I determined that, if I was to die, I would die in this position, like
a knot on the stay. The sea thundered on, over and past, and as it
roared by it revealed a hideous sight. The *Kon-Tiki* was wholly
changed, as by the stroke of a magic wand. The vessel we knew from
weeks and months at sea was no more; in a few seconds our pleasant
world had become a shattered wreck.

I saw only one man on board besides myself. He lay pressed flat
across the ridge of the cabin roof, face downward with his arms

stretched out on both sides, while the cabin itself was crushed in, like a house of cards, toward the stern and toward the starboard side. The motionless figure was Herman. There was no other sign of life, while the hill of water thundered by, in across the reef. The hardwood mast on the starboard side was broken like a match, and the upper stump, in its fall, had smashed right through the cabin roof, so that the mast and all its gear slanted at a low angle over the reef on the starboard side. Astern, the steering block was twisted round length-ways and the crossbeam broken, while the steering oar was smashed to splinters. The splashboards at the bow were broken like cigar boxes, and the whole deck was torn up and pasted like wet paper against the forward wall of the cabin, along with boxes, cans, canvas, and other cargo. Bamboo sticks and rope ends stuck up everywhere, and the general effect was of complete chaos.

I felt cold fear run through my whole body. What was the good of my holding on? If I lost one single man here, in the run in, the whole thing would be ruined, and for the moment there was only one human figure to be seen after the last buffet. In that second Torstein's hunched-up form appeared outside the raft. He was hanging like a monkey in the ropes from the masthead and managed to get on to the logs again, where he crawled up on to the debris forward of the cabin. Herman, too, now turned his head and gave me a forced grin of encouragement, but did not move. I bellowed in the faint hope of locating the others and heard Bengt's calm voice call out that all hands were aboard. They were lying holding on to the ropes behind the tangled barricade which the tough plaiting from the bamboo deck had built up.

All this happened in the course of a few seconds, while the *Kon-Tiki* was being drawn out of the witches' caldron by the back-wash, and a fresh sea came rolling over her. For the last time I bellowed "Hang on!" at the top of my lungs amid the uproar, and that was all I myself did; I hung on and disappeared in the masses of water which rushed over and past in those endless two or three seconds. That was enough for me. I saw the ends of the logs knocking and bumping against a sharp step in the coral reef without going over it. Then we were sucked out again. I also saw the two men who lay stretched out across the ridge of the cabin roof, but none of us smiled any longer. Behind the chaos of bamboo I heard a calm voice call out:

"This won't do."

I myself felt equally discouraged. As the masthead sank farther and farther out over the starboard side, I found myself hanging on to a slack line outside the raft. The next sea came. When it had gone by I was dead tired, and my only thought was to get up on to the logs and lie behind the barricade. When the backwash retreated, I saw for the first time the rugged red reef naked beneath us and perceived Torstein standing, bent double, on gleaming red corals, holding on to a bunch of rope ends from the mast. Knut, standing aft, was about to jump. I shouted that we must all keep on the logs, and Torstein, who had been washed overboard by the pressure of water, sprang up again like a cat.

Two or three more seas rolled over us with diminishing force, and what happened then I do not remember, except that water foamed in and out and I myself sank lower and lower toward the red reef over which we were being lifted in. Then only crests of foam full of salt spray came whirling in, and I was able to work my way in on to the raft, where we all made for the after end of the logs which was highest up on the reef.

At the same moment Knut crouched down and sprang up on to the reef with the line which lay clear astern. While the backwash was running out, he waded through the whirling water some thirty yards in and stood safely at the end of the line when the next sea foamed in toward him, died down, and ran back from the flat reef like a broad stream.

Then Erik came crawling out of the collapsed cabin, with his shoes on. If we had all done as he did, we should have got off cheaply. As the cabin had not been washed overboard but had been pressed down pretty flat under the canvas, Erik lay quietly stretched out among the cargo and heard the peals of thunder crashing above him while the collapsed bamboo walls curved downward. Bengt had had a slight concussion when the mast fell but had managed to crawl under the wrecked cabin alongside Erik. We should all of us have been lying there if we had realized in advance how firmly the count-less lashings and plaited bamboo sheets would hang on to the main logs under the pressure of the water.

Erik was now standing ready on the logs aft, and when the sea retired he, too, jumped up on the reef. It was Herman's turn next, and then Bengt's. Each time the raft was pushed a bit farther in, and, when Torstein's turn and my own came, the raft already lay so far in on the reef that there was no longer any ground for abandoning her. All hands began the work of salvage.

We were now twenty yards away from that devilish step up on the reef, and it was there and beyond it that the breakers came rolling after one another in long lines. The coral polyps had taken care to build the atoll so high that only the very tops of the breakers were able to send a fresh stream of sea water past us and into the lagoon, which abounded in fish. Here inside was the corals' own world, and they disported themselves in the strangest shapes and colors.

A long way in on the reef the others found the rubber raft, lying drifting and quite waterlogged. They emptied it and dragged it back to the wreck, and we loaded it to the full with the most important equipment, like the radio set, provisions, and water bottles. We dragged all this in across the reef and piled it up on the top of a huge block of coral, which lay alone on the inside of the reef like a large meteorite. Then we went back to the wreck for fresh loads. We could never know what the sea would be up to when the tidal currents got to work around us.

In the shallow water inside the reef we saw something bright shining in the sun. When we waded over to pick it up, to our astonishment we saw two empty tins. This was not exactly what we had expected to find there, and we were still more surprised when we saw that the little boxes were quite bright and newly opened and stamped "Pineapple," with the same inscription as that on the new field rations we ourselves were testing for the quartermaster. They were indeed two of our own pineapple tins which we had thrown overboard after our last meal on board the *Kon-Tiki*. We had followed close behind them up on the reef.

We were standing on sharp, rugged coral blocks, and on the uneven bottom we waded now ankle-deep, now chest-deep, according to the channels and stream beds in the reef. Anemones and corals gave the whole reef the appearance of a rock garden covered with mosses and cactus and fossilized plants, red and green and yellow and white. There was no color that was not represented, either in corals or algae or in shells and sea slugs and fantastic fish, which were wriggling about everywhere. In the deeper channels small sharks about four feet long came sneaking up to us in the crystal-clear water.

But we had only to smack the water with the palms of our hands for them to turn about and keep at a distance.

Where we had stranded, we had only pools of water and wet patches of coral about us; farther in lay the calm blue lagoon. The tide was going out and we continually saw more corals sticking up out of the water round us, while the surf which thundered without interruption along the reef sank down, as it were, a floor lower. What would happen there on the narrow reef when the tide began to flow again was uncertain. We must get away.

The reef stretched like a half-submerged fortress wall up to the north and down to the south. In the extreme south was a long island densely covered with tall palm forest. And just above us to the north, only 600 or 700 yards away, lay another but considerably smaller palm island. It lay inside the reef, with palm tops rising into the sky and snow-white sandy beaches running out into the still lagoon. The whole island looked like a bulging green basket of flowers, or a little bit of concentrated paradise.

This island we chose.

Herman stood beside me beaming all over his bearded face. He did not say a word, only stretched out his hand and laughed quietly. The *Kon-Tiki* still lay far out on the reef with the spray flying over her. She was a wreck, but an honorable wreck. Everything above deck was smashed up, but the nine balsa logs from the Quevedo forest in Ecuador were as intact as ever. They had saved our lives.

For Discussion

1. What plans did the crew of the *Kon-Tiki* make when it became clear that they were heading straight for the Takume reef? Why did each man have a "limited sphere of responsibility"?
2. Why was "order number one" so important? How did the men react as the *Kon-Tiki* drifted helplessly towards the dangerous reef?
3. Why was "holding on" so difficult? Were the men justified or not in feeling triumphant after three onslaughts from the breakers? Why?
4. What happened when the fourth great wave broke over the raft? Why did Heyerdahl question the good of holding on?
5. How did the waves help the men reach the safety of the reef? What was it like within the coral reef? Why did the crew have to get away from it?

6. The men chose to take refuge on a small palm island. What reason do you have for believing that they would not suffer any hardships and would soon be rescued?
7. Why did the author call the *Kon-Tiki* an "honorable wreck"? In your opinion, were the men as responsible as the raft for the successful outcome of this experience? Why or why not?
8. The book, *Kon-Tiki*, from which this selection came, is a personal reminiscence. Like an autobiography, it reveals the writer's response to people and events. In an autobiography, however, the focus is on the writer himself. In a personal reminiscence, the focus is on the experience the writer has chosen to share with the reader. Often, a personal reminiscence, such as *Kon-Tiki*, is such a stirring account of true adventure that it rivals fiction in its appeal. How did Heyerdahl make this hair-raising experience come to life? In what ways was it like a short story? In what ways was it different?
9. From this selection, what opinion do you have of Heyerdahl's character? Point out sentences to support your answer.
10. Heyerdahl's ability as a writer is revealed in his descriptive passages about the sea, the Raroia atoll, the shattered wreck, and the lagoon. Reread these passages. Point out those details which you consider particularly effective. Select five similes in the selection which Heyerdahl used to help the reader share his impressions of what he saw and heard.

For Composition

1. Write a composition in which you express your opinion of why the men of the *Kon-Tiki* might have taken this dangerous trip across the Pacific. Do you think they were wise to risk their lives as they did?
2. Heyerdahl does not tell you what the various members of the crew thought or felt during the battle with the breakers. Imagine that you are Eric, Knut, or one of the other members of the crew. Write an account of what you thought and felt during this experience.
3. Making a trip by rowboat, sailboat, canoe, or ship can be an enjoyable and sometimes exciting experience. If you have had such an experience, write an account of it. Select details that will bring the event vividly to life for the reader.

Eve Curie

Four Years in a Shed

Eve Curie (1904–   ), French writer, lecturer, and pianist, is the daughter of the famous scientists, Marie and Pierre Curie. Her outstanding biography of her mother, *Madame Curie*, was translated into twenty-five languages. In the introduction to this book, Eve Curie wrote: "My mother was thirty-seven years old when I was born. When I was big enough to know her well, she was already an aging woman who had passed the summit of renown. And yet it is the celebrated scientist who is strangest to me—probably because the idea that she was a 'celebrated scientist' did not occupy the mind of Marie Curie. It seems to me, rather, that I have always lived near the poor student, haunted by dreams, who was Marya Sklodovska long before I came into the world."

"Four Years in a Shed" is a chapter from *Madame Curie*. It tells how this small, frail woman, together with her husband, worked under almost insurmountable conditions to produce the first gram of radium salts from eight tons of pitchblende.

$\mathcal{A}$ MAN chosen at random from a crowd to read an account of the discovery of radium would not have doubted for one moment that radium existed: beings whose critical sense has not been sharpened and simultaneously deformed by specialized culture keep their imaginations fresh. They are ready to accept an unexpected fact, however extraordinary it may appear, and to wonder at it.

The physicist colleagues of the Curies received the news in slightly different fashion. The special properties of polonium and radium upset fundamental theories in which scientists had believed for centuries. How was one to explain the spontaneous radiation of the radioactive bodies? The discovery upset a world of acquired knowledge and contradicted the most firmly established ideas on the composition of matter. Thus the physicist kept on the reserve. He was violently interested in Pierre and Marie's work, he could perceive its infinite developments, but before being convinced he awaited the acquisition of decisive results.

The attitude of the chemist was even more downright. By definition, a chemist only believes in the existence of a new substance when he has seen the substance, touched it, weighed and examined it, confronted it with acids, bottled it, and when he has determined its "atomic weight."

Now, up to the present, nobody had "seen" radium. Nobody knew the atomic weight of radium. And the chemists, faithful to their principles, concluded: "No atomic weight, no radium. Show us some radium and we will believe you."

To show polonium and radium to the incredulous, to prove to the world the existence of their "children," and to complete their own conviction, M. and Mme. Curie were now to labor for four years.

The aim was to obtain pure radium and polonium. In the most strongly radioactive products the scientists had prepared, these substances figured only in imperceptible traces. Pierre and Marie already knew the method by which they could hope to isolate the new metals, but the separation could not be made except by treating very large quantities of crude material.

Here arose three agonizing questions:

How were they to get a sufficient quantity of ore? What premises could they use to effect their treatment? What money was there to pay the inevitable cost of the work?

Pitchblende, in which polonium and radium were hidden, was a costly ore, treated at the St. Joachimsthal mines in Bohemia for the extraction of uranium salts used in the manufacture of glass. Tons of pitchblende would cost a great deal; a great deal too much for the Curie household.

Ingenuity was to make up for wealth. According to the expectation of the two scientists, the extraction of uranium should leave, intact in the ore, such traces of polonium and radium as the ore contains. There was no reason why these traces should not be found in the residue. And, whereas crude pitchblende was costly, its residue after treatment had very slight value. By asking an Austrian colleague for a recommendation to the directors of the mine of St. Joachimsthal would it not be possible to obtain a considerable quantity of such residue for a reasonable price?

It was simple enough: but somebody had to think of it.

It was necessary, of course, to buy this crude material and pay for its transportation to Paris. Pierre and Marie appropriated the required sum from their very slight savings. They were not so foolish as to ask for official credits. . . . If two physicists on the scent of an immense discovery had asked the University of Paris or the French government for a grant to buy pitchblende residue they would have been laughed at. In any case their letter would have been lost in the files of some office, and they would have had to wait months for a reply, probably unfavorable in the end. Out of the traditions and principles of the French Revolution, which had created the metric system, founded the Normal School, and encouraged science in many circumstances, the State seemed to have retained, after more than a century, only the deplorable words pronounced by Fouquier-Tinville at the trial in which Lavoisier was condemned to the guillotine: "The Republic has no need for scientists."

But at least could there not be found, in the numerous buildings attached to the Sorbonne, some kind of suitable workroom to lend to the Curie couple? Apparently not. After vain attempts, Pierre and Marie staggered back to their point of departure, which is to say to the School of Physics where Pierre taught, to the little room where Marie had done her first experiments. The room gave on a courtyard, and on the other side of the yard there was a wooden shack, an abandoned shed, with a skylight roof in such bad condition that it admitted the rain. The Faculty of Medicine had formerly used the place as a dissecting room, but for a long time now it had not even been considered fit to house the cadavers. No floor: an uncertain layer of bitumen covered the earth. It was furnished with some worn kitchen tables, a blackboard which had landed there for no known reason, and an old cast-iron stove with a rusty pipe.

A workman would not willingly have worked in such a place: Marie and Pierre, nevertheless, resigned themselves to it. The shed had one advantage: it was so untempting, so miserable, that nobody thought of refusing them the use of it. Schutzenberger, the director of the school, had always been very kind to Pierre Curie and no doubt regretted that he had nothing better to offer. However that may be, he offered nothing else; and the couple, very pleased at not being put into the street with their material, thanked him, saying that "this would do" and that they would "make the best of it."

As they were taking possession of the shed, a reply arrived from Austria. Good news! By extraordinary luck, the residue of recent extractions of uranium had not been scattered. The useless material had been piled up in a no-man's-land planted with pine trees, near the mine of St. Joachimsthal. Thanks to the intercession of Professor Suess and the Academy of Science of Vienna, the Austrian government, which was the proprietor of the State factory there, decided to present a ton of residue to the two French lunatics who thought they needed it. If, later on, they wished to be sent a greater quantity of the material, they could obtain it at the mine on the best terms. For the moment the Curies had to pay only the transportation charges on a ton of ore.

One morning a heavy wagon, like those which deliver coal, drew up in the Rue Lhomond before the School of Physics. Pierre and Marie were notified. They hurried bareheaded into the street in their laboratory gowns. Pierre, who was never agitated, kept his calm; but the more exuberant Marie could not contain her joy at the sight of the sacks that were being unloaded. It was pitchblende, *her* pitchblende, for which she had received a notice some days before from the freight station. Full of curiosity and impatience, she wanted to open one of the sacks and contemplate her treasure without further waiting. She cut the strings, undid the coarse sackcloth and plunged her two hands into the dull brown ore, still mixed with pine needles from Bohemia.

There was where radium was hidden. It was from there that Marie must extract it, even if she had to treat a mountain of this inert stuff like dust on the road.

Marya Sklodovska had lived through the most intoxicating moments of her student life in a garret; Marie Curie was to know wonderful joys again in a dilapidated shed. It was a strange sort of beginning over again, in which a sharp subtle happiness (which probably no woman before Marie had ever experienced) twice elected the most miserable setting.

The shed in the Rue Lhomond surpassed the most pessimistic expectations of discomfort. In summer, because of its skylights, it was as stifling as a hothouse. In winter one did not know whether to wish for rain or frost; if it rained, the water fell drop by drop, with a soft, nerve-racking noise, on the ground or on the work-tables, in places which the physicists had to mark in order to avoid putting apparatus there. If it froze, one froze. There was no recourse. The stove, even when it was stoked white, was a complete disappointment. If one went near enough to touch it one received a little heat, but two steps away and one was back in the zone of ice.

It was almost better for Marie and Pierre to get used to the cruelty of the outside temperature, since their technical installation—hardly existent—possessed no chimneys to carry off noxious gases, and the greater part of their treatment had to be made in the open air, in the courtyard. When a shower came the physicists hastily moved their apparatus inside: to keep on working without being suffocated they set up draughts between the opened door and windows.

Marie probably did not boast to Dr. Vauthier of this very peculiar cure for attacks of tuberculosis.

> We had no money, no laboratory and no help in the conduct of this important and difficult task [she was to write later]. It was like creating something out of nothing, and if Casimir Dluski once called my student years "the heroic years of my sister-in-law's life," I may say without exaggeration that this period was, for my husband and myself, the heroic period of our common existence.
>
> . . . And yet it was in this miserable old shed that the best and happiest years of our life were spent, entirely consecrated to work. I sometimes passed the whole day stirring a mass in ebullition, with an iron rod nearly as big as myself. In the evening I was broken with fatigue.

In such conditions M. and Mme. Curie worked for four years from 1898 to 1902.

During the first year they busied themselves with the chemical separation of radium and polonium and they studied the radiation of the products (more and more active) thus obtained. Before long they considered it more practical to separate their efforts. Pierre Curie tried to determine the properties of radium, and to know the new metal better. Marie continued those chemical treatments which would permit her to obtain salts of pure radium.

In this division of labor Marie had chosen the "man's job." She accomplished the toil of a day laborer. Inside the shed her husband was absorbed by delicate experiments. In the courtyard, dressed in her old dust-covered and acid-stained smock, her hair blown by the wind, surrounded by smoke which stung her eyes and throat, Marie was a sort of factory all by herself.

I came to treat as many as twenty kilograms of matter at a time [she writes], which had the effect of filling the shed with great jars full of precipitates and liquids. It was killing work to carry the receivers, to pour off the liquids and to stir, for hours at a stretch, the boiling matter in a smelting basin.

Radium showed no intention of allowing itself to be known by human creatures. Where were the days when Marie naïvely expected the radium content of pitchblende to be *one per cent?* The radiation of the new substance was so powerful that a tiny quantity of radium, disseminated through the ore, was the source of striking phenomena which could be easily observed and measured. The difficult, the impossible thing, was to isolate this minute quantity, to separate it from the gangue [1] in which it was so intimately mixed.

The days of work became months and years: Pierre and Marie were not discouraged. This material which resisted them, which defended its secrets, fascinated them. United by their tenderness, united by their intellectual passions, they had, in a wooden shack, the "antinatural" existence for which they had both been made, she as well as he.

At this period we were entirely absorbed by the new realm that was, thanks to an unhoped-for discovery, opening before us [Marie was to write]. In spite of the difficulties of our working conditions, we felt very happy. Our days were spent at the laboratory. In our poor shed there reigned a great tranquillity: sometimes, as we watched over some operation, we would walk up and down, talking about work in the present and in the future; when we were cold a cup of hot tea taken near the stove comforted us. We lived in our single preoccupation as if in a dream.

. . . We saw only very few persons at the laboratory; among the physicists and chemists there were a few who came from time to time, either to see our experiments or to ask for advice from Pierre Curie, whose competence in several branches of physics was well-known. Then took place some conversations before the blackboard —the sort of conversation one remembers well because it acts as a stimulant for scientific interest and the ardor for work without interrupting the course of reflection and without troubling that

[1] **gangue:** the stony or earthy minerals occurring with the metallic ore

atmosphere of peace and meditation which is the true atmosphere of a laboratory.

Whenever Pierre and Marie, alone in this poor place, left their apparatus for a moment and quietly let their tongues run on, their talk about their beloved radium passed from the transcendent to the childish.

"I wonder what *It* will be like, what *It* will look like," Marie said one day with the feverish curiosity of a child who has been promised a toy. "Pierre, what form do you imagine *It* will take?"

"I don't know," the physicist answered gently. "I should like it to have a very beautiful color. . . ."

It is odd to observe that in Marie Curie's correspondence we find, upon this prodigious effort, none of the sensitive comments, decked out with imagery, which used to flash suddenly amid the familiarity of her letters. Was it because the years of exile had somewhat relaxed the young woman's intimacy with her people? Was she too pressed by work to find time?

The essential reason for this reserve is perhaps to be sought elsewhere. It was not by chance that Mme. Curie's letters ceased to be original at the exact moment when the story of her life became exceptional. As student, teacher or young wife, Marie could tell her story. . . . But now she was isolated by all that was secret and inexpressible in her scientific vocation. Among those she loved there was no longer anybody able to understand, to realize her worries and her difficult design. She could share her obsessions with only one person, Pierre Curie, companion. To him alone could she confide rare thoughts and dreams. Marie, from now on, was to present to all others, however near they might be to her heart, an almost commonplace picture of herself. She was to paint for them only the bourgeois side of her life. She was to find sometimes accents full of contained emotion to express her happiness as a woman. But of her work she was to speak only in laconic, inexpressive little phrases: news in three lines, without even attempting to suggest the wonders that work meant to her.

Here we feel an absolute determination not to illustrate the singular profession she had chosen by literature. Through subtle modesty, and also through horror of vain talk and everything superfluous, Marie concealed herself, dug herself in; or rather, she offered only one of her profiles. Shyness, boredom, or reason, whatever it may have been, the scientist of genius effaced and dissimulated herself behind "a woman like all others."

Marie to Bronya,[2] *1899:*

Our life is always the same. We work a lot but we sleep well, so our health does not suffer. The evenings are taken up by caring for the child. In the morning I dress her and give her her food, then I can generally go out at about nine. During the whole of this year we have not been either to the theater or a concert, and we have not paid one visit. For that matter, we feel very well. . . . I miss my family enormously, above all you, my dears, and Father. I often think of my isolation with grief. I cannot complain of anything else, for our health is not bad, the child is growing well, and I have the best husband one could dream of; I could never have imagined finding one like him. He is a true gift of heaven, and the more we live together the more we love each other.

Our work is progressing. I shall soon have a lecture to deliver on the subject. It should have been last Saturday but I was prevented from giving it, so it will no doubt be on this Saturday, or else in a fortnight.

This work, which is so dryly mentioned in passing, was in fact progressing magnificently. In the course of the years 1899 and 1900 Pierre and Marie Curie published a report on the discovery of "induced radioactivity" due to radium, another on the effects of radioactivity, and another on the electric charge carried by the rays. And at last they drew up, for the Congress of Physics of 1900, a general report on the radioactive substances, which aroused immense interest among the scientists of Europe.

The development of the new science of radioactivity was rapid, overwhelming—the Curies needed fellow workers. Up to now they had had only the intermittent help of a laboratory assistant named Petit, an honest man who came to work for them outside his hours of service—working out of personal enthusiasm, almost in secret. But they now required technicians of the first order. Their discovery had important extensions in the domain of chemistry, which demanded attentive study. They wished to associate competent research workers with them.

[2] **Bronya:** Marie Curie's sister

Our work on radioactivity began in solitude [Marie was to write]. But before the breadth of the task it became more and more evident that collaboration would be useful. Already in 1898 one of the laboratory chiefs of the school, G. Bémont, had given us some passing help. Toward 1900 Pierre Curie entered into relations with a young chemist, André Debierne, assistant in the laboratory of Professor Friedel, who esteemed him highly. André Debierne willingly accepted work on radioactivity. He undertook especially the research of a new radio element, the existence of which was suspected in the group of iron and rare clays. He discovered this element, named "actinium." Even though he worked in the physico-chemical laboratory at the Sorbonne directed by Jean Perrin, he frequently came to see us in our shed and soon became a very close friend to us, to Dr. Curie and later on to our children.

Thus, even before radium and polonium were isolated, a French scientist, André Debierne, had discovered a "brother," *actinium.*

At about the same period [Marie tells us], a young physicist, Georges Sagnac, engaged in studying X rays, came frequently to talk to Pierre Curie about the analogies that might exist between these rays, their secondary rays, and the radiation of radioactive bodies. Together they performed a work on the electric charge carried by these secondary rays.

Marie continued to treat, kilogram by kilogram, the tons of pitchblende residue which were sent her on several occasions from St. Joachimsthal. With her terrible patience, she was able to be, every day for four years, a physicist, a chemist, a specialized worker, an engineer and a laboring man all at once. Thanks to her brain and muscle, the old tables in the shed held more and more concentrated products—products more and more rich in radium. Mme. Curie was approaching the end: she no longer stood in the courtyard, enveloped in bitter smoke, to watch the heavy basins of material in fusion. She was now at the stage of purification and of the "fractional crystallization" of strongly radioactive solutions. But the poverty of her haphazard equipment hindered her work more than ever. It was now that she needed a spotlessly clean workroom and apparatus perfectly protected against cold, heat and dirt. In this shed, open to every wind,

iron and coal dust was afloat which, to Marie's despair, mixed itself
into the products purified with so much care. Her heart sometimes
constricted before these little daily accidents, which took so much of
her time and her strength.

Pierre was so tired of the interminable struggle that he would have
been quite ready to abandon it. Of course, he did not dream of dropping the study of radium and of radioactivity. But he would willingly
have renounced, for the time being, the special operation of preparing
pure radium. The obstacles seemed insurmountable. Could they not
resume this work later on, under better conditions? More attached to
the meaning of natural phenomena than to their material reality,
Pierre Curie was exasperated to see the paltry results to which Marie's
exhausting effort had led. He advised an armistice.

He counted without his wife's character. Marie wanted to isolate
radium and she would isolate it. She scorned fatigue and difficulties,
and even the gaps in her own knowledge which complicated her task.
After all, she was only a very young scientist: she still had not the
certainty and great culture Pierre had acquired by twenty years' work,
and sometimes she stumbled across phenomena or methods of calcu-
lation about which she knew very little and for which she had to make
hasty studies.

So much the worse! With stubborn eyes under her great brow, she
clung to her apparatus and her test tubes.

In 1902, forty-five months after the day on which the Curies announced the probable existence of radium, Marie finally carried off
the victory in this war of attrition: she succeeded in preparing a deci-
gram of pure radium, and made a first determination of the atomic
weight of the new substance, which was 225.

The incredulous chemists—of whom there were still a few—could
only bow before the facts, before the superhuman obstinacy of a
woman.

Radium officially existed.

It was nine o'clock at night. Pierre and Marie Curie were in their
little house at 108 Boulevard Kellermann, where they had been living
since 1900. The house suited them well. From the boulevard, where
three rows of trees half hid the fortifications, could be seen only a
dull wall and a tiny door. But behind the one-story house, hidden from
all eyes, there was a narrow provincial garden, rather pretty and very

quiet. And from the "barrier" of Gentilly they could escape on their bicycles toward the suburbs and the woods. . . .

Old Dr. Curie, who lived with the couple, had retired to his room. Marie had bathed her child and put it to bed, and had stayed for a long time beside the cot. This was a rite. When Irène did not feel her mother near at night she would call out for her incessantly, with that "Mé!" which was to be our substitute for "Mamma" always. And Marie, yielding to the implacability of the four-year-old baby, climbed the stairs, seated herself beside the child and stayed there in the darkness until the young voice gave way to light, regular breathing. Only then would she go down again to Pierre, who was growing impatient. In spite of his kindness, he was the most possessive and jealous of husbands. He was so used to the constant presence of his wife that her least eclipse kept him from thinking freely. If Marie delayed too long near her daughter, he received her on her return with a reproach so unjust as to be comic:

"You never think of anything but that child!"

Pierre walked slowly about the room. Marie sat down and made some stitches on the hem of Irène's new apron. One of her principles was never to buy ready-made clothes for the child: she thought them too fancy and impractical. In the days when Bronya was in Paris the two sisters cut out their children's dresses together, according to patterns of their own invention. These patterns still served for Marie.

But this evening she could not fix her attention. Nervous, she got up; then, suddenly:

"Suppose we go down there for a moment?"

There was a note of supplication in her voice—altogether superfluous, for Pierre, like herself, longed to go back to the shed they had left two hours before. Radium, fanciful as a living creature, endearing as a love, called them back to its dwelling, to the wretched laboratory.

The day's work had been hard, and it would have been more reasonable for the couple to rest. But Pierre and Marie were not always reasonable. As soon as they had put on their coats and told Dr. Curie of their flight, they were in the street. They went on foot, arm in arm, exchanging few words. After the crowded streets of this queer district, with its factory buildings, wastelands and poor tenements, they arrived in the Rue Lhomond and crossed the little courtyard. Pierre put the key in the lock. The door squeaked, as it had squeaked thousands of times, and admitted them to their realm, to their dream.

"Don't light the lamps!" Marie said in the darkness. Then she added with a little laugh:

"Do you remember the day when you said to me 'I should like radium to have a beautiful color'?"

The reality was more entrancing than the simple wish of long ago. Radium had something better than "a beautiful color": it was spontaneously luminous. And in the somber shed where, in the absence of cupboards, the precious particles in their tiny glass receivers were placed on tables or on shelves nailed to the wall, their phosphorescent bluish outlines gleamed, suspended in the night.

"Look . . . Look!" the young woman murmured.

She went forward cautiously, looked for and found a straw-bottomed chair. She sat down in the darkness and silence. Their two faces turned toward the pale glimmering, the mysterious sources of radiation, toward radium—their radium. Her body leaning forward, her head eager, Marie took up again the attitude which had been hers an hour earlier at the bedside of her sleeping child.

Her companion's hand lightly touched her hair.

She was to remember forever this evening of glowworms, this magic.

For Discussion

1. What task confronted Marie and Pierre Curie in their effort to prove that radium existed? What obstacles stood in their way? How were these obstacles eliminated?
2. Describe the Curies' working conditions. What qualities did Marie Curie reveal in the four years she and her husband worked in the shed? How do you explain her saying that those years were "the best and happiest years of our life"?
3. Why was Marie's letter to her sister, Bronya (page 148), so surprising a document? What explanation can you give for both the tone and content of the letter? What aspect of Marie Curie's personality did it reveal?
4. In the last stages of the work in the shed, how did Marie's attitude differ from Pierre's? What quality in Marie did the author think accounted for her final victory? Do you agree? Why or why not?
5. In what ways were Marie and Pierre an "ideal" couple? In what ways did they differ in temperament? Point out sentences from this selection to support your answer. What was revealed about their relationship in the brief scene about their child, Irène?

6. What were the "glowworms" referred to by the author in the final sentence? How did the author show a relation between Marie Curie, the scientist, and Marie Curie, the mother?

7. Perhaps the most popular form of nonfiction is the biography—the life story of an actual person, living or dead. To add life, color, and meaning to the story, anecdotes, dialogue, description, and analysis are all emphasized by a biographer. Point out how each of these was used by Eve Curie in this chapter from *Madame Curie*.

8. One quality that is important in a good biography is respect for the truth. The author should approach his subject with an open mind and not allow prejudices for or against the person to "color" the true story he has to tell. Since the author was Madame Curie's daughter, she had particular pitfalls to avoid in writing this biography. What might some of these pitfalls have been? In your opinion, do you think she avoided them? Explain.

9. Another quality which every good biographer strives for is accurate coverage of the facts, based on careful research. In this chapter, Eve Curie was dealing with a period in her mother's life which she could not know firsthand. What type of documentation did the author use to give authenticity in this selection? Did this documentation help bring Marie Curie to life for you? Why or why not?

For Composition

1. What criticisms did the author have of the French government's attitude toward the Curies? Write a short paper in which you state why you agree or disagree with this criticism.

2. Many famous people in the scientific and artistic fields have had to undergo personal hardships or public opposition before they achieved success. Write a character sketch of a well-known figure about whom you have read. Describe the difficulties he had to meet. You might read about the life of Pasteur, Beethoven, Samuel Johnson, or Eugene O'Neill.

3. You may have tried to perform an experiment, or make something in school or at home, and discovered that it was not so easy as you had imagined. Write an account of this experience, of the problem involved, and the difficulties you encountered.

Arthur Koestler

Earliest Memories

Arthur Koestler (1905–   ), perhaps the most widely read political novelist of our time, is best known for *Darkness at Noon*, the horrifying story of a communist who, realizing the error of the communist doctrine he promoted throughout his life, finally became a victim himself of its ruthless disregard of the individual. Born of Hungarian-Austrian parents, Koestler started his career as a student of science, but soon became a foreign correspondent, and then a novelist. About 1930, he became a fervent Marxist, and in 1931 he joined the Communist Party. After seven or eight years, he suffered disillusionment with the Party, a disillusionment which he described in part in *The God That Failed*. Since 1940, he has written in English.

Besides novels, Koestler has also written many works of nonfiction, including his autobiography, *Arrow in the Blue*, in which he tells of his constant quest for an absolute amid all his many experiences. In the following selection from this book, Koestler gives expression to the writer's desire to explore and analyze what goes on within a person's mind, even —or perhaps especially—when that person is himself.

*A*LL my earliest memories seem to group themselves about three dominant themes: guilt, fear, and loneliness.

Of the three, fear stands out most vividly and persistently. My formative experiences seem to consist of a series of shocks.

The first that I remember occurred when I was between four and five years old. My mother dressed me with special care, and we went for an outing with my father. This in itself was unusual; but even more peculiar was the strange and apologetic manner of my parents as they led me down Andrássy Street, holding on firmly to both my hands. We were to visit Dr. Neubauer, they said; he was going to take a look at my throat and give me a cough medicine. Afterwards, as a reward, I was to have some ice cream.

I had already been taken to Dr. Neubauer the week before. He had examined me, and had then whispered with my parents in a manner which had aroused my apprehensions. This time we were not kept waiting; the doctor and his woman assistant were expecting us. Their manner was oily in a sinister way. I was made to sit in a kind of dentist's chair; then, without warning or explanation, my arms and legs were tied with leather straps to the frame of the chair. This was done with quick, deft movements by the doctor and his assistant, whose breathing was audible in the silence. Half senseless with fear, I craned my neck to look into my parents' faces, and when I saw that they, too, were frightened the bottom fell out of the world. The doctor hustled them both out of the room, fastened a metal tray beneath my chin, pried my chattering teeth apart, and forced a rubber gag between my jaws.

There followed several indelible minutes of steel instruments being thrust into the back of my mouth, of choking and vomiting blood into the tray beneath my chin; then two more attacks with the steel instruments, and more choking and blood and vomit. That is how tonsillectomies were performed, without anaesthesia, A.D. 1910, in Budapest. I don't know how other children reacted to that kind of thing. In all probability I must have been sensitivized by some earlier, forgotten traumatic experience for I reacted with a shock that was to have a lasting effect.

Those moments of utter loneliness, abandoned by my parents, in the clutches of a hostile and malign power, filled me with a kind of cosmic terror. It was as if I had fallen through a manhole, into a dark underground world of archaic brutality. Thenceforth I never lost my awareness of the existence of that second universe into which one might be transported, without warning, from one moment to the other. The world had become ambiguous, invested with a double meaning; events moved on two different planes at the same time—a visible and an invisible one—like a ship which carries its passengers on its sunny decks, while its keel ploughs through the dark phantom world beneath.

It is not unlikely that my subsequent preoccupation with physical violence, terror, and torture derives partly from this experience, and that Dr. Neubauer paved the way for my becoming a chronicler of the more repulsive aspects of our time. This was my first meeting with "Ahor"—the irrational, Archaic Horror—which subsequently played such an important part in the world around me, that I designed this handy abbreviation for it. When, years later, I fell into the hands of the regime which I dreaded and detested most, and was led in handcuffs through a hostile crowd, I had the feeling that this was but a repetition of a situation I had already lived through—that of being, tied, gagged, and delivered to a malign power. And when my friends perished in the clutches of Europe's various dictators, I could, in writing about them, without much effort put myself in their place.

It may seem that I am exaggerating the effects of an experience which consisted, after all, in one of the most trivial surgical interventions carried out in a somewhat clumsy and brutal manner. More precisely, it may be thought that the study of psychiatry has equipped the author with a kind of dramatic hindsight. No one can guarantee the correctness of his memory; but the fact is that for more than a year after that experience I lived in a strange fantasy world of my own, playing hide-and-seek with an evil power which persecuted me. This power was personified by our gentle family physician, Dr. Szilagyi.

Shortly after the tonsil operation, I was in bed with an upset stomach. Dr. Szilagyi examined me, and after the usual consultation with my mother behind closed doors, he remarked with a jovial pat on my cheek: "Well, well! The best thing to do seems to be to cut your tummy open with a knife." With that he contentedly departed in his morning coat and striped trousers, carrying his black leather bag—and in it, no doubt, lay the knife.

I was old enough to understand that Dr. S.'s remark was meant to be a joke. But with the precocious child's uncanny ear for nuances, I caught an undertone which was not jocular. In fact, Dr. Szilagyi had discussed with my mother the advisability of getting rid of my appendix.

For a long time thereafter, my days became divided into dangerous and secure halves. The dangerous half was the morning, when the doctor made the rounds of his patients. The safe half was the afternoon when he received them in his consulting room. The situation was complicated by my father's habit of taking me on some mornings for rides in a hired horse-cab; while he was visiting his business acquaintances, I was left waiting in the cab. Before Dr. Szilagyi's threat had got hold of me, I used to enjoy those morning rides. Now I dreaded them because, while alone in the cab, I felt particularly vulnerable and exposed; if Dr. S. happened to pass by, he might remem-

ber his threat, snatch me out of the cab and take me with him. So on
every outing I pestered my father to take a closed carriage instead of
an open one. The closed carriages had little curtains which you could
pull across the windows. As soon as my father got out of the cab, I
pulled the curtains tight.

My obsession took even more extravagant forms. Once a fortnight
I had to accompany my father to the barber shop to have my hair
cut. The shop had an ill-lit back room which was reflected in the
mirror in front of the barber's chair. When the door was opened I
could catch a glimpse of the back room and vaguely distinguish several strange instruments which hung from hooks. The instruments
became somehow associated with the knife that was to cut my tummy
open, and the barber's shop became another place of terror.

It never occurred to me to confess my fears to my parents or to ask
for their protection; and I had no playmates to confide in. Since they
had sided with Dr. Neubauer and trapped and betrayed me, they
could no longer be trusted; the very mention of the matter might remind them of the temporarily shelved and forgotten project and
hasten its execution. I must have had at that period a greater capacity
for dissimulation than in later years, for my parents never guessed
what went on in my private underworld. But then, most children are
like that: while unable to keep a secret referring to the world of facts,
they are perfect conspirators in defence of the world of their fantasies.

I cannot recall how long this attack of mild paranoia lasted; but it
must have persisted for some months because in the meantime the
seasons changed, and the weather became too warm for closed and
curtained cabs. I was sent to school just after my sixth birthday, and
by that time this particular obsession had dissolved.

A second series of upheavals, which would have affected even a
normal child, occurred between my ninth and tenth year. I set fire to
our home, underwent two operations, and witnessed a disastrous conflict between my parents. The last mentioned of these shocks was
the worst, but for evident reasons cannot be discussed; it involved a
succession of lurid and harrowing scenes which, apart from their
frightening nature *per se*, taught me the anguish of split loyalties.
All my experiences of that critical year were silhouetted against this
background—which, for the time being, must remain a blank.

The year was 1914/15. The outbreak of the First World War had ruined my father's business in Budapest; we had given up our flat and moved to Vienna. From then on we never again had a permanent home.

The first station in our nomadic wanderings was a boarding house called Pension Exquisite; it was, and probably still is, on the fifth floor of an old building in the heart of Vienna, facing St. Stephen's Cathedral. One afternoon, at a time when the conflict between my parents was at its height, I was left alone in our rooms in the Pension. I was depressed, and thought that the glow of some colored candles which my mother had bought, would create a pleasant change of atmosphere. I lit them, put them on the window sill and, becoming absorbed in my reading, forgot all about them—until one of the candles fell into a wastepaper basket and set it alight. I tried to extinguish the flames by waving the basket in the air; and when the flames grew too hot, hurled it against the gauze curtains. The room, like every self-respecting boarding house room of the period, was richly draped with velvet and plush, and the fire spread rapidly. I was too frightened of being punished to call for help, and tore in a frenzy at the burning curtains in the thickening smoke. The next thing I remember is waking up on the bed of Fräulein Schlesinger, a French teacher who lived in the boarding house and with whom I was very much in love. My parents' return coincided with the arrival of the fire brigade; some three or four rooms facing the Cathedral were gutted before the fire was brought under control. I was not punished, not even in disgrace; the heroic dimensions of my misdeed had evidently transcended the limits of any possible retribution.

Not long after this event, I was again reading in my room one lonely afternoon when suddenly there was a loud report, and a hard object hit me on the back of the head, knocking me momentarily unconscious. A big can of tinned beans which had been standing on the radiator cover had exploded, presumably under the effect of fermentation. The elaborately far-fetched nature of this further catastrophe made the inmates of the Pension Exquisite regard me as a boy endowed with somewhat awe-inspiring potentialities, and I was much sought after for table-lifting seances, a popular pastime in those days.

Next, Dr. Szilagyi's long-standing threat materialized: an abscess of the appendix got me on the danger list. Feigning sleep, I overheard a conversation from which I gathered that I was to be operated on the next day. I was taken to the hospital in an ambulance. It was a bright, clear, winter morning; as we crossed the lovely courtyard of Vienna's Imperial Palace, small flakes of snow began to whirl down from the sunny sky. Through the window next to my pillow in the ambulance, I watched hungrily the dance of the white crystals in the air, and while I did so a curious change of mood came over me. I believe that in those moments I became for the first time aware of the gentle but overwhelming impact of beauty, and of the feeling of one's own self peacefully dissolving in nature as a grain of salt dissolves in the ocean. At the beginning of the journey I had watched the faces of passers-by in the street with impotent envy; they laughed and talked, their morrow would be like yesterday; only I was set apart. Under the snowflakes in the courtyard of the palace, I no longer minded; I felt reconciled and at peace.

That journey in the ambulance was a turning point. A few moments of terror were still to come: being wheeled into the operating theatre; and the panic of suffocation under the ether. But the phantoms of the netherworld had been made to retreat by some other power of even more mysterious origin. As it turned out, they were not routed, but merely forced to fall back to prepared positions.

I was told that the appendectomy, which had failed the first time, had to be repeated. I was now treated as a brave boy who is never afraid of the big bad wolf; but in fact I was in mortal fear of the ether mask, of a repetition of the choking agony before going under. The old enemy, Ahor, had appeared in a new guise. Then, one day, while reading the *Tales of Munchausen*,[1] I had an inspiration. The chapter I was reading was the delightful story of the boastful Baron falling into a bog and sinking deeper and deeper. When he has sunk down to his chin, and his remaining minutes seem to be counted, he saves himself by the simple expedient of grabbing his own hair and pulling himself out.

I was so delighted with the Baron's escape that I laughed aloud— and in that same instant found the solution to the problem which had been haunting me. I was going to pull myself out of the bog of

[1] *Tales of Munchausen:* hilarious and fantastic stories of the adventures of Baron Munchausen, originally published in England in 1785. The author is unknown.

my fears by holding the ether mask myself over my face until I passed out. In this way I would feel that I was in control of the situation, and that the terrible moment of helplessness would not recur.

I mentioned the idea to my mother who understood instinctively, and induced the surgeon to satisfy my whim. Although the operation was too long delayed and I again had to be rushed to hospital in the same ambulance, along the same road, I felt no fear when I put the mask on my face under the encouraging grin of the anaesthetist.

Since that episode I have learned to outwit my obsessions and anxieties—or at least to come to a kind of *modus vivendi* [2] with them. To arrive at an amicable arrangement with one's neuroses sounds like a contradiction in terms—yet I believe that it can be achieved, provided one accepts one's complexes and treats them with respectful courtesy, as it were, instead of fighting them and denying their existence. It is my profound belief that man has the power to pull himself by his own hair out of the mire. The Baron in the Bog, abbreviated "Babo," conqueror of "Ahor," has become for me both a symbol and a profession of faith. . . .

Next to guilt and to fear, loneliness played a dominant part in my childhood.

Until I went to school I had no playmates. Owing to my mother's settled conviction that she was an exile from glamorous Vienna in barbaric Budapest, we had no friendly ties with other families. I only had a chance to play with other children on the rare occasions when my mother was obliged to invite the family of some business relation of my father's to a *jour*—which, in Viennese French, means a ceremonial afternoon party complete with coffee, whipped cream, and cakes—or when we, in turn, had to attend a *jour* given by a family with a child of my own age. These events occurred perhaps once or twice a year. They were discussed for days in advance and, at my persistent nagging, my mother always did her best to describe the little boy or girl I was going to meet. But her descriptions were never detailed enough to satisfy my feverish curiosity and excitement; so I built up for myself fantasy portraits of my future playmates, made plans to squeeze the last drop of pleasure out of the short span of time vouchsafed me, deliberated which of my toys to parade, and which of the games to play that I had thought up and never had a

----

[2] *modus vivendi:* mode of living

partner to try with. As the hour of the visit approached I became almost sick with apprehension. Then came the agony of waiting—either for the doorbell to signal the visitors' arrival or, if we were going out, for my mother to finish dressing, to put the last touches to her hair, and give her ultimate orders to the servants about polishing the silver and cleaning the polar-bear rug during our absence.

The first minute or so after meeting the other child, I felt petrified with timidity. The worst moment was the formal pumping of hands under the encouragement of the grownups with their grotesquely honeyed, piping voices. The other child was always startlingly different from what I had imagined, and this caused me both to be disappointed and to fall in love at once with the unexpected apparition, so real and so alive. For the other child, even if stupid and ugly, was in my eyes always a happy prince, bathed in the glory of having brothers or sisters, or regular playmates; it lived in that fairy-tale world where children played together day and night, and into which I was only admitted for a short and irretrievable hour.

However, as soon as the adults had settled down at the *jour* table and we children were left alone in the nursery, my timidity wore off and I changed into a frenzied little maniac. The ingenious games I had devised in my daydreams all had to be tried out during those infinitely precious moments. The other child, whether younger or older, would usually be swept off its feet by this torrent of new games and ideas, and within a quarter of an hour I would become transformed from a tongue-tied puppet into a fierce bully who had to have it all his own way. Then, in the midst of this revelry, I would suddenly be struck by the thought that the afternoon would soon be over, that it might in fact be broken up at any minute by the grownups; and this dread would further increase my fever and give it a morbid taste. Thus I taught myself early the art of poisoning my pleasures by reminding myself of their ephemeral nature. After the guests had left or we were home again, I became depressed and intractable, and there would follow renewed disgrace, culminating in Bertha's promise that I would never, never be allowed to play with other children again.

The pattern was repeated on the equally rare occasions when I was taken by my parents to the circus or the theatre. If the play had three acts, I would tell myself at the end of the first: now one third of the pleasure is already gone; and from the middle of the second act on I felt with growing melancholy that I was gliding down a slope towards the inescapable end. Later, when I became a soccer enthusiast, I would keep glancing at my watch during an exciting game to find out how many of the ninety minutes of playing time were left.

This obsession with the hour-glass character of pleasure never left me. As I grew up, it gradually changed its object from self-pity to pity for others who were engrossed in the pursuit of pleasure without being aware of its treacherous nature. I read with a scorching pity Gogol's story of the little clerk who buys, at the price of a lifetime of privations, a magnificent, warm overcoat, goes to a party to celebrate its purchase, and is robbed of it on his way home, having only worn it once. A few days later he dies of pneumonia and a broken heart; but his ghost goes on robbing other people of their coats at night in the snow-covered, deserted squares of Moscow.

When I was about fifteen, and the misery of the post-war inflation years in Vienna was at its peak, I saw one day an elderly man standing in front of Gerstner's luxurious tearoom. He had the fine intellectual head of the dying race of Viennese patricians, and was dressed with meticulous care in what was obviously his one remaining good suit, freshened up with a damp brush. He tried to act as if he had just paused casually in front of Gerstner's sparkling window, but his gaze was riveted on the colorful pastries and chocolates behind the polished pane, and there was a desperate, childish greed in his eyes. For several minutes I watched him standing there, and although I had outgrown my taste for sweets, my mouth filled with a vicarious flow of saliva. After a while he became restless, then seemed to waver and finally to reach a decision. I was standing a few steps away, on the edge of the pavement, and I read the various phases of his pathetic inner struggle from the almost imperceptible shifts of his shoulders and his back. When his resolution was made, his shoulders straightened in a youthful, almost jaunty manner, and an instant later he entered the shop through the narrow, elegant door with its gilt rococo ornaments.

I followed behind. The air inside Gerstner's was hot, perfumed, and sweet; the sounds were muffled to a low murmur by the thick, soft carpets on the floor, the silk tapestry covering the walls, and the velvet curtains on the doors; it was like the padded interior of a chocolate box. The people who sat chatting and smiling at the small, polished tea-tables all looked wealthy and well-groomed and happy. They were mostly *nouveaux riches*,[3] speculators and profiteers, for the old bourgeoisie of Vienna had been destroyed by the inflation as finally and completely as if it had been buried by a landslide; nevertheless, this new clientele of Gerstner's looked perfectly civilized and did not even try to assume blasé manners. The people of Vienna had never learned that an air of boredom is an essential part of *savoir faire*;[4] and so warmly saturated with tradition was the atmosphere of their city, that the parvenus had already acquired the unique Viennese art of being not only rich but actually enjoying it. They had that courteous gaiety and amused self-mockery and warm malice and flickering erotic spark, which had prevailed at Gerstner's in the past Imperial days. So that elderly man, hesitantly entering the tearoom, could not even comfort himself with the thought that the new patrons were lacking in appreciation of the pleasures which for him had become unobtainable and part of a lost paradise.

Once inside, he would probably have preferred to get out again; but it was too late. It was folly on his part to go to Gerstner's, where at that time a cup of tea or chocolate with *petits fours*[5] cost two or three thousand Kronen, or as much as his monthly salary amounted to. Blindly, he chose a table in a quiet corner and picked up the gilded menu-card with its astronomical prices printed in small, graceful italics. Then, with a pathetic show of assurance he gave the waitress his order and sat back, bracing himself for the desperate task of enjoying every minute of his ruinous escapade.

I bought a packet of peppermints at the counter and left; I could not bear watching him any longer. The wrench of pity which I felt was not caused by his poverty, but by the transitoriness of his enjoyment, the knowledge that the golden *petits fours* would turn to dust on his palate. I have often wondered why this little scene left such a deep, aching impression in my memory—so deep indeed that I had to include it in this text though I am unable to define its relevance. Apparently I must have identified myself with that lonely figure, whom I only saw for a few minutes, by virtue of a kind of Cinderella Complex. He was a solitary outcast like myself, a man with a spiritual

[3] *nouveaux riches:* those who have newly become rich (French)
[4] *savoir faire:* knowledge of just what to do in any situation; tact (French)
[5] *petits fours:* small tea cakes (French)

face and an abject craving for sweets, victim of the same hour-glass which counted my pleasures and made them run out as the sand runs through its hole. But that, of course, isn't much of an explanation.

For Discussion

1. During Koestler's childhood, what did "Ahor" represent to him? How did his visit to Dr. Neubauer contribute to this idea? In your opinion, was Koestler's "double" way of seeing the world accurate? Why or why not?

2. How do you explain the fact that Koestler never revealed to his parents his fears about the family doctor and the barber shop? Why might children be "perfect conspirators in defense of the world of their fantasies"?

3. How did the author come to the idea of "Babo"? What did it represent to him? Explain how it worked at the time of his second operation. Would you say that "Ahor" and "Babo" were childhood concepts or ideas that every person must make sense of in his life? Explain your answer.

4. In his relations with other children, Koestler shuttled between being timid and being a bully. How might his concept of "Ahor" have indirectly resulted in both of these attitudes?

5. What was Koestler's "obsession with the hour-glass character of pleasure"? What did it reveal about his attitude toward the world? Do you think there is a more positive way of seeing the momentary pleasures of reality? If so, how would you describe this way?

6. Why did the incident about the elderly gentleman at Gerstner's leave such a lasting impression on the author? What would you say was the chief reason for Koestler's feeling like "a solitary outcast"?

7. A good autobiographer must not only have a good memory for recalling people and events accurately, he must also have the ability to see himself objectively and analyze his motives and behavior honestly. From this section of Koestler's autobiography, would you say he fulfills the requirements of a good autobiographer? Why or why not?

8. The autobiographer uses many of the techniques of the novelist in order to make his life story interesting. He must characterize the people who were important to him. He must also bring to life his emotional responses to people and events so that the self-portrait he draws will have the qualities of a real flesh-and-blood person. Point out details in Koestler's characterization of the elderly gentleman at Gerstner's which reveal the author's abilities as a novelist.

9. Choose an incident from this selection which reveals Koestler's ability to describe an event and his responses to it in a true-to-life way. What details did he employ to achieve this?

For Composition

1. Write a short character sketch of Koestler, based on what you have learned about him for this selection.
2. One reason for Koestler's objectivity in "Earliest Memories" is that he wrote about the events of his childhood almost fifty years after they occurred. Write a short account of an event in your childhood, which you can now look back on with objectivity. Explain the difference between how you see the event now and how you saw it when it occurred.
3. Write a short essay in which you express your views on how a child might be presented with the idea of evil without frightening him and driving him into a private world within himself.

Karel Čapek

London Streets and English People

Karel Čapek * (1890–1938) was a Czech journalist, playwright, and novelist whose popularity arose from his ability to treat serious themes with humor. His plays, notably *The Insect Comedy* and *R.U.R.* (see page 274), have been successfully produced all over the world. Among his many works are several humorous travel books, including *Letters from England*, in which he gives his good-natured though critical impressions of the country and its people. The following selection from the book reveals a European's lighthearted view of the Anglo-Saxon world.

As regards London itself, it smells of petrol, burnt grass, and tallow, thus differing from Paris, where unto these are added the odor of powder, coffee and cheese. In Prague each street has a different smell; in this respect there is no place to beat Prague. The voices of London are a more complicated matter; the inner districts, such as the Strand or Piccadilly, sound, I assure you, like a spinning mill with thousands of spindles; it clatters, rattles, whirs, mutters, whizzes and rumbles with thousands of packed motor-lorries, buses, cars, and steam tractors; and you sit on the top of a bus which cannot move forward and clatters to no purpose, you are shaken up by its rattling and leap about on your seat like some queer stuffed puppet. Then there are side streets, gardens, squares, roads and groves and crescents up to the wretched street in Notting Hill, where I am writing this: all of them streets of Two Pillars, streets of Similar Railings, streets of Seven Steps In Front of Each House, and so on; now here, a sort of desperate series of variations on the sound "i" proclaims the milkman, a woeful "ieiei" merely denotes firewood, "uó" is the coalman's war cry, and the ghastly yell of a delirious sailor announces that a youth is hawking five cabbage heads in a perambulator. And by night the cats make love as savagely as on the roofs of Palermo, in spite of all reports about English Puritanism. Only the people here

* kå'rel cha'pek

166

are quieter than elsewhere; they talk to each other half-heartedly, and their aim is to get home with the least possible delay. And that is the strangest thing about the English streets: here you do not see respectable ladies telling each other on the kerb what happened at the Smiths or the Greens, nor courting couples strolling arm-in-arm like sleepwalkers, nor worthy citizens seated on their doorstep with their hands on their knees (by the way, here I have not yet seen a carpenter or a locksmith or a workshop or a journeyman or an apprentice; here are nothing but shops, nothing but shops, nothing but Westminster Bank and Midland Bank, Ltd.), nor men drinking in the street, nor benches in the market-square, nor idlers, nor tramps, nor servant-girls, nor pensioners—in short, nothing, nothing, nothing; the London streets are just a gulley through which life flows to get home. In the streets people do not live, stare, talk, stand or sit; they merely rush through the streets. Here the street is not the most interesting of places, where a thousandfold spectacle meets your gaze, and where a thousand adventures address themselves to you; a place where people whistle or scuffle; bawl, flirt, rest, poetize or philosophize, and enjoy life and indulge in jokes or politics and band themselves together in twos, in threes, in families, in throngs, or in revolutions. In our country, in Italy, in France, the street is a sort of large tavern or public garden, a village green, a meeting place, a playground and theater, an extension of home and doorstep; here it is something which belongs to nobody, and which does not bring anyone closer to his fellows; here you do not meet with people, and things, but merely avoid them.

In our country a man thrusts his head out of the window, and he is right in the street. But the English home is separated from the street not merely by a curtain in the window, but also by a garden and a railing, ivy, a patch of grass, a door knocker and age-old tradition. The English home must have its own garden, for the street does not provide it with a queer and delightful pleasaunce; in the garden it must have its own swing or playground, because the street does not provide it with a playground or the diversions of a skating rink. The poetry of the English home exists at the expense of the English street which is devoid of poetry. And here no revolutionary throngs will ever march through the streets, because these streets are too long. And also too dull.

Thank goodness that there are buses here, vessels of the desert, camels bearing you on their backs through the infinity of bricks and mortar which is London. One of the things which puzzle me is that they do not miss the way, although, for the greater part, they do not steer by sun or stars, owing to the cloudy condition of the atmosphere here. I still do not know by what secret signs the driver distinguishes Ladbroke Grove from Great Western Road or Kensington Park Road. I do not know why he should prefer to take a trip to East Acton, instead of riding to Pimlico or Hammersmith. For all these places are so curiously alike that I cannot imagine why he should have specialized in East Acton. Perhaps he has a house there, one of those with two pillars and seven steps by the door. These houses look rather like family vaults; I tried to make a drawing of them, but do what I would, I was unable to obtain a sufficiently hopeless appearance; besides, I have no grey paint to smear over them.

Before I forget: of course, I went to look at Baker Street, but I came back terribly disappointed. There is not the slightest trace of Sherlock Holmes there: it is a business thoroughfare of unexampled respectability, which serves no higher purpose than to lead to Regent's Park, which, after a long endeavor, it almost manages to achieve. If we also briefly touch upon its underground railway station, we have exhausted everything, including our patience.

In England I should like to be a cow or a baby; but being a grown-up man I viewed the people of this country. Well, it is not true that the English wear loud check suits, with pipe and whiskers; as regards the latter, the only true Englishman is Dr. Bouček in Prague. Every Englishman wears a mackintosh, and has a cap on his head and a newspaper in his hand. As for the Englishwoman, she carries a mackintosh or a tennis racket. Nature here has a propensity for unusual shagginess, excrescences, woolliness, spikiness, and all kinds of hair; English horses, for example, have regular tufts and tassels of hair on their legs, and English dogs are nothing more nor less than absurd bundles of forelocks. Only the English lawn and the English gentlemen are shaved every day.

What an English gentleman is cannot be stated concisely; you would have to be acquainted, firstly, with an English club waiter, or with a booking clerk at a railway station, or, above all, with a policeman. A gentleman, that is a measured combination of silence, courtesy, dignity, sport, newspapers and honesty. The man sitting opposite you in the train will anger you for two hours by not regarding you as worthy of a glance; suddenly he gets up and hands you your bag which you are unable to reach. Here the people always manage to help each other, but they never have anything to say to each other, except about the weather. That is probably why Englishmen have invented all games, and why they do not speak during their games. Their taciturnity is such that they do not even publicly abuse the Government, the trains or the taxes; on the whole, a joyless and reticent people. In the place of taverns, where one can sit, drink and talk, they have invented bars, where one can stand, drink and hold one's peace. The more talkative people (like Lloyd George) take to politics, or to authorship; an English book must have at least four hundred pages.

It is perhaps through sheer taciturnity that the English swallow half of every word, and then the second half they somehow squash; so it is difficult to understand them. I used to travel every day to Ladbroke Grove; the conductor would come and I would say: "Ledbruk Grröv." ". . . ? ? Eh?" "Ledbhuk Ghöv!" ". . . ? ? ? Eh?" "Hevhuv Hev!" "Aa, Hevhuv Hov!" The conductor would rejoice and give me a ticket to Ladbroke Grove. I shall never learn this as long as I live.

But if you get to know them closer, they are very kind and gentle; they never speak much because they never speak about themselves. They enjoy themselves like children, but with the most solemn leathery expression; they have lots of ingrained etiquette, but at the same time they are as free-and-easy as young whelps. They are hard as flint, incapable of adapting themselves, conservative, loyal, rather shallow and always uncommunicative; they cannot get out of their skin, but it is a solid and, in every respect, excellent skin. You cannot speak to them without being invited to lunch or dinner; they are as hospitable as St. Julian, but they can never overstep the distance between man and man. Sometimes you have a sense of uneasiness at feeling so solitary in the midst of these kind and courteous people; but if you were a little boy, you would know that you can trust them more than yourself, and you would be free and respected here more than anywhere else in the world; the policeman would puff out his cheeks to make you laugh, an old gentleman would play at ball with you, and a white-haired lady would lay aside her four-hundred-page novel to gaze at you winsomely with her grey and still youthful eyes.

For Discussion

1. It is clear from this selection that Čapek did not like London streets. In your opinion, what was his chief complaint about the city? According to the author, how did London differ in its atmosphere from cities in France or Czechoslovakia?

2. Why didn't Čapek like the sounds and smells of London? How did the people differ from those on the Continent?

3. What objections did the author have to London homes and various sections of the city? Might these objections apply to homes and sections of an American city? Why or why not?

4. According to Čapek, why would it be good to be a cow or a child in England? Why might a European adult feel lonely among the English?

5. What did the author seem to like best about the people of England? What did he like least about them?

6. From this selection, the reader gets not only a picture of London streets and the English people, but, indirectly, of the author himself. From this selection, what kind of person would you say Čapek was? Cite sentences to support your answer.

7. Satire is a kind of writing that criticizes customs and manners by holding them up to ridicule. Čapek writes satirically, though good-naturedly, about what he observed on his visit to England. Point out instances of this good-natured satire.

8. Although this selection is very different from Heyerdahl's "At the Mercy of the Breakers," both are personal reminiscences. Explain why.

For Composition

1. You may never have visited another country as Čapek did, but you may have visited another town, city, or state that was different from your own. Write a description of such a place and your impressions of the people. Choose specific details which will bring the streets, houses, shops, and inhabitants vividly to life for the reader.

2. Čapek's impressions of London were unfavorable. Write a short composition in which you describe the favorable or unfavorable impression a person might get in visiting your home town.

Jan de Hartog

A Ghost in the Subway

Jan de Hartog (1914–   ), born in Haarlem, Holland, is a well-known writer of plays, fiction, and nonfiction. His book, *Waters of the New World*, written in 1961, is an account of his travels by boat through the United States, and his impressions of what he saw. However, as de Hartog himself says of this book, "I realized that what I had started to write were not impressions of America, but sketches for a self-portrait." The following short sketch from the book reveals the author's keen eye for significant details, as well as a sensitive man's search for truth in the everyday world around him.

WHEN I became a pupil of Amsterdam Naval College, which took pride in its historic background, I was, like the rest of the new boys, handed a book written by a retired Merchant Navy captain. It contained advice for young sailors ashore in foreign parts; to hand it to us at that moment was a stroke of genius. For we were still a long way from foreign parts, doomed for the next three years to confinement to the cavernous barracks of the college and the concrete courtyard with the concrete training ship, its yardarms and ratlines scuffed bare by generations of cadets; a book about how to behave in Hong Kong, Port Said and Valparaiso made it all seem temporary and less bleak. One remark from the old captain particularly struck my fancy: "If you want to get to know a city, take the horse tram." It was a piece of advice that I have followed ever since, for though the horse tram had already vanished with the author when I was given the book, it was obviously not the horse that counted but the tram.

So, in New York City, I took the subway. It was just after office hours; the train was full of commuters. There were office girls; junior executives with narrow-brimmed straw hats; a few elderly people, gray with exhaustion. The atmosphere was one of resignation; no key to the mood of the city seemed evident. This subway train might be running underneath any major city of the world at this hour: the Tube in London, the Metro in Paris, the Underground in Moscow.

171

Then a small communicating door at the far end opened jerkily, and in staggered a drunk.

He was an old man with a lumberjack's plaid cap, a short coat with moth-eaten fur collar and patched blue jeans. He came in with a rollicking shout of joy and slapped the nearest commuter on the shoulder, crying, "Ha ha!" He had reached that fleeting stage when a fifth of whisky has more effect on the human heart than two thousand years of Christianity. The junior executive whose shoulder he had slapped ignored him and he moved down among the benches, spreading cheer, good humor, snatches of song and, in the bends of the track, the hopping remnants of an Irish jig. His high spirits and passionate desire for communication with all his brothers on this earth were irresistible; then he came up to two adjoining benches where several young men, as identical as sparrows, sat talking. He pointed at one, indiscriminately, and said, "You remind me of me Oncle Henry, me boy," and he sang something tuneless but exuberant. Yet his ebullient joy seemed to be waning, and no wonder, because something was happening to him that I had never witnessed anywhere else on earth.

In any other subway in the world, had this man come in, people would have reacted with embarrassment or irritation, but they would have reacted. Women would have exchanged disapproving looks behind his back and men indulgent smiles; they might have tried to evade his insistent advances by ignoring him when addressed, but at some point they would have betrayed an awareness of his presence. Not so in this subway in New York City. It was not a tacit agreement, it was a natural mode of behavior; nobody gave any sign whatsoever that there was a drunk about in the carriage, dancing, singing, throwing his cap in the air, hanging on to the strap like a mischievous chimpanzee. They did not lock him out of their consciousness; he simply did not exist. The junior executives went on talking to one another across the aisle, even when the drunk, frightened by now, put himself between them. "Hey!" he called, his face swaying like a poppy amidst the straw hats. "Look at me! How are ye, me boys? Hey! Look at me!" But no one looked. The people behind the drunk's back exchanged not a glance, not the shimmer of a smile. They were not aware of his presence. He was invisible, inaudible, nonexistent.

I saw a human being wake up in the other world, after death. The terror on the drunk's face when he was finally convinced that he was dead, a ghost in the subway, was unforgettable. He reeled out of the carriage in panic. He staggered through the narrow door into the next, a ghost trying to escape from hell.

The old captain's advice still held good. If you want to get to know a city, take the horse tram.

For Discussion

1. What did the old captain mean by the remark: "If you want to get to know a city, take the horse tram"? Do you agree or disagree with this? Why?
2. What did de Hartog learn about New York from riding the subway? What relation is there between de Hartog's criticisms of New Yorkers and Čapek's criticism of Londoners in the previous essay? Why might both authors have felt as they did, though they came from different countries?
3. Why did de Hartog call the drunk "a ghost"? How do you explain the behavior of the people in the subway? Do you agree that this behavior could not have happened "anywhere else on earth"? Why or why not?
4. Although this selection seems to be specifically about New Yorkers, do you think the author had a more general theme in mind when he wrote this? If so, what is that theme? Why did de Hartog call this piece "A Ghost in the Subway" rather than "*The* Ghost in the Subway"?
5. This essay, like "London Streets and English People," is a personal reminiscence. "A Ghost in the Subway," however, has more of the vignette or story quality. Point out elements of the short story in this selection.

For Composition

1. Write a description of a ride you took on a public conveyance, such as a train or bus. Describe the people around you—how they looked, what they were doing, and how they reacted to a specific occurrence. You may, unlike de Hartog, want to show another side to people, such as their kindness or friendliness.
2. Both de Hartog and Čapek are Europeans giving their impressions of another country, but the approach to their material is different. Write a short essay in which you compare and contrast "A Ghost in the Subway" and "London Streets and English People."

Jacques Maritain

Some American Illusions

Jacques Maritain * (1882–   ), French philosopher and central figure in the "neo-Thomist" school of contemporary Christian thought, was raised in the tradition of liberal Protestantism. While a student at the Sorbonne, he met his wife Raïssa, herself a poet and writer of distinction. Together they persisted in a quest for the Absolute, and were led first to the teachings of Bergson and ultimately to the Catholic faith. Influenced by the "ardent faith" of Leon Bloy, the Maritains found the universal harmony for which they were searching; in 1906 Maritain and his wife were baptized.

Maritain has applied the teachings of St. Thomas Aquinas to philosophy and esthetics. A prolific writer, he has striven in his major works, including *Three Reformers: Luther, Descartes, Rousseau* and *Art and Scholasticism*, to urge the Thomistic union of reason and faith. Nor has he been oblivious to political realities. In his 1940 volume *Scholasticism and Politics*, in *France, My Country* (1941), and in numerous articles and lectures he has examined such present-day movements as Marxism and Francoism and explored the role of Christianity in the political world.

An opponent of Nazism and, in particular, of the puppet regime established at Vichy, Maritain left France for America in 1940. Since then he has spent a great deal of time in the United States, writing and lecturing at various universities. *Reflections on America* (1958), from which the following selection was taken, grew out of a series of lectures he delivered at the University of Chicago. Here Maritain subjects several aspects of American life to a keen but sympathetic analysis. Commenting on such matters as American materialism, bigotry, and morality, Maritain does not attempt to document his observations but, rather, to state with uncompromising candor his private responses to the American scene.

* zhäk′ ma rē tan′

$\mathcal{T}HE$ illusions I shall point to in this chapter are in no way specifically American. But they seem to me to be not infrequent in this great country; so that their very generality allows me to speak of them as "some American illusions."

Illusion number one. In some respects the American conception of life appears as a continuation of the eighteenth-century optimistic views on Man and Nature.

At first glance it would even seem that this country fosters belief in the goodness of Nature, the natural goodness of man, in the Rousseauist sense. Everything would be all right if Nature were not repressed, and were left to its own inclinations (without distinguishing between the metaphysical essence of man and the particular nature and existential condition of each one). In other words, there is no hidden root of evil in our nature, no original sin, no need for divine grace. In this way of thinking, which is seemingly accepted here and there but remains quite superficial, and concerns words and the conversational approach more than concepts or any reasoned-out conviction, we have to do with a trend toward naturalism more insidious, I think, than the threat of materialism. The assumption (rather general in our modern world) is that man will attain a state of merely natural perfection and merely natural bliss, and triumph over evil by the sole instrumentality of human energy and human science, and that he is his own Saviour (with the additional guarantee, if you need the solace of religion, of God's approval and encouragement).

Yet there is some serious inconsistency in this very naturalism, because we are confronted with a quite opposite tendency, originating, I think, in a residue of (and bitterness against) old Puritanism.

And from this other point of view Nature is not so good. There is an idea that human nature is fundamentally miserable—a set of brute instincts and desires which clash with each other, and which are not disciplined from within by moral conscience, to be sure, but only repressed from without by social taboos.

As a result, if it were not for the existence of psychologists and engineers, we should say with the ancient Greeks: it were better for man never to have been born. . . .

Illusion number two. It is generally believed that success is a thing good in itself, and which it is, from an ethical point of view, mandatory to strive for.

In this American concept of success there is no greediness or egoism. It is, it seems to me, rather an over-simplified idea that "to succeed" is to bear fruit, and therefore to give proof of the fact that psychologically and morally you are not a failure.

This is a very old illusion, already denounced by Socrates: mistaking external success, which depends on a great many ingredients extraneous to ethical life—good connections, cleverness, good luck, ruthlessness, and so forth—for genuine "success" in the metaphysical sense, that is, for the genuinely human happy issue which is internal, and consists in having, as Socrates said, a "good and beautiful soul."

Illusion number three. This is an illusion into which ethically minded people are liable to fall, and which boils down to mistaking the part for the whole.

What I mean is that given a particular objective—for instance, such and such group interest, or business interest, or national interest—which, considered in itself, is, moreover, morally good, some responsible people happen to make this particular good into a universal or an absolute, disregarding the superior and more general good on which, under the circumstances, the rightness of our conduct depends.

Then they believe that what is good for their business or for the particular job with which they are entrusted is good for America, and for mankind. And they believe it *with a perfectly clear conscience* —a fact which enrages more cynical people, who know very well that if *they* had taken the same course of action they would have done so without bothering about any moral justification.

Illusion number four. Every professor is liable to meet young men or young women who loathe, in the name of equality, the very notion of any kind of hierarchy—even if it is a question of the degrees of knowledge (it is offensive to say that wisdom is superior to science, or philosophy to chemistry).

Illusion number five. Americans seem sometimes to believe that if you are a thinker you must be a frowning bore, because thinking is so damn serious.

Illusion number six. You seem, also, to believe that you don't obey any man—but only law; and that your condition as free men demands that you should be governed not by other men, exercising authority under the law of the land and according to law—but by Law itself, with a capital "L," by an abstract entity which has neither soul nor hands.

Illusion number seven. A number of Americans seem to consider that marriage must be both the perfect fulfillment of romantic love and the pursuit of full individual self-realization for the two partners involved.

For Discussion

1. Maritain opened his reflections with a qualification in which he explained why he considered these illusions typically American. On what basis did he classify them as American? Perhaps he might also have given his reasons for calling them "illusions" instead of, say, "characteristics" or "traits." Do you, in fact, consider the qualities noted by Maritain illusions, or misconceptions, or do you think they have some basis in reality? Discuss.

2. What contradictory American point of view did Maritain identify in "Illusion number one"? On what basis did he criticize that illusion? Show how it is reflected in American arts—for instance, in films (westerns, heroes like Gary Cooper or John Wayne), literature (novels by James Fenimore Cooper, Mark Twain), and slogans (such as "the new frontier").

3. List the characteristics that Illusion one, and Illusions four through seven have in common. How have these illusions contributed to or detracted from American political, social, and economic success?

4. What did Maritain describe as "genuine" success in "Illusion number two"? Give examples from your own experience of "Illusion number three," which Maritain summarized as "mistaking the part for the whole." Are Illusions two and three typically American or are they more widespread? Discuss.

5. How did Maritain's views of America differ from those that a native American might have expressed? What is the American stereotype or "image" abroad? (If you do not know, consult newspapers, editorials, magazine articles, books of political science, or other sources.) Tell why you do or do not think that Maritain's view was in any way affected by that stereotype or "image."

For Composition

1. To Maritain's list and description of "Some American Illusions," add and provide examples of a few more that you have encountered or observed.
2. Write a few paragraphs in which you analyze your own views in the light of Maritain's comments. For example, consider such questions as the following: Which of the illusions noted by Maritain influence your conduct? Do you, indeed, consider them illusions? Have Maritain's observations inspired you to abandon illusions?

Boris Pasternak

Translating Shakespeare

Boris Leonidovich Pasternak (1890–1960), whose work is an eloquent testament to the unconquerable human spirit, achieved international fame as a poet and translator even before he was awarded the Nobel Prize in 1958 for his novel, *Dr. Zhivago*. Forbidden under pain of exile by the Soviet government to accept the award, Pasternak rejected it and lived in quiet seclusion until his death. He now lies buried within the shadows of the Orthodox Church of the Transfiguration outside Moscow.

Pasternak grew up in a cultural atmosphere, which was later reflected in his work. His mother was a concert pianist; his father, a painter, whose close friendship with Leo Tolstoy influenced the entire Pasternak household. Pasternak's writings in Russian, which fill some fifty volumes, include poems, short stories, novels in verse, and translations. Among his most successful works are translations of the plays of Shakespeare, considered by many to be the best in the Russian language.

OVER the years I have translated several of Shakespeare's plays: *Hamlet, Romeo and Juliet, Antony and Cleopatra, Othello, King Henry IV* (Parts I and II), *King Lear* and *Macbeth*.

The demand for simple and readable translations is great and seemingly inexhaustible. Every translator flatters himself with the hope that he, more than others, will succeed in meeting it. I have not escaped the common fate.

Nor are my opinions on the aims and problems of translating literary works exceptional. I believe, as do many others, that closeness to the original is not ensured only by literal exactness or by similarity of form: the likeness, as in a portrait, cannot be achieved without a lively and natural method of expression. As much as the author, the translator must confine himself to a vocabulary which is natural to him and avoid the literary artifice involved in stylization. Like the original text, the translation must create an impression of life and not of verbiage.

179

Shakespeare's Poetic Style

Shakespeare's dramas are deeply realistic in their conception. In his prose passages and in those dialogues in verse which are combined with movement or action, his style is conversational. For the rest, the flow of his blank verse is highly metaphorical, sometimes needlessly so and in such cases at the cost of some artificiality.

His imagery is not always equal to itself. At times it is poetry at its highest, at others it falls plainly into rhetoric and is loaded with dozens of inadequate substitutes for the one right word which he had on the tip of his tongue and which escaped him in his hurry. Nevertheless, at its worst as at its best, his metaphorical speech conforms to the essentials of true allegory.

Metaphorical language is the result of the disproportion between man's short life and the immense and long-term tasks he sets himself. Because of this, he needs to look at things as sharply as an eagle and to convey his vision in flashes which can be immediately apprehended. This is just what poetry is. Outsized personalities use metaphor as a shorthand of the spirit.

The stormy quickness of the brushstrokes of a Rembrandt, a Michelangelo, or a Titian was not the fruit of their deliberate choice. Possessed by the need to paint the universe, they could not paint in any other way.

Shakespeare's style combines opposite extremes. His prose is finished and polished. It is the work of a genius in the art of comic detail, a master of conciseness, and a brilliant mimic of everything strange and curious in the world.

In complete contrast to this is his blank verse. Voltaire and Tolstoy were shocked by its inward and outward chaos.

Shakespeare's characters, who often go through several stages of completion, occasionally speak first in poetry and later in prose. In such cases the scenes in verse produce the impression of being sketches and those in prose of being finished and conclusive.

Verse was Shakespeare's most rapid and immediate method of expression. It was his quickest way of putting down his thoughts. So true is this that many of his verse passages read almost like the rough drafts of his prose.

His poetry draws its strength from its very quality of sketchiness, powerful, uncontrollable, disorderly, and abundant.

Shakespeare's Use of Rhythm

Shakespeare's rhythm is the basic principle of his poetry. Its momentum determines the speed and sequence of questions and answers in his dialogues and the length of his periods and monologues.

It is a rhythm which reflects the enviably laconic quality of English, a quality which makes it possible to compress a whole statement, made up of two or more contrasted propositions, into a single line of iambic verse. It is the rhythm of free speech, the language of a man who sets up no idols and is therefore honest and concise.

Hamlet

Shakespeare's use of rhythm is clearest in *Hamlet*, where it serves a triple purpose. It is used as a method of characterization, it makes audible and sustains the prevailing mood, and it elevates the tone and softens the brutality of certain scenes.

The characters are sharply differentiated by the rhythm of their speech. Polonius, the King, Guildenstern and Rosencrantz speak in one way; Laertes, Ophelia, Horatio, and the rest in another. The credulity of the Queen is shown not only in her words but also by her singsong manner of drawing out her vowels.

So vivid is the rhythmic characterization of Hamlet himself that it creates the illusion of a leitmotif, as though a musical phrase were reiterated at his every appearance on the stage, although in fact no such leitmotif exists. The very pulse of his being seems to be made audible. Everything is contained in it: his inconsistent gestures, his long, resolute stride and the proud half-turn of his head, as well as the way in which the thoughts he utters in his monologues leap and take flight, the mocking arrogance of his ripostes to the courtiers who mill round him, and his manner of staring into the distance of the unknown whence his father's ghost once summoned him and where it may at any moment speak again.

Neither the music of Hamlet's speech nor that of the play as a whole lends itself to quotation: it is impossible to give an impression of it by any one example. Yet, disembodied though it is, so ominously and so closely is it woven into the texture of the tragedy that, given the subject, one is tempted to describe it as Scandinavian and as suited to the climate of apparitions. It consists in a measured alternation of solemnity and disquiet and, by thickening the atmosphere to its utmost density, it brings out the dominant mood. What is this mood?

According to the well-established view of critics, *Hamlet* is a tragedy of the will. This is true. But in what sense is it to be understood? Absence of will power did not exist as a theme in Shakespeare's time: it aroused no interest. Nor does Shakespeare's portrait of Hamlet, drawn so clearly and in so much detail, suggest a neurotic. Hamlet is a prince of the blood who never, for a moment, ceases to be conscious of his rights as heir to the throne; he is the spoilt darling of an ancient court, and self-assured in the awareness of his natural gifts. The sum of qualities with which he is endowed by Shakespeare leaves no room for flabbiness: it precludes it. Rather, the opposite is true: the audience, impressed by his brilliant prospects, is left to judge of the greatness of his sacrifice in giving them up for a higher aim.

From the moment of the ghost's appearance, Hamlet gives up his will in order to "do the will of him that sent him." *Hamlet* is not a drama of weakness, but of duty and self-denial. It is immaterial that, when appearance and reality are shown to be at variance—to be indeed separated by an abyss—the message is conveyed by supernatural means and that the ghost commands Hamlet to exact vengeance. What is important is that chance has allotted Hamlet the role of judge of his own time and servant of the future. *Hamlet* is the drama of a high destiny, of a life devoted and preordained to a heroic task.

This is the overall tone of the play, so concentrated by the rhythm as to be almost palpable. But the rhythmic principle is applied in still another way. It has a softening effect on certain harsh scenes which would be intolerable without it.

Thus for instance, in the scene in which he sends Ophelia to a nunnery, Hamlet speaks to the girl who loves him, and whom he tramples underfoot, with the ruthlessness of a self-centered Byronic rebel. His irony is out of keeping with his own love for her, which he painfully suppresses in himself. But let us see how this heartless scene is introduced. Immediately before it comes the famous speech, "To be or not to be," and the fresh music of the monologue still echoes in the opening verses which Hamlet and Ophelia exchange. The bitter and disorderly beauty of the monologue in which Hamlet's perplexities crowd and overtake each other and remain unsolved recalls the sudden chords, abruptly cut off, tried out on the organ before the opening of a requiem.

No wonder that the monologue heralds the beginning of the cruel denouement. It precedes it as the funeral service precedes the burial. The way is opened by it for whatever is inevitable, and whatever follows is washed, redeemed, and lent majesty in advance not only by the spoken thoughts but by the ardor and purity of the tears which ring in it. . . .

Othello

The division of the plays into acts and scenes was not made by Shakespeare but later, by his editors. Nevertheless it was not forced on them: they lend themselves to it easily by virtue of their inward structure.

The original texts, printed without a break, nevertheless stood out by a rigor of construction and development which is rare in our time.

This applies particularly to the thematic development usually contained in the middle of the drama, that is to say in the third and some parts of the second and fourth acts. This section is, as it were, the box which holds the mainspring of the mechanism.

At the beginning and conclusion of his plays Shakespeare freely improvises the details and, with as light a heart, disposes of the loose ends. The swiftly changing scenes are full of life, they are drawn from nature with the utmost freedom and with a staggering wealth of imagination.

But he denies himself this freedom in the middle section, where the threads have been tied up and must begin to be unravelled; here Shakespeare shows himself to be the child and slave of his age. His third acts are riveted to the mechanics of the plot in a measure unknown to the dramatic art of later centuries, though it was from him that it learned its honesty and daring. They are ruled by too blind a faith in the power of logic and in the real existence of ethical abstractions. The lively portraits drawn at the beginning, with their convincing light and shade, are replaced by personified virtues and vices. The sequence of actions and events ceases to be natural and has the suspect tidiness of rational deductions, as of syllogisms in an argument.

When Shakespeare was a child, moralities constructed in accordance with the formal rules of medieval scholasticism were still shown on the English provincial stage. He may well have seen them, and his old-fashioned industry in working out his plot may have been a remnant of the past which had fascinated him in his childhood.

Four-fifths of his writings are made up of his beginnings and endings. This is the part that made the audience laugh and cry; it is on this that his fame is based, and it accounts for all the talk about his truthfulness to life in opposition to the deadly soullessness of neoclassicism.

But a thing may be rightly observed, yet wrongly explained. One often hears extravagant praise of the "mousetrap" in *Hamlet* or of the iron necessity in the development of this or that passion or in the consequences of this or that crime in Shakespeare. Such admiration starts from false premises. It is not the mousetrap that deserves to be admired, but Shakespeare's genius which shows itself even where his writing is artificial. What should cause wonder is that the third acts, which make up one-fifth of his work and which are often devitalized and contrived, do not circumvent his greatness. He survives, not because of, but in spite of them.

For all the passion and the genius concentrated in *Othello*, and for all its popularity on the stage, what has been said above applies in a considerable measure to this play.

Here we have the dazzling quays of Venice, Brabantio's house, the arsenal; the extraordinary night session of the Senate, and Othello's account of the gradual beginnings of his and Desdemona's feeling for each other. Then the storm at sea off the coast of Cyprus and the drunken brawl at night on the ramparts. And, before the end, the famous scene of Desdemona preparing for the night, in which the still more famous "Willow" song is sung, tragically natural before the dreadful illumination of the finale.

But what happens in between? With a few turns of the key, Iago winds up like an alarm clock the suspicions of his victim, and the course of jealousy, obvious and labored, unwinds, creaking and shuddering like a rusty mechanism. It will be said that such is the nature of jealousy or that such is the tribute paid to the convention of the stage with its insistence on excessive clarity. It may be so. But the damage would be less if the tribute were paid by an artist of less genius and less consistency. In our time another aspect of the play has a topical interest.

Can it be an accident that the hero is black, while all that he holds dear in life is white? What is the significance of this choice of colors? Does it mean only that all peoples have an equal right to human dignity? Shakespeare's thought went much further.

The concept of the equality of peoples did not exist in his time.

What did exist and was fully alive was a different and wider notion of their equal opportunities. Shakespeare was not interested in what a man had been at birth, but in the point he had reached, in what he had changed into, what he had become. In Shakespeare's view, Othello, who was black, was a human being and a Christian who lived in historic times, and this interested him the more because living side by side with Othello was Iago, who was white, and who was an unconverted prehistoric animal. . . .

The Audience

Shakespeare's chronicles of English history abound in hints at the topical events of his day. There were no newspapers: to hear the news (as G. B. Harrison notes in his *England in Shakespeare's Day*) people gathered in taverns and theaters. Drama spoke in hints. Nor is it surprising that the common people understood them since they concerned facts which were close to everyone.

The political open secret of the time was the difficulties of the war with Spain, started with enthusiasm but which had soon become a bore. For fifteen years it had been waged by land and sea, off the coast of Portugal and in the Netherlands and in Ireland.

Falstaff's parodies of martial speeches amused the simple, peaceful public, which plainly understood what was meant, and which laughed still more heartily at his recruiting scene (where the recruits bribe their way out) because it knew the truth of it by experience.

A great deal more astonishing is another example of the intelligence of the contemporary audience.

The works of Shakespeare, as of all Elizabethans, are full of appeals to history and ancient literature and of mythological examples and names. To understand them nowadays, even reference book in hand, one needs to be a classical scholar yet we are told that the average Londoner of those days caught these flickering allusions in mid-air and digested them without the least trouble. How are we to believe this?

The explanation is that the school curriculum was very different from ours. A knowledge of Latin, which is now taken for a sign of higher education, was then the lowest step to learning, just as Church Slavonic used to be in Russia. In the primary, so-called grammar schools—and Shakespeare went to one of them—Latin was the spoken language and, according to the historian Trevelyan, the schoolboys were not allowed to use English even in their games. Those London apprentices and shop assistants who could read and write were as much at home with Fortune, Herakles, and Niobe as a modern schoolboy with internal combustion and the elements of electricity.

Shakespeare was born in time to find a well-established, century-old way of life still in being. His age was a festive period in England's history. By the end of the next reign the balance of things had already been upset.

Authenticity of Shakespeare's Authorship

Shakespeare's work is a whole and he is everywhere true to himself. He is recognizable by his vocabulary. Certain of his characters appear under different names in play after play and he sings the same song over and over to different tunes. His habit of repeating and paraphrasing himself is particularly noticeable in *Hamlet*.

In a scene with Horatio, Hamlet tells him that he is a man and cannot be played upon like a pipe.

A few pages further on he asks Guildenstern, in the same allegorical sense, whether he would like to play the pipe.

In the first player's monologue about the cruelty of Fortune in allowing Priam to be killed, the gods are urged to punish her by breaking her wheel, the symbol of her power, and flinging the pieces down from heaven to Tartarus. A few pages further on, Rosencrantz, speaking to the King, compares a monarch's power to a wheel fixed on a mount which, if its foundations are shaken, destroys everything on its way as it hurtles down.

Juliet takes the dagger from dead Romeo's side and stabs herself with the words "This is thy sheath." A few lines further on her father uses the same words about the dagger resting in Juliet's breast instead of in the sheath on Romeo's belt. And so on, almost at every step. What does this mean?

Translating Shakespeare is a task which takes time and effort. Once it is undertaken, it is best to divide it into sections long enough for the work not to get stale and to complete one section each day. In thus daily progressing through the text, the translator finds himself reliving the circumstances of the author. Day by day he reproduces his actions and he is drawn into some of his secrets, not in theory but practically, by experience.

Stumbling on such repetitions as I have mentioned and realizing how close together they are, he cannot help asking himself in surprise: "Who and in what conditions would remember so little of what he had put down only a few days earlier?"

Then, with a tangible certainty which is not given to the biographer or the scholar, the translator becomes aware of the personality of Shakespeare and of his genius. In twenty years Shakespeare wrote thirty-six plays, not to speak of his poems and sonnets. Forced to write two plays a year on an average, he had no time to revise and, constantly forgetting what he had written the day before, he repeated himself in his hurry.

At this point the absurdity of the Baconian theory becomes more striking than ever. What need was there to replace the simple and in no way improbable account of Shakespeare's life by a tangle of mysterious substitutions and their alleged discoveries?

Is it conceivable that Rutland, Bacon, or Southampton should have disguised himself so unsuccessfully; that, using a cypher or a faked identity, he should have hidden from Elizabeth and her time only to reveal himself so carelessly to later generations? What cunning, what ulterior purpose can be imagined in the mind of this highly reckless man who undoubtedly existed, who was not ashamed of slips of the pen, and who, yawning with fatigue in the face of history, remembered less of his own work than any high school pupil knows of it today? His strength shows itself in his weaknesses.

There is another puzzling thing. Why is it that ungifted people are so passionately interested in those who are great? They have their own conception of the artist, a conception which is idle, agreeable, and false. They start by assuming that Shakespeare was a genius in the sense in which they understand genius; they apply their yardstick to him and he fails to measure up to it.

His life, they find, was too obscure and workaday for his fame. He had no library of his own and his signature at the bottom of his will is a scrawl. It strikes them as suspicious that a man who knew the soil, the crops, the animals, and all the hours of the day and night as simple people know them should also have been at home with law, history, diplomacy, and the ways and habits of courtiers. And so they are astonished, amazed, forgetting that so great an artist must inevitably sum up everything human in himself. . . .

There is no pure comedy or tragedy in Shakespeare. His style is between the two and made up of both; it is thus closer to the true face of life than either, for in life, too, horrors and delights are mixed. This has been accounted to him as a merit by all English critics, from Samuel Johnson to T. S. Eliot.

To Shakespeare, the difference between tragedy and comedy was not merely the difference between the lofty and the commonplace, the ideal and the real. He used them rather as the major and minor keys in music. In arranging his material he employed poetry and prose and the transitions from one to the other as variations in music.

These transitions are the chief characteristic of his dramatic art; they are at the very heart of his stagecraft and they convey that hidden rhythm of thought and mood which I referred to in my note on *Hamlet.*

All his dramas are made up of swiftly alternating scenes of tragedy and tomfoolery. One aspect of this method is particularly marked.

On the edge of Ophelia's grave the audience is made to laugh at the philosophizing of the gravediggers. At the moment when Juliet's corpse is carried out, the boy from the servants' hall giggles at the musicians who have been invited to a wedding, and the musicians bargain with the nurse who is trying to get rid of them. Cleopatra's suicide is preceded by the appearance of the half-wit Egyptian snake charmer with his absurd reflections on the uselessness of reptiles— almost as in Maeterlinck or in Leonid Andreyev!

Shakespeare was the father and the prophet of realism. His influence on Pushkin, Victor Hugo, and other poets is well known. He was studied by the German romantics. One of the Schlegels translated him into German and the other drew on him for his theory of romantic irony. Goethe, as the symbolist author of *Faust,* was his descendant. Finally, to keep only to the essentials, as a dramatist he is the predecessor of Chekhov and of Ibsen.

It is in this same spirit, which he transmitted to his heirs, that he makes vulgar mediocrity snort and rush in on the funereal solemnity of his finales.

Its eruption makes the mystery of death, already inaccessibly remote from us, withdraw still further. The respectful distance we keep between ourselves and the threshold of what is lofty and frightening grows a little longer still. No situation as seen by the artist or the thinker is final; every position is the last but one. It is as if Shakespeare were afraid lest the audience should believe too firmly in the seemingly unconditional finality of his denouements. By breaking up the rhythm at the end he re-establishes infinity. In keeping with the character of modern art and in contrast to the fatalism of the ancient world, he dissolves the mortal, temporal quality of the individual sign in its immortal, universal significance.

Macbeth

Macbeth might well have been called *Crime and Punishment*. All the time I was translating it I was haunted by its likeness to Dostoyevsky's novel.

Planning the murder of Banquo, Macbeth tells his hired murderers:

> Your spirits shine through you. Within this hour at most
> I will advise you where to plant yourselves,
> Acquaint you with the perfect spy o' the time,
> The moment on't; for't must be done tonight,
> And something from the palace . . .

A little further on, in the third scene of the third act, the murderers, lying in ambush for Banquo, watch the guests arriving through the park.

SECOND MURDERER:
> Then 'tis he: the rest
> That are within the note of expectation
> Already are i' the court.

FIRST MURDERER:
> His horses go about.

THIRD MURDERER:
> Almost a mile: but he does usually—
> So all men do—from hence to the palace gate
> Make it their walk . . .

Murder is a desperate, dangerous business. Everything must be thought out, every possibility must be foreseen. Both Shakespeare and Dostoyevsky endow their heroes with their own foresight and imagination, their own capacities for timeliness, detail, and precision. Both the novel and the play have the sharp, heightened realism of detection and of detective fiction: the cautious wariness of the policeman who looks over his shoulder as often as the criminal himself.

Neither Macbeth nor Raskolnikov [1] is a born criminal or a villain

[1] **Raskolnikov:** main character in Dostoyevsky's *Crime and Punishment*

by nature. They are turned into criminals by faulty rationalizations, by deductions from false premises.

In one case the impetus is given by the prophecy of the witches who set the vanity of Macbeth ablaze. In the other, it comes from the extreme nihilistic proposition that, if there is no God, everything is allowed, and therefore a murder is in no way different from any other human act.

Of the two, Macbeth feels particularly safe from retribution. What could threaten him? A forest walking across a plain? A man not born of woman?—Such things don't exist, they are blatant absurdities. In other words, he may shed blood fearlessly. And what, in any case, has he to fear from justice once he has seized kingly power and become the only source of law? It all seems so clear and logical! What could be more simple and obvious? And so the crimes follow in quick succession—many crimes over a long time—until the forest suddenly moves and sets out on its way and an avenger comes who is not born of woman.

Incidentally, about Lady Macbeth—coolness and will power are not her predominant qualities. I think that what is strongest in her is something more generally feminine. She is one of those active, insistent wives, a woman who is her husband's helper, his support, for whom her husband's interests are her own and who takes his plans on faith once and for all. She neither discusses them nor judges nor selects among them. To reason, to doubt, to make plans—that's her husband's business, it's his lookout. She is his executive, more resolute and consistent than he is himself. Miscalculating her strength, she assumes the excessive burden and is destroyed, not by conscience but by spiritual exhaustion, sadness, and fatigue.

For Discussion

1. What are the principal points made by Pasternak concerning the translation of a literary work? In your opinion, why might idioms present a problem to a translator? What other problems might he meet? What reasons do you have for thinking that a translation of a play by Shakespeare might have drawbacks for a reader?
2. Explain Pasternak's statement on page 180: "Outsized personalities use metaphor as a shorthand of the spirit."
3. From your knowledge of *Hamlet*, would you say that it is a drama of "duty and self-denial"? Explain.
4. To what contemporary issue did Pasternak relate Shakespeare's *Othello?*

What, according to Pasternak, was Shakespeare's view on this issue? Compare Shakespeare's view (as Pasternak described it) with prevalent present-day opinion.

5. Why, according to Pasternak, were Elizabethan audiences so aware of the topical events alluded to in Shakespeare's historical plays? Explain how it was possible for these audiences to understand the difficult literary, historical, and classical allusions in his plays.

6. From your knowledge of *Macbeth*, do you agree or disagree with Pasternak's analysis of Lady Macbeth's character? Explain your answer.

7. What reason did Pasternak give to support his conviction that Shakespeare existed and that his plays were not written by Francis Bacon or anyone else?

8. Often the structure of an essay indicates whether it is a formal or informal essay. Thus, if the writer is interested in a logical and serious expository presentation of certain ideas, his arrangement of the material is almost predetermined. However, in a familiar essay this formal exposition of material is not primary. The arrangement of the material may seem to follow no form other than that of a casual association of ideas as the author attempts to convey his opinions and reflections on the subject. In the light of these remarks, comment on Pasternak's essay. Is it formal, informal, or both? Explain.

For Composition

1. Write one or more paragraphs expressing your thoughts on Pasternak's comment: "But a thing may be rightly observed, yet wrongly explained."

2. Pasternak described Shakespeare's verse as "uncontrollable" and "disorderly." Write a paper in which you present reasons for your agreement or disagreement with this description. Include lines from any play of Shakespeare you have read to support your viewpoint.

3. "There is no pure comedy or tragedy in Shakespeare ... for in life, too, horrors and delights are mixed." Write a short informal essay which supports or rejects this statement of Pasternak's.

Pablo Casals and
José Maria Corredor

Before and During Exile

Pablo Casals * (1876–   ), master of the violincello since the beginning of the century, has become, in his own lifetime, a symbol of artistic integrity and social commitment. Excelling as a conductor, performer, composer, and teacher, Casals has also voiced strong and vigorous protests against totalitarian governments that have violated human freedom and dignity. Thus, he has refused to live or perform in his native Spain until the people are again given the right to elect a government of their choice. True to his convictions, Casals has maintained his voluntary exile from Spain and is now living in Puerto Rico, the birthplace of his mother.

During World War II Casals fled from Spain to Prades, a French town in the Pyrenees, remarkably Spanish in its geography and population. When his hopes were disappointed for the downfall of the Franco regime after the war, he refused to play before audiences in those countries that, in his view, were abandoning the Spanish people's democratic ideals. Because Casals would not appear in public concerts, renowned musicians from all over the world gathered in Prades in 1950 to hear the master play, thus setting the precedent for what was to become the annual Prades Festival. There Casals would startle his audiences with his brilliant performances of Bach, his favorite, Beethoven and others, ending always with the Catalan folk tune "El Cant des Ocells" ("Song of the Birds").

José Maria Corredor, Casals' fellow countryman and devoted friend, transcribed a series of conversations that he had with the master and incorporated them in a volume called Conversations with Casals, from which the following selection was taken. By allowing Casals to speak for himself and by directing him with relevant and intelligent questions, Corredor succeeded in presenting a full-bodied portrait of the musician. Indeed, even in the final pages of the book, Corredor encouraged Casals to summarize his life-long credo as no one else could: "I am now prepared for everything! Nothing that happens will surprise me. The pursuit of music and love for my neighbors have been inseparable with me, and if the first has given me the purest and most exalted joys, the second has brought me peace of mind, even in the saddest moments of my life. I am every day convinced that the mainspring of any important human enterprise must be moral strength and generosity."

* pä′blō kä sä′lz

192

*I*S *it a long time since you went to play in Russia for the last time?*
Yes. I have often spoken to you about my great friend Siloti, who
was the beloved disciple of Liszt. His wife came from a great Russian
family. His father-in-law had founded the Museum of Modern Art in
Moscow and made a gift of it to the city. Siloti lived in St. Peters-
burg. He devoted all his talent and work to the cause of popular
education, and by so doing raised the mental standards of the people.
He and a few friends subsidized the running of an important orchestra,
which gave concerts for the students and the workers. He led a simple
life, free from ostentation. He lived for his art and for the people. The
most eminent Russian musicians met at his house. Then came the
October Revolution, when everything was taken from him and he
was subjected to all the usual inquisitions and interrogations. He became ill; as a living-place for his wife and five children he was given the
kitchen of his own house and a small adjacent room. The rest of his
house was occupied by young men of the new *régime* where they led a
life of debauchery. In order to survive, Siloti and his family had to do
the most impossible and degrading things. The only valuable they
managed to hide was a necklace. And it was thanks to the value of this
that after two or three years of martyrdom they managed to escape to
Finland.

I was very worried about them, since I did not receive any news.
But one day, when I was in Barcelona, there was a letter from Antwerp
from Siloti saying "We are here." I went off immediately, and when I
met them at Antwerp I could hardly recognize them; they looked like
ghosts. Since that day I have never wanted to go back to Russia. I do
realize that in a revolution certain excesses cannot, unfortunately, be
avoided, but I don't accept that, under the pretext of forming a new
social order, these leaders think they can persecute blindly the very
people who have *practiced* fraternity with the workers and the people.

One can read in Dostoyevsky's The Brothers Karamazov *the often
quoted question, "Would you sacrifice the child who is in front of you
to follow a revolutionary doctrine?"*

No, never! The end does not justify the means. I have protested
and always shall protest against inhuman means.

*And a few years later we had the Nazis who began persecuting
people. . . .*

Ah . . . when I saw that Einstein, Thomas Mann, Bruno Walter and so many illustrious personalities of science and the arts had to expatriate themselves, some persecuted because of their race,[1] others because of their ideas, I thought it was my duty to protest, and I declared I would not go back to Germany until intellectual and artistic liberties were restored. When, later on, Mussolini imitated the Nazis, I adopted the same attitude towards Italy.

The only weapons I possess are the cello and the conductor's baton. They are not very deadly, but I have no others, and do not wish to have any. In the circumstances I used what I had to protest against what I considered was disgraceful and ignominious.

However, the German public had a great veneration for you.

For me, it was very painful to leave them, but I thought that by taking this attitude I was more faithful to Bach and Beethoven, and all they stood for, than to the people who through weakness or fanaticism soiled the honour of a great country.

This attitude, and the one you took later, have raised a lot of comment on the subject of the relation between art and politics.

I am not a politician. I never have been and do not pretend to be one. I am simply an artist. But the question is whether art is to be a pastime, a toy for men to play with, or if it should have a deep and human meaning. Politics do not belong to an artist but, to my mind, he is under an obligation to take sides, whatever sacrifice it means, if human dignity becomes involved. Besides, the word politics, if not used in good faith, can cover up much confusion. It may mean the ordinary legislation of each nation, in which I have no right to interfere unless it concerns my own country. But the politics we spoke of concern the governments which betrayed the general rights of human nature. In this case moral principles are involved which prevail above all frontiers; all men of good will should fight against the violation of these principles.

Since the affaire Dreyfus [2] *the goodwill of men seems to have declined, and for some time now we have been in a period called the "time of contempt." You are a glorious "survival."*

[1] "Casals is the only Aryan artist who has made a definite stand against the new barbarians."—Emil Ludwig.

[2] *affaire Dreyfus:* a scandal involving a French army officer who was convicted of treason in 1894 and later released when it was discovered that he was a victim of anti-Semitism and conspiracy

But is it possible that moral principles (which are not the same thing as political formulas) should become unfashionable? If a persecution was unjust fifty years ago, would it not be so today? The great victory of our civilization is that it gives us a guarantee against being persecuted for our ideas or feelings; also that the power which rules us instead of being absolute and irresponsible, will be elected and controlled by the people without exception. If this conquest is lost (and we have sad instances of it) we see the appearance of barbarous despots, and the fear and trembling of the subordinates. When it gets to that state my conscience forces me to protest.

The artist in his ivory tower?

It would be too easy, under the pretext of artistic neutrality, to retire into it, instead of fighting injustice. I have shown to you my conception of all art, which should elevate and not degrade us. Considering that an artist is a man, he cannot as a man withdraw from his solidarity with his fellow creatures.

When I see innocent blood spilled and the tears of the victims of injustice, it becomes more important to me than my music and all my cello recitals!

In the course of the first and terrible phase of the Spanish tragedy, I got so indignant one day that I did not hesitate to risk my life to save a man who was persecuted. I was at Sant Salvador practicing the cello. Two armed men entered my room and said, "We have been told that Mr. X is here." (He was a businessman from Barcelona who spent the summer in a house next to mine.) "He is not here," I said. They went off. A moment later they returned with poor Mr. X, whom they had arrested, and who already feared the worst; his wife was at his side crying. "We know you have a telephone and we want to telephone to Vendrell to get them to send a cart." (Those famous carts they used for carrying condemned people to be shot.)

I faced them and said: "I shall do the telephoning, not you. Why did you arrest this man? You can do what you like but you will not take Mr. X away, do you hear?" They had revolvers and guns. I had nothing: but the tone of my voice made them understand that I meant what I said. They had a moment of hesitation which was decisive. They muttered, "We had orders from the Mayor of Vendrell." I took the telephone and talked to the man who was supposed to be the mayor. My words were of such a kind that he got frightened and said:

"These men have made a mistake. I told them to go somewhere else." The tone of his voice belied his words. I communicated his answer to the men and told them they could go and that Mr. X would stay. As they went through the door they gave me a look of hatred and threatened me as well.

It shows that you had taken a stand.

Yes. For me and most of the Spanish intellectuals it was a question of principle: the main responsibility for the civil war fell on those who tried to abolish by force a legitimate Government (which had been elected by popular votes a few months before). And when their *pronunciamento* [3] failed, they tried to secure the help of Fascist Italy and Nazi Germany. In all civilized countries one should accept the decision of the people, and those who are not satisfied should wait for the next elections.

The Barcelona University bestowed on you the title of Doctor honoris causa *in rather strange circumstances.*

Very strange, when you think that the authorities of the Academy signed the diploma the day before Franco's Army came into Barcelona! That was the last meeting of the Catalonia University. Italian aircraft were flying over the town all the time, evacuation had already started, and yet, at a time as painful and critical as it was, my country thought of paying me such a moving tribute. I shall never forget it.

When the civil war ended, did you decide to live in Prades immediately?

No. I had been away a little while, playing at concerts, and when the war ended I was in Paris, ill with all the symptoms of nervous depression. I was staying with an old pupil and was kept all day in complete darkness, as I could not bear any light. I felt broken and worn out. The news I got from home was terrible: oppression had begun in Catalonia; thousands of refugees were shut up in concentration camps in the South of France; my house in Sant Salvador was occupied and ransacked by the Franco troops; my brother Luis was maltreated in Vendrell because he was my brother.... His situation obsessed me. He had such a fine character. During an epidemic of cholera at Vendrell he had done some wonderful acts of devotion without telling anybody. A friend from Barcelona came to see me in Paris. He was the first person who told me about Prades, where he had

[3] *pronunciamento:* an edict proclaiming a change in government

been a resident. He said it was a pretty little town at the foot of the Canigou, where almost everyone talks Catalan. This got me out of my torpor. I left Paris and went to Perpignan, where I met my friend Pichot. We visited many places on the coast as I am very fond of the sea. This was in the autumn of 1939: everything was already closed and I did not fancy any of the places I saw. Then I decided to go and live in Prades.

Did you enjoy your stay?

As soon as I got there the Catalan landscape acted on me like a sedative.

You had some hard work in front of you?

As soon as I felt better I gave myself up to the task of relieving my unfortunate compatriots who were living in the camps. Some Catalan friends, exiled in Prades also, helped me to organize everything with the greatest enthusiasm. I took a room in an hotel where we set up a regular office to centralize all the gifts, the purchases, the demands and distribution. We had lorries loaded with food and garments going to the camps. I wrote to friends for funds and we were glad of any gifts.

You visited the camps pretty often?

Yes, specially those at Argeles, Rivesalte, Vernet, Septfonds and some others. These camps were frightful, not because of deliberate cruelty but simply because of the improvisation and confusion which prevailed when they were established. The unfortunate people who were shut up there lacked the most elementary commodities. I realized that my visits brought some consolation to those who had lost contact with the world outside and who were lamentably demoralized, hopeless and abandoned. I tried to send small gifts to all those who asked me, and wrote little notes of encouragement. In those days I wrote thousands of letters and postcards.

The Second World War had started. Did you expect any danger?

Yes, I did. And my friends abroad even more. I received so many letters from American friends advising me to leave Europe and come to them.

To be exiled in America, sheltered from all danger, and also able to make a fortune with playing . . .

No, I could not do that. My duty was to stay with my compatriots who, like myself, had been hunted from their country, and try to comfort them with my presence. Also, since I had taken a stand against totalitarians, I had a moral obligation to stay when the war started which was supposed to rid Europe of totalitarianism—at least that is what I then believed would happen.

When the French defeat came in June 1940, you must have found yourself in a difficult position.

Very. At that time I thought all was lost in Europe. Also the rumor was spreading that the Spanish Army, taking advantage of the French retreat as the Italians had done, would cross the Pyrenees. Some refugee friends and I hired two cars to go to Bordeaux, in the hope of sailing to England from there. Before leaving I had burnt all the compromising papers I had, to save my correspondents from pursuit. (How I regretted the destruction of thousands of letters I had received from the camps. They formed a human document of such extraordinary interest.) When we reached Bordeaux we heard that the ship we hoped to sail in had been sunk by the German Air Force the day before. We tried other ships but it was all impossible, and we had to return to Prades, which we reached after a very difficult journey as all the roads were filled with refugees. There was such a panic at the time that when we got back to our hotel at Prades, in the middle of the night, no one would open the door, and it was only because the tobacconist opposite heard us and let us in that we did not spend the night outside. After that I went to live in the *Villa Colette* for a few years.

I went on with the work of helping my compatriots in the camps. Some of them had been transformed into what they called *Compagnies de Travailleurs,* which was a modern version of organized slavery. But with the news of the wonderful *résistance anglaise* we got more confident in the final issue of the conflict. Like millions of people, we anxiously listened every night to the radio from London. Things were difficult and food was seriously restricted.

Did you continue to give concerts during these years?

Before and after June 1940 I went to Switzerland in order to get the necessary funds to live on. When the French armistice was signed I thought I ought to help the French, who were going through a very difficult time, and gave concerts for charity in the free zone, Lyons, Marseilles, Perpignan; but after the Allied landing in North Africa the whole of France was occupied. I would not leave Prades, and with the German troops everywhere I thought silence was the only possible attitude.

Did the Germans worry you?

Once some agents of the Gestapo came to the *Villa Colette* and went through every bit of paper I had, and when they retired said: "Be careful. If our suspicions are confirmed we will arrest you."

The atmosphere became more and more intolerable; one day from my room window I saw three German officers coming through the gate and I thought we were done for. They came in, behaved extremely well, and said, after a military salute, "We are great admirers of yours and we have come to greet you and find out how you are." They sat down and started a conversation which lasted over two hours. "So you are the Casals our fathers and grandfathers told us about?" "I am." After a series of praises they came to the usual question: "And why don't you go and play in Germany?" "For the same reason I do not go and play in Spain." "We think you are mistaken. Hitler is a great man, who protects artists and the arts." "That is your opinion; I have mine." "Wouldn't you like to come and play in Berlin again? Hitler himself will come and hear you, and if you like we'll put a railway carriage at your disposal." "No, thank you." I guessed they wanted me to play to them, but I was determined I would not do it. So when they asked me to take my cello, I told them I had had rheumatic pains in the shoulder for some days, and could not play. They insisted and said, "Just a few notes." I refused. They saw my instrument and plucked the strings. I felt disturbed at the thought that perhaps these hands had spilled blood or were tainted. "Is this the cello you played on in Germany?" "Very often." The Commandant sat at the piano and started a Bach aria to get me going . . . it was useless.

"We cannot go away without a souvenir from you." I understood their chief would ask them for proof of their visit; I signed a photograph on which I wrote: "In remembrance of your visit to Prades." As they went, and I looked out of the window, they asked me if they could take a photograph (another proof). I did not see them again. But I had not played for them.

After the Allied landing in Normandy, the situation must have been even more tense.

Yes. A young man who was engaged to the daughter of a friend of mine, and who had joined the "French Militia" [4] so that he would not

---

[4] **French Militia:** French soldiers commissioned by the Vichy government. Tools of the German occupation, their function was to hunt down patriots and Communists.

be sent to Germany, told me he had seen my name on a list of people who were to be arrested, and heard the local chief say "When the time comes, Casals will see what is in store for him." This young man had the courage to stand up to him and said it was infamous and that he would lodge a protest in front of anyone concerned.

For some reason we were left at liberty after the landing took place. During those days every hour seemed like a hundred years. There was a moment of great danger: the *Maquis* [5] operating in the Pyrenees came to Prades and attacked the house where the Gestapo were operating. One German got killed and many were wounded. What would be the reprisals? We could have been shot. Fortunately the Mayor of Prades went to the military commander and told him all the responsibility for the attack should be his. Nothing happened, and shortly afterwards the moment we had been waiting for arrived. The German troops evacuated the town. Hope became a reality. Our exile (at least so we thought) was nearing its end.

Two weeks later the young man of the Militia, of whom I have spoken, was on trial at Perpignan with three others. I was summoned as a witness after I had written to the President of the Tribunal to explain what he had done for me. The atmosphere of the court was thick with excitement and hatred for this Militia. I was feeling sick with fear for the life of the young man. I stuck to what I had said in my letter. Out of the four accused, three were given the death penalty and executed; the fourth, my young friend, was given thirty years' solitary confinement, but he only stayed in prison two or three years and was released.

You probably saved his life.

He, first, had probably saved mine. In any case, in those horrible days it was a small comfort to have been able to save one human life.

[5] **Maquis:** French guerrilla fighters who resisted the Nazis during World War II

For Discussion

1. Casals here stated his reasons for his self-imposed exile from Communist Russia, Nazi Germany, Franco's Spain, and Fascist Italy. What did those regimes have in common that Casals found repellent?

2. Casals distinguished between his political and moral involvement in the internal affairs of a state. Why did he feel that an artist ought not to take sides in the political controversies of a foreign country? Why, on the other hand, did he feel that an artist was obliged to take a stand on a moral issue affecting any country? Do you agree or disagree with Casals in this matter? Discuss.

3. Describe the particular incidents that embittered Casals against the governments of Russia, Spain, and Germany, and the ways in which he chose to demonstrate his distaste for their policies. What personal qualities did Casals exhibit in the final incident? What was his principal weapon against those countries whose policies he deplored? Tell why you do or do not consider this an effective weapon.

4. Would you say that Casals' retreat to Prades, France was also a retreat from the world? Discuss. How did he participate in the Allied cause during that time? Why did he refuse to take refuge in America?

5. This conversation communicates a strong emotional tone. How did Casals convey his emotional involvement in the events he described? Which subjects do you think aroused his strongest emotional response? Why?

6. Note the techniques employed by José Maria Corredor, the interviewer. Above all, he tried to ask questions that would elicit pertinent information from Casals, and would also allow the musician to expand upon an idea and to volunteer additional details. How did Corredor achieve those ends? In your opinion, what was Corredor's attitude toward Casals? How do you know? Did that attitude influence the tone of the interview in any way? If so, how? Tell why you do or do not consider this an effective interview.

7. Many people think of the artist as an isolated figure, alienated and aloof from the world, observing human folly from an "ivory tower." Casals, of course, did not subscribe to that view. Why? Tell why you do or do not consider this popularly maintained conception of the artist a valid one. Think of past or contemporary artists that you know about. Were they involved in world affairs? If so, how do you think their involvement changed or affected their work?

8. What do you think ought to be the artist's role in the world? Should he function as an objective observer or as an active participant? Does the artist have a greater responsibility than a private individual to take a stand on a particular issue? If so, why? What, in fact, should be the role that each private citizen plays in world affairs? Should he be involved or detached? Discuss.

For Composition

1. Two important questions that Corredor asked Casals were the following: (a) "Would you sacrifice the child who is in front of you to follow a revolutionary doctrine?" and (b) "The artist in his ivory tower?" Write an essay in which you take up either of these problems, analyze it, and propose a solution. Or, write a short story using either of these questions as a central problem in an incident that the main character confronts.

2. Set up and carry out an interview with an individual—for instance, a school official, a public servant, or someone involved in community affairs. Prepare questions that will go straight to the point and that will enable you to learn enough about your subject's life, as well as about his intellectual and emotional opinions. Write a sketch of your subject in the form of a conversation.

François Mauriac

An Interview with Greta Garbo

François Mauriac * (1885–   ) has been writing novels, plays, poems, and stories since 1913. Many consider him the greatest contemporary Catholic novelist. He was awarded the Nobel Prize for Literature in 1952. Some of his best-known novels include *Thérèse*, *Woman of the Pharisees*, and *The Desert of Love*.

The world in which Mauriac's characters live and the moral law by which they survive are determined by theology. Mauriac is primarily interested in the struggle between human love and divine love, between sin and divine grace, and he explores with accuracy and subtlety the psychology of people and what motivates them to act as they do. Most of his works contain harsh criticisms of man and of the family in particular.

Because of his pessimistic outlook, Mauriac has been severely reproved by some Catholic critics. In answer, he reminds his detractors that the way into the supernatural often starts from the depths. "And so I pride myself," he says, "on painting a world in revolt against the Tribunal of conscience, a miserable world, devoid of grace, and so, without rejecting any of my freedom as a writer, to reach an indirect apology for Christianity. It is quite impossible, I said to myself, to reproduce the modern world as it exists, without displaying the violation of a holy law."

Beneath the dark colors with which Mauriac paints his world, one can discern his fundamental faith in human dignity and salvation. His numerous literary, religious, reflective, and impressionistic essays, including the following imaginary conversation with the famous film star, Greta Garbo (from *Second Thoughts*), reflect his ambivalent perspective: on the one hand, his despairing vision of death and calamity, and on the other hand, his awareness of the redemptive power of human suffering and God's love.

G RETA Garbo seems to me a kind of deer relentlessly pursued by a pack of journalists baying at her heels. She has left luggage behind her in hotels to throw the bloodhounds off the scent; she has many times cowered in secret hideaways. Last night, however, in a dream, Greta Garbo opened the door to my study, walked into the room and

* frän swä′ mô ryäk′

sat down across from me, as if she had come for an interview—a thing that was all the more strange since I have never been one of her hunters.

It was toward the end of a November day; the shutters were still open, but the lamps had already been lighted. I could not see her face very clearly, yet I knew it was she. Perhaps I should have gotten up and offered a suitable welcome to such a famous beauty. I didn't. I lay on my couch and did not say a word. Any gesture of welcome would have seemed as crazy as if, while I sat in some movie house, my lips had tried to pursue those beautiful hands of hers across the screen.

Miss Garbo began talking to me. Without preamble, she begged me not to think badly of her for hating interviews so. Her motives, she insisted, were not selfish ones. It wasn't that she cared only for her own comfort, she said, it wasn't even a need for rest and privacy that made her so elusive. "Try to understand me, Monsieur," she said, almost pleadingly. "Imagine how often I have sat way in the back of some theater—whether in New York, Chicago, Vienna, Berlin, or Paris doesn't matter—and in the hazy half-light watched the enormous crowd fascinated by my face. It's always the same crowd—or, rather, as it seems to me, the same captive monster from which floats up like incense toward my face the smoke from thousands and thousands of cigarettes.

"My face—" she paused. "The terrible thing is, all those rapt eyes are devouring a face that isn't mine, that is not my real face. Mine is bruised and stained with kisses and tears, it's even a little lined. Pain and grief, you know, leave a mark on any face, no matter how beautiful or cherished it is.

"But the public doesn't dream that what they see isn't my real face. Even I have forgotten what it's like. I've had to change the face God gave me as a child in order to offer people the ageless miracle they worship on the screen. . . . Who can tell whether I have eyebrows that are truly mine? Even I can't. My lashes—they're very famous, but are they real, are they mine? My body is still young, of course, but even I can't be sure that it's alive and warm. How could it be, through all the creams and powder and paint? . . . Perhaps, Monsieur, I have destroyed myself. I sometimes feel that I have sacrificed my real self to become an image: the image of a beautiful woman who can gratify each of thousands of hopeless expectations and frustrated desires. The real Greta Garbo has been transformed into the vision of what the adolescent will never find, what the middle-aged man has spent fifty futile years searching for, what this woman or that wishes desperately she were so that she could hold on to the man who is slipping away from her. Now, Monsieur, do you see why I hide? I hide out of pity for all these people, for all of them, because I don't want them to know that I do not really exist."

This is what Greta Garbo said to me: she confessed that she did not really exist. As I listened, I intuitively understood, half accepted what she said, yet there she sat and with my own eyes I saw her. Or rather, in the uncertain evening light, I glimpsed the marvelous outline of her features. She had marvelous features, yet they were not, I observed, too unlike many others. The short veil stopping just above her mouth hid what little was not already invisible under the layer of paint that coats all womankind today. It struck me as strange that the cinema requires its stars to wear such excessive makeup in order to project to us the pure essence of a face. The mysterious barrier of the screen lets only the imperishable elements of nose and mouth filter through. Perhaps the paints and salves help to absorb and dissolve all the ephemeral parts. Perhaps, too, God's intent in creating such a face shows forth in the heavenly simplicity of this design, cleansed of all stains, readied as if for Eternity. I could understand how anyone in the world would be tempted to fall to his knees before such a vision, such a revelation, if the screen, unfortunately, did not also isolate and emphasize and rivet our eyes on the dangerous appeal that exists for each of us in too great beauty.

A feverishly susceptible boy, lost in the countless crowds of moviegoers, must in his solitude struggle with the immense turmoil Greta Garbo's marvelous eyes arouse in him. Desire is secretly stirred by this woman who is so real, even though she is also inaccessible. She smiles, she parts her lips, she arches her neck, she half closes her eyes. All these things she does with impunity. She is vibrant, "present" in the fullest physical sense, offered to millions of men; yet if one of them were to be seized by frenzy and rush toward her, he would find a piece of cloth stretched across a space—the rag that decoys the bull—and he would embrace emptiness. Does Greta Garbo know, perhaps, that on a certain evening, in Philadelphia or in Buenos Aires or in Melbourne, one of her nameless lovers suddenly started up from his seat and ploughed his way through a mass of furious bodies, trampling on the crowd as if he were walking on water? Does she know that he reached for that figure, visible but forever beyond his grasp, and with a ripping of cloth plunged headfirst through the screen? . . . It is a strange scene to imagine, yet it recalls a line of Rimbaud: *"Puis, o désespoir, la cloison devint vaguement l'ombre des arbres, et je suis abîmé sous la tristesse amoureuse de la nuit. . . ."* [1]

"Yes," Greta Garbo admitted in a low voice, "I have unleashed that kind of madness, I know, and I am afraid of it. It is fear, too, which makes me shun people. I have been unfaithful to millions of men; I have indeed betrayed all mankind. I ask myself about this flood of humanity, this carnal ocean that fills the dark caves of the film houses night and day and is renewed hour after hour—I wonder won't it someday spew forth someone, some boy perhaps, bent on revenge?

"Of course," she went on, as if to reassure herself, "he would never recognize me. He would not dare strike a woman who looks like any other woman. He would see that in real life I am not the Greta Garbo he knows, that I don't look at all like the star in the movie magazines he reads."

Greta Garbo sat in silence before me. Her magical eyes looked at me, begging for some word of comfort, and I thought how only the cinema puts men at the mercy of our eternal adversary; it removes all the cares that engulf and disarm women in daily life and that make real women less dangerous. Only at the films can we understand the full meaning of those lines of de Vigny:

> *Et les rois d'Orient ont dit dans leurs cantiques*
> *Ton regard redoutable à l'égal de la mort . . .* [2]

"Have you ever thought," I asked Miss Garbo, "that a great many crimes may be committed because of you? It is hard for a young man of feeling to go back to his drab routine after an evening at a movie, an evening spent in dreaming he has been with you. And while the ostentatious luxury of the films is an abomination, still your face makes the abomination almost irresistibly appealing. It's ironic, isn't it, that we should call it 'high life' when it is the lowest, most abject thing in the world? But you are so beautiful that a boy's brief spree can appear altogether glamorous. The poor fellow—he forgets about his philoso-

---

[1] "Then, O despair, the partition vaguely became the shadow of the trees, and I was plunged beneath the amorous sadness of the night. . . ."

[2] "And the kings of the Orient said in their hymns
Your formidable glance is equal to death . . ."

phers and his poets and all the things he treasures, to dream that he is some broad-shouldered, athletic hero swaggering into an expensive restaurant behind a woman whose name is magic, and that the whispers fly from table to table: 'Greta Garbo! Look, that's Greta Garbo!' "

I saw Miss Garbo's body sag in the shadows, and she dropped her head. The lamp lighted her pale gold hair. "No, don't," I said. "You're wrong to hide your face. This mountain—better, this sea—of adoration and desire that batters against your multiplied image does not rise from an impure source. Millions of hearts cherish you because they know instinctively that truth is not found in the words of the philosophers or in the formulas of learned men. They know that truth is not abstract but carnal and alive, and that it is possible for them to find it and meet it and talk to it; they know that truth is *Someone*. Like you, truth has a forehead, a glance, a voice, a heart—a name among all other names. Saint John attested to this when he wrote of 'What we have heard, what we have seen with our eyes, what we have looked upon and our hands have handled . . .'

"You occupy the place of that Presence, and your face hides its absence, for you are a replacement, a double, a reflection. You give the lie to man's hunger and thirst for beauty, and that is why you can hold the miserable human herd motionless before a screen. Yet, and this is what I have often dreamed, think of the beauty and the magic of those other Features, of that other celestial, dazzling Face were it suddenly to appear on a piece of cloth stretched before the fascinated multitudes in all the movie palaces of this world!"

For Discussion

1. Notice how Mauriac set the scene for his interview with Greta Garbo. Identify such details as the setting, time, the condition of the narrator, the appearance and dress of Miss Garbo. What kind of mood did these details contribute to the interview? Tell why you do or do not consider this mood an appropriate one for the conversation that developed.

2. In an attempt to explain why she shunned interviews, Miss Garbo differentiated between her public and private selves. She summed up this insight as follows: "I have sacrificed my real self to become an image . . ." What did she consider her "real self"? What was her "image"? Miss Garbo concluded: "I hide out of pity for all these people, for all of them, because I don't want them to know that I do not

really exist." Whom did she mean by the "I" who did not "really exist"—her "real self" or her "image"? Support your answer.

3. The moviegoers who attended her films, on the other hand, were misled into thinking that the two Greta Garbos were one. Which Garbo did they believe in? How did their impression of Garbo influence their imaginative lives and their attitudes toward their own everyday activities? What did the reaction of one of these moviegoers during a performance of a Garbo film indicate about the possible effect of the cinema on the viewer? Why do you think he reacted in this particular way?

4. Yet when this fan attempted to "rush toward her" he was confronted with a "piece of cloth stretched across a space—the rag that decoys the bull—and he would embrace emptiness." What did this "emptiness" suggest to you? In answering this question, consider the following possibilities: Miss Garbo's admitted nonexistence; the futility and disappointment of high hopes and strivings; the misleading nature of the cinema; and the delusive quality of fantasy.

5. This same fan apparently mistook the world of his fantasy for reality. Try to identify the differences between reality and fantasy (illusion, dream, the imagination, and so forth). Should an individual always face up to reality? What purpose or value is there in fantasy? When does fantasy become dangerous? How did fantasy here endanger or benefit the moviegoer, Garbo, and the essayist himself? Consider these questions in the light of this essay and of your own experience.

6. Mauriac noted several paradoxes in this essay, including the following: "It struck me as strange that the cinema requires its stars to wear such excessive makeup in order to project to us the pure essence of a face." And "while the ostentatious luxury of the films is an abomination, still your face makes that abomination almost irresistibly appealing." Try to resolve these paradoxes in the context of this essay.

7. But these paradoxes were secondary to the major paradox: that of Greta Garbo's "multiplied image"—her "real self" versus her "image." Locate those passages that depict Miss Garbo as a hunted animal, a goddess, an ordinary woman. Taking into account her multifaceted personality as described in this essay, give your impression of the *real* Greta Garbo.

8. In the final paragraphs, Greta Garbo became something more than a human being; her face masked or concealed a reality greater than herself. What reality did it conceal? Why, therefore, did people long for her so ardently? What was Mauriac saying here about the nature of the true reality? Tell why you do or do not consider Greta Garbo an appropriate image, symbol, or mask for that "reality."

For Composition

1. In Romain Gary's "The Search" (page 48), you met Luc Martin, a young boy who was seriously affected by films. In a well-organized paper, compare and contrast the effect the cinema had on the characters in this essay and on Luc. What impact has the cinema had on your own life? Also answer such questions as the following: What kinds of reactions do films evoke? Why do films elicit such responses? Do movies constitute a healthy and worthwhile medium of communication?

2. Like the narrator in Leonid Andreyev's "Laughter" (page 84), Greta Garbo wore a mask. Write a composition in which you discuss the similarities and differences between the masks worn by these two characters, their respective reasons for wearing the masks, and their attitudes toward them. Also consider the following questions: What masks do you wear? Why do you feel impelled to wear them? When do you wear your masks? Do you consider them a necessity, a burden, a delight?

POETRY

𝒯WENTIETH-CENTURY poets in Europe, like their colleagues in the fields of fiction and drama, have wanted to show life honestly and truthfully, untouched by romantic coloring. They have gone about this in various ways. In the early decades of this century, the emphasis on realism brought about a new social awareness in poetry. Poets wrote about the working man as worthy of respect and dignity. They criticized the injustices of modern civilization and pointed to the dangers of ignoring spiritual values. Each poet, however, expressed his ideas in his own unique way and in a style particularly his own.

Contemporary poets have not only been concerned with the relation of man to his environment, they have also shown a great interest in the motives and inner conflicts of the individual. Frequently, this poetry has been so personal in its expression, that it has resulted in an obscurity which has baffled many readers. At its best, however, the exploration of individual consciousness in poetry has been bold and courageous, and the poet's feelings have been given a form which successfully mingles the personal with the impersonal.

Despite the emphasis on realism in European literature, romantic elements have persisted in poetry. Lyric poetry, for example, has continued to flourish in the work of such poets as Federico García Lorca and Rainer Maria Rilke. Rilke has musically expressed a nostalgia which prompts "tears from the depth of some divine despair." Jiménez expresses his love of nature; and Yevtushenko, his love of freedom. An admiration for the culture of the Middle Ages is to be seen in the poetry of Stefan George. These and other poets have continued certain trends of the nineteenth century, though often in ways quite different from their predecessors.

An important characteristic of contemporary European poetry is the use of symbols, begun in the previous century by Baudelaire, Rimbaud, Mallarmé and others, and continued in the twentieth century by Paul Valéry and his followers. The symbolists are strongly opposed to the sentimental and didactic in poetry. They see poetry as a search for the mystery of reality behind the everyday world perceived through the senses. The main instruments in this search are

210

the music of poetry and the poetic symbol, in which an emotional experience is most truthfully expressed through an image drawn from the external world. The poetry of a writer like Valéry is, as a result, suggestive rather than direct in its statement, and its meaning is often difficult to get at immediately.

Unlike Valéry, Guillaume Apollinaire broke radically with previous poetic forms in an attempt to capture the spirit of the twentieth century, with its blare and hubbub. Apollinaire eliminated punctuation from his poetry, introduced slang and modern rhythms, and used surprising images from everyday life, such as billboards, motion pictures, and factory workers. The effect was like that of the surrealists in art. The spirit of experimentation in Apollinaire's verse was part of the breaking with old traditions which pervaded much of the literature in the early part of the century. Today, modern poets, particularly in France, are still influenced by the surrealism of Apollinaire, as they are by the symbolism of Valéry.

Since World War II, poets have reflected the general spirit of uneasiness which exists in the world today. They have been realists, but also sad romantics. They have been energetic, but most often without any positive direction or faith. They have acted confident, but have revealed a deep-seated insecurity. "How can anyone be sure of anything in this age of anxiety?" they ask.

Still, poetry persists. Man has a desire to give form to the welter of experience he meets, to give symmetry to his contradictory and often puzzling thoughts and feelings. The poet does this. He shows that order can be found in what seems disorderly, and that even the complaints and criticisms of man can be expressed beautifully. The poet in the twentieth century, with all his uncertainties, is still affirming the fact that poetry, through the fusion of sounds and pictures, reveals reality as a mighty oneness of freedom and order, the everyday and the wonderful, the impermanent and the permanent. He continues to affirm Rimbaud's belief that poetry is a means of detaching us from the facile aspect of reality in order to put us into communication with a more authentic reality.

Alexander Blok

Although Alexander Blok (1880–1921) became alienated from the revolutionary movement in Russia before his death, he has enjoyed great popularity among the Russian people throughout the present century. In 1904, he saw his first book of poems published, and by World War I, his reputation as one of the foremost poets of his generation was clearly assured.

Blok's early verse, which was both realistic and symbolic, expressed his feelings about the futility of life, as in "Night in Petrograd." This sense of futility, however, was a superficial thing, a face he showed to the world. Beneath it there was a deep idealism and a yearning for a total change in man's life. That is why he reacted optimistically to the Russian Revolution in 1918. He immediately wrote what is often considered his finest poem, "The Twelve," a dramatic narrative about twelve pillaging Red soldiers. In 1918, he also wrote "The Scythians," in which he identified the Russians with the Scythians of classical times who destroyed the outposts of the Roman Empire. In this poem, Blok warned Europe of Russia's new power. Though much of his poetry is permeated with a bitter irony, he also wrote lyrics, such as "Little Catkins." Today, Blok is one of the few symbolist poets whose work is countenanced by the Soviet regime.

Night in Petrograd

Night: the street, a foolish lamp giving
A dingy light, a druggist's store:
For a quarter of a century go on living,
No escape. All will be as before.

You die: afresh you start life boldly,   5
Just as of old each detail repeat.
Night, the canal rippling so coldly,
The druggist's store, the lamp, the street.

(*tr. V. de Sola Pinto*)

212

Little Catkins[1]

Little boys and little maidens
Little candles, little catkins
   Homeward bring.

Little lights are burning softly,
People cross themselves in passing—   5
   Scent of spring.

Little wind so bold and merry,·
Little raindrops, don't extinguish
   These flames, pray!

I will rise tomorrow early,   10
Rise to greet you, Willow Sunday,
   Holy day.

               (*tr. Babette Deutsch*)

[1] On the eve of Palm Sunday, which the Russians call Willow Sunday, consecrated sprigs of pussy willow and lighted candles are carried home from church.

from The Scythians

Panmongolism—a slogan quite bizarre,
But none the less like music to my ear.
          —VLADIMIR SOLOVYOV

You are the millions, we are multitude
And multitude and multitude.
Come, fight! Yea, we are Scythians,
Yea, Asians, a slant-eyed, greedy brood.

For you—the centuries, for us—one hour.   5
Like slaves, obeying and abhorred,
We were the shield between the breeds
Of Europe and the raging Mongol horde.

For centuries the hammers of your forge
Drowned out the avalanche's boom;   10
You heard like wild, fantastic tales
Of Lisbon's and Messina's sudden doom.   .

For centuries your eyes were toward the East.
Our pearls you hoarded in your chests
And mockingly you bode the day   15
When you could aim your cannon at our breasts.

The time has come. Disaster beats its wings.
Each day the insults grow apace.
The hour will strike, and it may chance
Your Paestums [1] will go down and leave no trace.   20

Oh, pause, old world, while life still beats in you,
Oh, weary one, oh, worn, oh, wise!
Halt here, as once did Oedipus
Before the Sphinx's enigmatic eyes.

Yea, Russia is a Sphinx. Exulting, grieving,   25
And sweating blood, she cannot sate
Her eyes that gaze and gaze and gaze
At you with stone-lipped love for you, and hate.

Yea, you have long since ceased to love
As our hot blood can love; the taste   30
You have forgotten of a love
That burns like fire and like fire lays waste.

All things we love: pure numbers' burning chill,
The visions that divinely bloom;
All things we know: the Gallic light   35
And the parturient Germanic gloom.

And we remember all: Parisian hells,
The cool of Venice's lagoons,
Far fragrance of green lemon groves,
And Cologne's masses that the smoke festoons.   40

---

[1] **Paestum:** an ancient Roman city

And flesh we love, its color and its taste,
Its deathy odor, heavy, raw.
And is it our guilt if your bones
May crack beneath our powerful supple paw?

It is our wont to seize wild colts at play: 45
They rear and impotently shake
Wild manes—we crush their mighty croups.
And shrewish women slaves we tame—or break.

Come unto us from the black ways of war,
Come to our peaceful arms and rest.   50
Comrades, before it is too late,
Sheathe the old sword; may brotherhood be blest.

If not, we have not anything to lose.
We too can practice perfidies.
By sick descendants you will be   55
Accursed for centuries and centuries.

To welcome pretty Europe, we shall spread
And scatter in the tangled space
Of our wide thickets. We shall turn
To you our alien Asiatic face.   60

Go, all of you, to Ural fastnesses;
We clear the ground for the appalling scenes
Of war between the savage Mongol hordes
And pitiless science with its massed machines.

Know that we will no longer be your shield   65
But, careless of the battle cries,
We'll watch the deadly duel seethe,
Aloof, with indurate and narrow eyes.

We will not move when the ferocious Hun
Despoils the corpse and leaves it bare,   70
Burns towns, herds cattle in the church,
And smell of white flesh roasting fills the air.

For the last time, old world, we bid you rouse,
For the last time the barbarous lyre sounds
That calls you to our bright fraternal feast   75
Where labor beckons and where peace abounds.

(*tr. Babette Deutsch*)

For Discussion

"Night in Petrograd"

1. Man has been both optimistic and pessimistic. He has seen life as
meaningful and meaningless. Clearly, "Night in Petrograd" expresses
Blok's pessimism. What aspect of life is emphasized in this poem?
What aspect has been left out? Why might Blok have seen life in this
way in 1912, when he wrote the poem?
2. Blok chose a few realistic details which symbolically convey the theme
of this poem. A symbol is an object which stands for something else,
usually an idea. What is the symbolism of "night" in this poem?
Explain the symbolism of the other details.
3. What does the image of the canal in line 7 add to the general mood
of the poem? The last line repeats the three objects of lines 1 and 2.
Why is this effective in conveying the theme of the poem?

"Little Catkins"

1. In this simple lyric, Blok has created a picture through words and
details that are rich in connotation. Point out the words and details
which contribute effectively to the mood of this poem.
2. In what meter is this written? What effect does this rhythm have
on the mood?

"The Scythians"

1. This is a long narrative poem written in 1918, clearly containing a
message. What is the message? What details did Blok use to convey
his idea visually to his readers?
2. Why was "the multitude" angry? In your opinion, was the anger
justified? Why or why not?
3. In what ways did Blok contrast Europe and Asia? Was he essentially·
accurate or inaccurate in his description? Why? Do you see any parallel
between the state of mind of the "multitude" in this poem and peoples in the world today? Give reasons for your answer.
4. When Blok called Russia "a Sphinx" (line 25), he was using a metaphor. A metaphor is a figure of speech in which two things are com-

pared without the use of *like* or *as*. Why might a poet use metaphors? Do you find the metaphor in lines 25-28 dramatically effective? Why or why not?

5. It is clear that "The Scythians" is an intense poem. According to Coleridge, however, every poem is a reconciliation of intensity and calm. Frequently the "calm" is achieved through the structure or form of a poem; that is, through a regular metrical beat and the use of rhyme, which give symmetry and order to the lines. Select one of the intense stanzas in "The Scythians." Show how the structure of the stanza gives it symmetry and order. In your opinion, would the intensity be weakened if the poem were less structured? Why or why not?

For Composition

1. Read in an encyclopedia about the Scythians' pillaging of the Roman Empire. Write an evaluation of Blok's comparison of this event with the situation of Russia and Western Europe in 1918. Do you think it is a valid comparison? Why or why not?
2. Write a paragraph that creates a meditative or religious mood. Make sure that each detail contributes to the overall effect you are trying to achieve.
3. For centuries, people have been saying two contradictory things: "Nothing ever changes; there is nothing new," and "Everything changes; nothing is permanent." Write a composition in which you express your views on these two observations. What relation do you see between permanence and change in the universe?

Yevgeny Yevtushenko

Yevgeny Yevtushenko * (1933–   ) was born too late to be personally scarred by the Russian Revolution, the ensuing civil war, the death of Lenin, or even World War II. In "Zima Junction," an autobiographical poem in which he described a return visit to his native Siberian town of Zima, he recalled that though Hitler was "not far from Moscow . . . we were children and accepted a lot lightly." As a grown man he turned away from the rural society of Zima, the woods, the rustic entertainment, the family scandals, and the politics of collective farm life that he had sketched so vividly in his poem. But always "the voice of Zima Junction" spoke to him, counseling him to

> Count happiness connatural to the mind
> more than truth is, and yet
> no happiness to exist without it.

This credo of staunch integrity and commitment to truth has governed his conduct and his poetry from the time of his childhood to the present. A vigorous advocate of the Soviet system, he has nevertheless persistently exposed what he saw as Party dishonesty and lack of concern for the individual. Testimony of his readiness to puncture Communist shibboleths and self-righteous platitudes is his attack on latent Soviet anti-Semitism in "Babii Yar," a poem that exploded upon the Soviet Union and the world with unprecedented force. His poetry is generally autobiographical and realistic, and reflects his idealism, hopefulness, his love and acceptance of life. The language is colloquial, the rhythms are lively, and often his poems have the quality of a folk tune. Indeed, several have been set to music and have become quite popular in that form.

Admired for his forthright, direct poetry, Yevtushenko has nonetheless been attacked by official Party publications for his unconventional opinions and behavior. Although his poems have been criticized by some as "middlebrow," they appeal to wide and dissimilar audiences because they speak of immediate and universal matters. He has established a strong following among the youth in the Soviet Union and in the rest of the world, where he is much in demand as a lecturer and a public reader of his own poetry.

* yev zhe'nĕ   yev toŏ shen'kō

I Congratulate You, Mamma

I congratulate you, mamma,
                    on your son's birthday.
You worry about him,
                    and your worry is strong.
Here he lies,   5
            so gaunt,
                    large and untidy,
married unwisely,
                    unprofitable for the home.
You gaze on him   10
                    with eyes bright and misted ...
Congratulations, mamma,
                    on the birthday of your worry!
You have made him a present
                    of his ruthless love for this age,   15
a hard,
        proud faith
                in the Revolution.[1]
You gave him neither fame,
                    nor riches,   20
but you've given him instead
                    the ability not to fear.
Open the windows then
                    on the leaves
                        and the warbling birds,   25
awake his eyes
            with a kiss.
Make him a present
            of a notebook and inkstand,
give him his fill of milk   30
                    and speed him on his journey ...
                    (*tr. George Reavey*)

---

[1] **Revolution:** the Russian Revolution of 1917, during which the Bolsheviks
under Lenin overthrew the Czarist regime and established the Communist state

When Your Face Came Rising

When your face came rising
above my crumpled life,
the only thing I understood at first
was how meager were all my possessions.
But your face cast a peculiar glow   5
on forests, seas, and rivers,
initiating into the colors of the world
uninitiated me.
I'm so afraid, I'm so afraid,
the unexpected dawn might end,   10
ending the discoveries, tears, and raptures,
but I refuse to fight this fear.
This fear—I understand—
is love itself. I cherish this fear,
not knowing how to cherish,   15
I, careless guardian of my love.
This fear has ringed me tightly.
These moments are so brief, I know,
and, for me, the colors will disappear
when once your face has set . . .   20

                    (*tr. George Reavey*)

Babii Yar

"Babii Yar" is a protest against the failure of the Soviet government to
erect a monument at Babii Yar, a suburb of Kiev where 35,000 Jews
were slaughtered in 1941 by Hitler's advancing armies. The poem is also
an indictment of private and official anti-Semitism in the Soviet Union.
Since the publication of this poem and of similar protests, the Soviet
government has established a memorial at Babii Yar.

No monument stands over Babii Yar.
A drop sheer as a crude gravestone.
I am afraid.
          Today I am as old in years
as all the Jewish people.   5

Now I seem to be
        a Jew.
Here I plod through ancient Egypt.
Here I perish crucified, on the cross,
and to this day I bear the scars of nails. [10]
I seem to be
        Dreyfus.[1]
The Philistine [2]
        is both informer and judge.
I am behind bars. [15]
        Beset on every side.
Hounded,
      spat on,
        slandered.
Squealing, dainty ladies in flounced Brussels lace [20]
stick their parasols into my face.
I seem to be then
        a young boy in Byelostok.[3]
Blood runs, spilling over the floors.
The bar-room rabble-rousers [25]
give off a stench of vodka and onion.
A boot kicks me aside, helpless.
In vain I plead with these pogrom [4] bullies.
While they jeer and shout,
        "Beat the Yids.[5] Save Russia!" [30]
some grain-marketeer beats up my mother.
O my Russian people!
      I know
        you
are international to the core. [35]
But those with unclean hands
have often made a jingle of your purest name.

---

[1] **Dreyfus:** Alfred Dreyfus, French army officer convicted of treason in 1894, and later released when it was discovered that he was a victim of conspiracy and anti-Semitism
[2] **Philistine:** smug, narrow-minded person, lacking in culture
[3] **Byelostok:** Russian town, once the home of many Jews
[4] **pogrom:** organized massacre of Jews
[5] *Yids:* derogatory term for Jews

I know the goodness of my land.
How vile these antisemites—
                            without a qualm   40
they pompously called themselves
"The Union of the Russian People"! [6]
I seem to be
                Anne Frank [7]
transparent   45
                as a branch in April.
And I love.
                And have no need of phrases.
My need
            is that we gaze into each other.   50
How little we can see
                    or smell!
We are denied the leaves,
                        we are denied the sky.
Yet we can do so much—   55
                            tenderly
embrace each other in a dark room.
They're coming here?
                    Be not afraid. Those are the booming
sounds of spring: 60
                    spring is coming here.
Come then to me.
                Quick, give me your lips.
Are they smashing down the door?
                            No, it's the ice breaking . . .   65
The wild grasses rustle over Babii Yar.
The trees look ominous,
                    like judges.

<hr>

[6] **"The Union of the Russian People"**: ultranationalistic, anti-Semitic organization founded in Russia in 1905

[7] **Anne Frank**: Author of *The Diary of a Young Girl*, Anne and her family hid from the Nazis in a secret annex in an Amsterdam house. After more than two years, they were discovered by the Germans and taken to Bergen-Belsen, the concentration camp, where Anne died.

Here all things scream silently,
                              and, baring my head,   70
slowly I feel myself
                    turning gray.
And I myself
            am one massive, soundless scream
above the thousand thousand buried here.   75
I am
      each old man
                    here shot dead.
I am   80
      every child
                    here shot dead.
Nothing in me
                shall ever forget!
The "Internationale," [8] let it
                              thunder   85
when the last antisemite on earth
is buried forever.
In my blood there is no Jewish blood.
In their callous rage, all antisemites
must hate me now as a Jew.   90
For that reason
            I am a true Russian!
                    (*tr. George Reavey*)

[8] **"Internationale"**: official Soviet anthem

For Discussion

"I Congratulate You, Mamma"

1. Who is the speaker in this poem? Support or reject the following possibilities: an outside narrator, the son himself, the mother herself, another member of the family, a close friend, the poet.

2. What gifts had the mother given her son in the past? What kind of life could and did the son lead using these gifts? Do you think the poet felt that these gifts provided the proper tools with which a person could be successful in life? Explain.

3. According to the final lines of the poem, what presents should the mother give her son now? With these gifts, what kind of life would the son be likely to lead? From the tone of these lines, what would you say was the speaker's attitude toward that kind of life or profession? For example, equipped with these gifts, could the son find happiness, could he live a free life, would others admire and respect him?

4. The conflict between the ideal and the real is a major theme in this poem. What hopes would an individual probably have for the outcome of any revolution? Do you detect any note of disillusionment here with the outcome of the Russian Revolution? Explain. Did the Revolution occur during the son's lifetime or during the mother's? What had the Revolution given to the son? Is the "ability not to fear" always a positive characteristic, or can this ability sometimes be dangerous? Explain.

5. Tell why you do or do not think that Yevtushenko used the word "congratulate" ironically. What were the mixed or contradictory emotions expressed toward the son and the mother? Indicate specific lines to support your ideas. Have you ever had ambivalent feelings—simultaneous conflicting emotions such as love and hate—towards a person or thing? Describe your experience and emotions.

"When Your Face Came Rising"

1. This poem is united by a central metaphor: the rising and setting of the sun. Trace this metaphor as it is developed in the poem. What do the sun and its movements represent in this metaphor? How do the colors change as the metaphor progresses?

2. How did the speaker evaluate his life before the "face came rising"? What effect did the rising face have on his perception of nature, of life, of his inner self, of love's meaning? How did the changes in color illustrate that effect?

3. During moments of intense happiness, people often become aware of the passing of time and the transient nature of joy. Point out those lines that show the speaker's awareness of this contradictory nature of happiness. Why did the speaker refuse to "fight this fear"? Why did he "cherish" it? In what way can fear be "love itself"? Have you ever felt such emotions? Describe your experience.

"Babii Yar"

1. While standing at Babii Yar, the scene of the massacre of Jews, the speaker felt "as old in years as all the Jewish people." What did he

mean by this statement? Why did this scene inspire such a feeling? How did the speaker illustrate (a) his identification with the Jews; (b) the age of the Jews; and (c) the suffering of the Jews?

2. In lines 11–42, the speaker drew a sharp contrast between the persecuted and the persecutor. What were the differences between the victim and his tormentor in the Dreyfus affair? in the bar-room scene in Russia?

3. How did the Russian anti-Semites justify their brutal treatment of the Jews (line 30)? Tell why you do or do not consider this a valid justification for their actions. What contradictory feelings did the speaker have about Russia and the Russian people?

4. In lines 43–65, the speaker seemed "to be Anne Frank." During the time Anne spent hiding with her family in the Amsterdam annex, she fell in love with Peter Van Daan, a Dutch boy whose family was also in hiding with the Franks. Who, then, were the two speakers in these lines? What was happening to them at this moment? Since they had to hide indoors, in what form did they experience spring? What ideas come to your mind when you think of spring? What is the irony of the expression "the booming sounds of spring"?

5. When the speaker identified himself with Anne Frank, how was his tone different from that of the preceding lines? What expressions created a mood of delicacy, sensitivity, love, and tenderness?

6. In lines 66–84, the speaker returns to the subject of the first few lines of the poem. How do these later lines reinforce the earlier ones? Why did the trees look like judges? Whom were they judging? How did the speaker re-emphasize his age here? Why did "all things scream silently"? Why was the speaker's own scream "massive" and "soundless"?

7. What significance did anti-Semitism have for the speaker? Since he was not directly threatened by anti-Semitism, why do you think he was "afraid" (line 3)? Was he still afraid by the end of the poem? Support your answer. After imaginatively going through the cycle of Jewish history, why did the speaker call himself a "true Russian"? According to the speaker, what are the qualities of a "true Russian"?

For Composition

1. George Reavey, the editor and translator of these poems by Yevtushenko, wrote this appraisal of the poet: "But if Yevtushenko is at times the moralist, he is far from being entirely so; and the lyrical quality of his poetry has been growing richer rather than poorer." Using

the above three poems as your points of reference, write a composition in which you support or reject this evaluation of Yevtushenko's poetry. Consider also the question of whether a poet should address himself to moralistic, topical, political matters or, rather, exclusively to personal (lyrical), universal, and unchanging concerns.

2. Here is what Yevtushenko wrote about Alexander Blok:

> Lights and shadows fly to meet him,
> and stars in splinters fall on the roadways,
> and the waxen fingers of his clasped hands
> show something higher than dismay.

Reread the poems by Blok on pages 212–216. Write a paper in which you identify those aspects of Blok's style and themes that Yevtushenko is noting here. Do you agree with Yevtushenko's characterization of Blok's work? Compare and contrast the style and subjects of Blok and Yevtushenko.

Stefan George

Born of a middle-class Catholic family, Stefan George * (1868–1933) became one of Germany's outstanding modern poets. He believed in "art for art's sake" and a detachment from everyday life. In the late 1880's, he became the influential leader of a group of poets who called themselves the *Georgekreis* (the "George Circle") and who shared his convictions. George was a visionary who wanted to develop a poetic art which would separate the individual from the pervading corruptions of contemporary civilization. In his poetry he called for a European spiritual culture which would find its inspiration in the ideas and beliefs of the Christian Middle Ages and ancient Greece. In championing this cause, he frequently pointed to the German nation. This was erroneously interpreted by some of his contemporaries as propaganda for Nazism, which was then growing in influence in Germany. After George received the Goethe prize for poetry in 1927, he was looked on by the Nazis as a prophet of their cause, but he scorned their patronage. He refused to accept any honors they wished to confer on him which might indicate that he agreed with or consented to the doctrines of the Nazi government. Because of this, he chose to live as an exile in Switzerland during the last years of his life.

My Boy's Come Home

My boy's come home,
His hair still by the sea wind blown,
　　His step still buoyant
With vanquished fears and wanderlust of youth.

By the salty spray　　　　　　　　　　　　　5
His burnished cheek is still inflamed:
　　Fruit ripened swift
In foreign climes' wild heat and fragrances.

Already slant his glance
As with a secret I shall never know,　　　　10

* ste'fän gā'órgə

227

And a little dulled
Since coming from the springtime to our cold.

So opened wide
The bud, I scarcely dared to look,
And kept myself   15
From lips reserved already for other lips to kiss.

My arms enclose
What has despite me in a world apart
Grown up and bloomed—
My own and from me endlessly afar.

(*tr. Kate Flores*)

Leo XIII

Now that the thrones are held by brazen idlers,
With mien of brokers and with boastful rattle:
Our spirit avid to revere and trembling
Before the only actual majesty,
Turns to the grave paternal face of him,   5
The three-fold Crowned, the verily Anointed,
Who after life well lived a hundred years,
Peers as a shadow from his sacred stronghold.

When he has done the work for all his peoples,
The vineyard fills his leisure: heavy clusters   10
Of grapes his snowy fingers handle lightly.
His fare is bread and wine and weightless mallow,
And never are his sleepless midnights filled
With vain ambition, for on hymns he muses
For her, the world's delight: Our Blessèd Lady,   15
And for her radiant, her almighty Child.

"Come, Sainted Boy, and help the riven world,
Lest wretchedness destroy it, Sole Redeemer!
A gentler age shall bloom beneath your sign,
And rise untouched from all the desecrations . . .   20

May joys of long-desired peace return,
May Love bind each to each and make them brothers!"
So sings the poet and the prophet knows:
New love alone begets a new salvation.

When all adorned with symbols of his office,   25
Uplifted with the baldachin [1]—a pattern
Of lofty splendor and divine dominion—
Ensheathed in veils of incense and of candles,
To all the globe of earth he grants his blessings,
Then prostrate on the ground we sink: believers,   30
Who melt into the thousand-headed masses,
That moved with mystery, grow beautiful.

(*tr. Carol North Vanhope and Ernst Morwitz*)

[1] **baldachin:** a fixed canopy of metal, wood, or stone above the high altar of a church

The Tapestry

Framed by a silken fringe, in strange accord
Here men are intermeshed with beasts and plants,
And sickles blue with stars of white are scored
And traverse them in the arrested dance.

Through lavish broideries run barren lines,   5
And part for part is tangled and at strife,
And none the riddle of the snared divines . . .
Then, on a night, the fabric comes to life.

Then frozen branches tremulously veer,
The beings close in line and circle fused   10
Emerge before the knotted tassels clear
And bring the answer over which you mused!

Not at your beck it is, and not for each
Accustomed hour, nor guild's enriching share,
And never for the many and through speech,   15
It comes incarnate rarely to the rare.

(*tr. Carol North Vanhope and Ernst Morwitz*)

Poem for This Age

I am your conscience, I the voice that pierces
Through your faint wrath that curses and throws down:
"None reign now but the vile; the dead were noble;
Now faith is swept away and love is withered.
How can we flee from this dry rotten sphere?"   5
Let them hold torches for you where the ruin
Of this age festers, which yourselves created
With heated senses and unraveled hearts.

Ye turned your heads so far ye saw not beauty,
Nor grandeur saw ye more—and then denied them   10
And tore their image down of past and present.
Ye raised above the bodies and the earth
Of smoke and dust and haze the structure. Giant
It rose and swiftly, walls and arched turrets;
Yet in the vault that floated higher throbbed   15
Foreboding of the hour when it would fall.

Then crept ye into caverns and ye cried:
"There is no day. He only who has killed
The body has redemption's fee: endurance."
So melted ancient pale and fevered seekers   20
Of gold their brass with liquids in a crucible.
And outside many walked on paths of sunlight.
When ye stirred up a soul from filth and venom,
Ye scattered out the rest of fluids good.

I saw the thousand-year-old eyes of rulers   25
Compact of stone, yet from our present dreamings
From our tears heavy . . . They as we knew this:
With deserts gardens change, and cold with heat;
Night comes for daylight—penance for delight.
And when the dark devours us and our sorrow   30
One thing (none knows it) lasts that always was,
And flowers and youth will laugh and song will sound.

(*tr. Reginald H. Phelps*)

For Discussion

"My Boy's Come Home"

1. What was the emotion of the parent-speaker in this poem? Why did he or she feel this way? How and why had the son changed? In what ways had he remained the same?
2. To what is the son compared? Do you think the metaphor is convincing? Why or why not?
3. The situation in this poem might have been expressed in prose. What qualities does the poem have that a prose statement would lack?

"Leo XIII"

1. What is George's attitude toward Pope Leo? Point out lines to support your answer.
2. In the Pope's invocation to the Christ Child (lines 17-22), what criticisms of existing conditions are implied? Quote other lines in the poem which support this criticism. What is the poet's solution to what is occurring in the world?

"The Tapestry"

1. Describe the scene in "The Tapestry." What might this scene represent symbolically?
2. Why is the tapestry a riddle? Why does the answer to the riddle come "rarely to the rare"? What do you think is meant by "the fabric comes to life"?
3. The tapestry in this poem is a study in rest and motion. What phrase in the first stanza reveals this fusion of opposites? The scene, while fixed and unmoving, has a great deal of motion going on in it. Point out words which communicate this sense of motion.
4. Stefan George was very much concerned with technique in his poetry, particularly with the sounds and rhythms of words. The translator of "The Tapestry" has adhered closely to George's rhythms, including his use of the caesura. (The caesura is a pause or break in the rhythm of a line of verse, usually near the middle of the line.) Point out the caesura in each line of the first stanza of "The Tapestry." What is the meter and rhyme scheme of the poem?

"Poem for This Age"

1. What is the tone of this poem? How is the poem like "Leo XIII"?
2. Describe specifically George's picture of modern civilization. Do you agree or disagree with this picture? Why? Explain the last stanza.

3. Explain the meaning of "unraveled hearts" in line 8. Point out other images which you feel effectively contribute to the mood of the poem.

4. Note George's use in this poem of the archaic "ye" and his occasional use of an inverted word order. Point out phrases in which the words are not in their natural order. How do these archaic devices affect the tone of the poem?

For Composition

1. "The Tapestry" may remind you of Keats' "Ode on a Grecian Urn." Reread Keats' poem. Write a short paper comparing and contrasting these two poems.

2. Choose two of the poems by Stefan George translated by different authors. Write a comparison of these poems, pointing out which you feel is more effective in English and why.

3. Stefan George was a central figure in the art-for-art's sake movement after World War I. This movement was meant to counteract the moralistic purpose of many nineteenth-century authors who felt that literature and art should "enforce the religious sentiments of men" and should influence their conduct. Write a paper in which you present your views on the purpose of George's poetry. Do you think that his poems were wholly contrary to the aims of nineteenth-century authors? Refer to specific poems to support your opinion.

4. Write a well-organized paragraph in which you express what you think the purpose of literature should be.

Rainer Maria Rilke

Rainer Maria Rilke (1875–1926) is regarded by most critics as the greatest German lyric poet of modern times. A restless and unhappy person, he constantly felt a sense of isolation and loneliness. Much of his time was spent traveling in Europe. For a time, he was secretary to the French sculptor, Rodin. From him, Rilke learned the value of craftsmanship and the importance of expressing universal experiences, rather than passing moods and emotions. After World War I, he produced his two greatest books of poems, *Duino Elegies* and *Sonnets to Orpheus*. Early in his career, he also wrote several excellent short stories (see page 41). His well-known prose poem, "The Cornet," became a bestseller in its second edition of 1912.

Rilke was greatly influenced by Stefan George. Although there are religious elements in his poetry, art was his religion. His dedication to poetry was the one permanent value in his life. He struggled constantly to reconcile the contradictions he saw in reality and in himself, and although he achieved this reconciliation successfully in his poetry, he was unable to apply the principles of his art to his personal life. As a result, the view of the world reflected in his poetry is essentially a tragic one.

Autumn

The leaves are falling, falling as from far,
as though above were withering farthest gardens;
they fall with a denying attitude.

And night by night, down into solitude,
the heavy earth falls far from every star.   5

We are all falling. This hand's falling too—
all have this falling-sickness none withstands.

And yet there's One whose gently-holding hands
this universal falling can't fall through.

(tr. J. B. Leishman)

233

Childhood

The school's long stream of time and tediousness
winds slowly on, through torpor, through dismay.
O loneliness, O time that creeps away . . .
Then out at last: the streets ring loud and gay,
and in the big white squares the fountains play,   5
and in the parks the world seems measureless.—
And to pass through it all in children's dress,
with others, but quite otherwise than they:—
O wondrous time, O time that fleets away,
O loneliness!   10

And out into it all to gaze and gaze:
men, women, women, men in blacks and greys,
and children, brightly dressed, but differently;
and here a house, and there a dog, maybe,
and fear and trust changing in subtle ways:—   15
O grief uncaused, O dream, O dark amaze,
O still-unsounded sea!

And then with bat and ball and hoop to playing
in parks where the bright colors softly fade,
brushing against the growups without staying   20
when ball or hoop their alien walks invade;
but when the twilight comes, with little, swaying
footsteps going home with unrejected aid:—
O thoughts that fade into the darkness, straying
alone, afraid!   25

And hours on end by the grey pond-side kneeling
with little sailing-boat and elbows bare;
forgetting it, because one like it's stealing
below the ripples, but with sails more fair;
and, having still to spare, to share some feeling   30
with the small sinking face caught sight of there:—
Childhood! Winged likenesses half-guessed at, wheeling,
oh, where, oh, where?

                                    (*tr. J. B. Leishman*)

Before Summer Rain[1]

Quite suddenly, from all the green around,
something—you hardly know just what—has gone;
you feel the park itself drawing in upon
the windows and growing silent. The last sound

is the rain-piping dotterel in the wood,   5
reminding you of somebody's *Jerome*[2]—
there rises so much zeal and solitude
from that one voice the downpour soon will come

responding to. The lofty walls, arrayed
with ancient portraits, as though recollecting   10
they should not listen to our talk, withdraw.

The faded tapestries are now reflecting
the uncertain light we in our childhood saw
those afternoons when we were so afraid.

(*tr. J. B. Leishman*)

[1] Written after a visit to the château at Chantilly
[2] Rilke is referring to the many paintings showing St. Jerome alone in his
cave zealously working at his translations.

Annunciation to Mary

The angel's entrance (you must realize)
was not what made her frightened. The surprise
he gave her by his coming was no more
than sun- or moon-beam stirring on the floor
would give another,—she had long since grown   5
used to the form that angels wear, descending;
never imagining this coming-down
was hard for them. (O it's past comprehending,
how pure she was. Did not, one day, a hind
that rested in a wood, watchfully staring,   10
feel her deep influence, and did it not
conceive the unicorn, then, without pairing,

the pure beast, beast which light begot.—)
No, not to see him enter, but to find
the youthful angel's countenance inclined   15
so near to her; that when he looked, and she
looked up at him, their looks so merged in one,
the world outside grew vacant suddenly,
and all things being seen, endured and done
were crowded into them: just she and he;   20
eye and its pasture, vision and its view,
here at this point and at this point alone:—
see, this arouses fear. Such fear both knew.

Then he sang out and made his tidings known.
(tr. J. B. Leishman)

Saint Sebastian[1]

Like one lying down he stands there, all
target-proffered by his mighty will.
Far-removed, like mothers when they still,
self-inwoven like a coronal.

And the arrows come, and, as if straight   5
out of his own loins originating,
cluster with their feathered ends vibrating.
But he darkly smiles, inviolate.

Only once his eyes show deep distress,
gazing in a painful nakedness;   10
then, as though ashamed of noticing,
seem to let go with disdainfulness
those destroyers of a lovely thing.
(tr. J. B. Leishman)

[1] There are many paintings of the martyrdom of St. Sebastian by Renaissance artists, but Rilke would seem to have had more particularly in mind that by Botticelli in the Kaiser Friedrich Museum at Berlin.

Imaginary Career

A childhood, reckless of renunciation,
endless and aimless. O unconscious joy!
Then terrors, limits, schooling, subjugation,
and fallings-in with forces that destroy.

Defiance. Now the bent becomes the bender,   5
and wreaks on others his own overthrow.
Loved, feared, contender, triumpher, defender
and overcomer, blow for blow.

Then lonely in the vaster, rarer, colder.
Yet deep within the figure now displayed   10
a silent yearning for the earlier, older . . .

And then God hurtled from his ambuscade.
                                   (*tr. J. B. Leishman*)

Requiem—for the Death of a Boy

Why did I print upon myself the names
Of elephant and dog and cow,
So far-off now, already so long ago,
And zebra, too . . . what for, what for?
What holds me now   5
Climbs like a water line
Up past all that. What help was it to know
I was, if I could never press
Through what's soft, what's hard, and come at last
Behind them, to the face that understands?   10

And these beginning hands . . .

Sometimes you'd say: "He promises . . ."
Yes, I promised. But what I promised you,
That was never what I felt afraid of.
Sometimes I'd sit against the house for hours   15

And look up at a bird.
If only I could have turned into the looking!
It lifted me, it flew me, how my eyes
Were open up there then! But I didn't love anybody.
Loving was misery—   20
Don't you see, I wasn't we,
And I was so much bigger
Than a man, I was my own danger,
And, inside it, I was the seed.

A little seed. The street can have it.   25
The wind can have it. I give it away.
Because that we all sat there so together—
I never did believe that. No honestly.

You talked, you laughed, but none of you were ever
Inside the talking or the laughing. No.   30
The sugar bowl, a glass of milk
Would never waver the way you would waver.
The apple lay there. Sometimes it felt so good
To hold tight to it, a hard ripe apple.
The big table, the coffee cups that never moved—   35
They were good, how peaceful they made the year!
And my toy did me good too, sometimes.
It was as reliable, almost, as the others,
Only not so peaceful. It stood halfway
Between me and my hat, in watchfulness forever.   40
There was a wooden horse, there was a rooster,
There was the doll with only one leg.
I did so much for them.
I made the sky small when they saw it
Because, almost from the start, I understood   45
How alone a wooden horse is. You can make one,
A wooden horse, one any size.
It gets painted, and later on you pull it,
And it's the real street it pounds down, then.
When you call it a horse, why isn't it a lie?   50
Because you feel that you're a horse, a little,

And grow all maney, shiny, grow four legs—
So as to grow, some day, into a man?
But wasn't I wood a little, too,
For its sake, and grew hard and quiet,   55
And looked out at it from an emptier face?

I almost think we traded places.
Whenever I would see the brook I'd race it,
And the brook raced, too, and I would run away.
Whenever I saw something that could ring I rang,   60
And whenever something sang I played for it.
I made myself at home with everything.
Only everything was satisfied without me
And got sadder, hung about with me.
Now, all at once, we're separated.   65
Do the lessons and the questions start again?
Or, now, ought I to say
What it was like with you? That worries me.
The house? I never got it right, exactly.
The rooms? Oh, there were so many things, so many . . .   70
Mother, *who* was the dog really?
That, in the forest, we would come on berries—
Even that seems, now extraordinary.

Surely there're some other children
Who've died to come play with me. They're always dying;   75
Lie there in bed, like me, and never do get well.

Well . . . How funny that sounds, here.
Does it mean something, still?
Here where I am
No one is ill, I think.   80
Since my sore throat, so long ago already—

Here everyone is like a just-poured drink.

But the ones who drink us I still haven't seen.
                                        (*tr. Randall Jarrell*)

For Discussion

"Autumn"

1. In this poem, Rilke begins with the fact of leaves falling. Then, according to the poet, the leaves seem to be falling from heaven, as if heaven were a garden. In your opinion, is this image an intensification of the facts, a revealing of new possibilities in the way ordinary events can be seen, or is it simply "poetic" and untrue to the facts? Explain your answer.
2. From the poem, what would you say is Rilke's viewpoint about people? Explain lines 4-5. What did he mean by "We are all falling"? Is he at all hopeful? Explain.
3. The entire poem, like the leaves, has a downward motion. How did the poet achieve this technically?

"Childhood"

1. Many of Rilke's poems are about childhood and life at school. In "Childhood," what contradictory emotions did he associate with his early life? How did he feel about school, about other children, about adults? Point out lines to support your answers.
2. Explain line 15—"and fear and trust changing in subtle ways." Do you think this is an accurate description of childhood? Why or why not?
3. What meaning do you see in the last stanza? Is it consistent with the mood of the rest of the poem? Explain your answer.
4. Detail piled on detail in a poem may make for monotony, or it may make for an intensification of an experience, as the poet reveals in more and more ways what he saw and felt. In "Childhood," Rilke employed many details to convey impressions of his early life. In your opinion, what is the effect of all these details? Do they make for monotony or for intensification? Do you think any of the details are unnecessary? Do you think there are details omitted which should have been included? Explain your answer.

"Before Summer Rain"

1. Would you say that Rilke was accurate in his observations about air, light, and sound just before a summer storm? Point out details to support your answer.
2. What is the meaning of the last stanza? What relation does it have to the poem "Childhood"?

"Annunciation to Mary"

1. Why was Mary not frightened by the angel's entrance? What does this tell you about Mary? How do lines 8-13 add to the characterization of Mary?
2. What was the cause of Mary's "fear"? Do you think it was fear in the ordinary sense? Explain lines 21-23.
3. Why might the angel also have felt this fear? In your opinion, can a person be "afraid" in the presence of great beauty? Explain.

"Saint Sebastian"

1. What did you find out about St. Sebastian from Rilke's poem? What was the saint's attitude to his destroyers?
2. From what you know of Rilke, what reasons do you have for believing that the poet identified himself with St. Sebastian?
3. Do you think that Rilke was excessively sympathetic to the martyr? Why or why not?
4. Explain the contradiction in lines 1-2.

"Imaginary Career"

1. Describe briefly the narrative in this poem. Explain the last line.
2. In stanza 1, the world seems to be an enemy to the child. Do you think this is wholly accurate? Why or why not?
3. You will note that this poem consists almost entirely of abstractions, unlike "Childhood," which contains many specific images. Why do you think Rilke used abstractions predominantly in "Imaginary Career"? What would you say is gained or lost by this use of abstractions?

"Requiem—for the Death of a Boy"

1. The person speaking in this poem is the young boy who is dead. To whom is he speaking? With what is he concerned in lines 7-10?
2. What criticisms did the boy have of other people? How did he feel about objects and his toys? Point out specific lines to support your answer.
3. What was the boy's attitude toward life? Do you think this attitude is unusual, or is it shared by many people? Explain.
4. Point out lines which reveal the boy's loneliness. What relation do you see between this poem and "Childhood"? How do the two poems differ in their images and rhythms?
5. This poem is a monologue. Do you think Rilke has, or has not, captured the youthful quality of the boy in the way he speaks? Explain.

For Composition

1. Write a paper on Rilke's attitude toward life, including childhood, as revealed in his poetry. Where do you agree and disagree with him? Refer to specific poems or lines from poems wherever possible.

2. Read St. Luke's account of the Annunciation. Write a short composition in which you point out how the account in the Gospel and in Rilke's poem "Annunciation to Mary" are alike and different in their emphases.

3. Write a descriptive paragraph of an everyday occurrence in nature, such as a rainstorm, snow falling, or trees budding in spring. Try to communicate to the reader the mood this occurrence aroused in you. Employ several accurate similes or metaphors in your description as a means of communicating this mood.

4. Rilke was aware of how important technique is in expressing an idea, an emotion, or a mood in a poem. He knew that it was through technique that the idea, emotion, or mood was communicated vividly and musically to the reader. Based on the poems you have read, write an analysis of some of the technical means used by Rilke to achieve his purpose. Point out, for example, Rilke's effective use of rhyme, alliteration, metaphor, and simile. Give examples.

Juan Ramón Jiménez

Juan Ramón Jiménez * (1881–1958), winner of the Nobel Prize for Literature in 1956, published his first poems when he was fourteen years old. During his lifetime, he wrote poetry noted for its originality, lyrical quality, and daring imagery. His best-known prose work, *Platero and I,* has sold over a million copies.

All his life, Jiménez dedicated himself to the search for truth and beauty. As a result, he changed and revised his poems, reworking every image so that he might achieve what he hoped was the quintessence of poetry. Nature was one of his chief subjects. He identified himself with birds, hills, trees, water, and the seasons. For him, nature was a means of affirming his relationship with reality. In his later years, Jiménez considered the poet something of a prophet, the person who fused the temporal with the eternal in each poem, thus creating beauty.

October

I laid myself down on the earth in front of
The infinite countryside of Castile,
Autumn was swathing the fields in the yellow
Sweetness shed by the clear light of its sunset.
Slowly the plow in parallel furrows   5
Spread apart the dark soil and with simple gestures
The open hand was scattering the seed
In its honestly parted inner recesses.
I thought to snatch out my heart and fling it,
Full of its lofty and profound feelings,   10
Along the broad furrow of tender farmland
To see if, by shredding it and sowing it,
The coming spring would reveal to the world
The tree of love, so pure and eternal.

(tr. H. R. Hays)

* hwän ra mōn' hē me'neth

243

I Am Like a Distracted Child

I am like a distracted child
Whom they drag by the hand
Through the fiesta of the world.
My eyes cling, sadly,
To things ...   5
And what misery when they tear me away from them!

> (*tr. H. R. Hays*)

Prelude to Autumn

In the open window I await you, autumn. Come
And cool my temples
With the spreading fragrance
Of a withered rose.

The early morning hour is lost in shadow. And all things   5
Come to an end in another way.
And love magnifies itself in an intense pulsation,
A huge journeying.

Life is farther away. The intimate landscape
Plaits foam and lace.   10
And yonder, where the tranquil branches leave spaces,
Sublime circles
Bury themselves within.

And the sweetness is wandering and unquiet.
And a vivid coolness   15
Arises from the soil ... autumn I grow impatient. Come
And caress my temples.

> (*tr. H. R. Hays*)

The Coming Star

The star is in the orange tree.
Let us see who can capture it!

Come quickly with pearls,
Fetch nets made of silk!

What an odor of springtime   5
From its flask of eternal life!

The star is in all eyes.
Let us see who can capture it!

In the air, in the grass,
Take care, do not lose it!   10

The star is in love!
Let us see who can capture it!

(*tr. H. R. Hays*)

Dream Nocturne

The earth leads through the earth;
but you, sea,
lead through heaven.
With what a steady light of gold and silver
do the stars show us   5
the way!—One would say
that the earth is the way
of the flesh,
that the sea is the way
of the soul—.   10
Yes, it seems
that the soul is the only traveler
of the sea, that the flesh, alone,
remained there on the shore

without her, saying farewell,   15
heavy and cold, like unto death.
    A voyage on the ocean,
how it resembles the voyage to death,
voyage to life eternal!

                     (*tr. Eleanor Laurelle Turnbull*)

Without Tedium or Rest

If I have gone out so much in the world
It has been only and always
To meet you, longed-for god,
Among so much head and so much breast
Of so many men.   5

(Gigantic city, great concourse,
Which returns to me in a gray reflection of water,
In this blue sun in a south full of light,
Of this longed-for and longing god,
Eyes, and eyes, and eyes,   10
With sparkling instantaneous movements
Of the eternal in motion.)

So much mover of thought and feeling,
(Black, white, yellow, red, green
In body) with the soul   15
Drifting toward you,
Becoming itself,
Happening in me,
Without knowing it, or I or they knowing it!

                     (*tr. H. R. Hays*)

Aphorisms

1. You find in solitude only what you take to it.
2. What a conflict within me between my good and my best!

3. The true sign of poetry is contagion; this does not mean (take care!) imitation.
4. What youth thinks of us is very important, for youth is the beginning of our posterity.
5. My best work is my constant repentance for my work.
6. The poem should be like a star which is a world and looks like a diamond.
7. If anyone seeks me in this life (and in death) let him look only in beauty.
8. Let us cultivate, above all, the will to reject.

For Discussion

"October"

1. Jiménez often identified himself with nature. How did he do this in "October"? Do you think this identification is valid? Why or why not?
2. What emotion did October arouse in the poet? Point out details that evoked this emotion. What do you think nature represented to Jiménez?

"I Am Like a Distracted Child"

1. What is the theme of this poem? Did the image employed by Jiménez convey the theme effectively? Why or why not?
2. In a poem, a poet always blends richness and economy. In this brief poem, Jiménez clearly emphasized economy. Point out how he also conveyed a sense of richness.

"Prelude to Autumn"

1. In your opinion, what does autumn symbolize in this poem? Point out specific lines to support your answer. Compare the mood of "Prelude to Autumn" with that of "October."
2. State the idea expressed in the poem. What is lacking in your prose statement that is essential to the poem? Do you agree or disagree that *how* things are said in this poem is part of what is said? Why?

"The Coming Star"

1. The poet saw the star "in the orange tree," "in all eyes," and "in the air, in the grass." What do you think the star represents?
2. What did Jiménez mean by "The star is in love"?

"Dream Nocturne"

1. How are earth and sea contrasted in this poem? What reasons might Jiménez have had for seeing the sea as "the way of the soul"?
2. Do you think that the image of an ocean voyage "to life eternal" is more convincing than an image of a train or automobile trip? Why or why not?
3. Explain the personification in this poem. Would you say this is an optimistic or a pessimistic poem? Why?
4. In what way does the music of the lines in this poem differ from that of "The Coming Star"? How do the two poems differ in mood?

"Without Tedium or Rest"

1. Jiménez expressed the idea that his happiness depended upon his identification with outside reality. Point out lines in the poem which support this statement. Do you agree or disagree with this idea?
2. Do you think that even when a poet is expressing his dislike or criticisms of things, he is affirming his relation with reality? Explain your answer.
3. Is the title of this poem appropriate or inappropriate? Why?

Aphorisms

Throughout his life, Jiménez wrote many aphorisms. An aphorism is a short, pithy sentence stating a general doctrine or truth. Explain the meaning of aphorism 3. Point out and explain the aphorisms which reveal Jiménez's attitude toward his work and toward beauty.

For Composition

1. Write a character sketch of Jiménez based on what you learned about the poet from his poems. Quote lines wherever they are pertinent to your sketch.
2. Write a short critical paper on one poem by Jiménez that you particularly liked or disliked. With specific references to the poem, state why you liked or disliked it.
3. Write a composition in which you express your agreement or disagreement with one of Jiménez's aphorisms. Give examples from your own experience to prove or disprove his statement.

Federico García Lorca

The plays and poems of Frederico García Lorca (1899–1936) excel those of most of his Spanish contemporaries. He did not achieve international fame, however, until after his untimely death during the Spanish Civil War. One of his notable achievements was his successful use of old Andalusian verse forms which were influenced by the Arabic culture that permeates much of the southern part of the Iberian peninsula. Lorca produced poems distinguished for their musical quality and their sensuous imagery. He has often been compared to the French surrealists and the American imagists. Like the surrealists, he sometimes juxtaposed seemingly unrelated ideas and realistic and nonrealistic images, making for strange, dreamlike effects. Like the imagists, he was intensely interested in using language precisely, as a means of achieving dramatic power in his poetry.

The Guitar

The lament begins
Of the guitar.
The wine cups of dawn
Are splintered afar.
The lament begins   5
Of the guitar.
It's impossible, useless,
To get it to stop.
It weeps montonously,
As the rain, drop by drop,   10
Or as the wind weeps
On the snowpeak's top.
It is impossible
To get it to stop.
It grieves for things   15
Far out of sight—

249

Like the hot southern sands
For camellias white.
It weeps, the targetless arrow,
The eve without morrow, 20
And the first bird on the bough
To perish in sorrow.
O the guitar, the heart
That bleeds in the shades
Terribly wounded 25
By its own five blades!

(*tr. Roy Campbell*)

Song of the Horseman

Córdoba.
Remote and lonely.

Jet-black mare and full round moon,
With olives in my saddle bags,
Although I know the road so well 5
I shall not get to Córdoba.

Across the plain, across the wind,
Jet-black mare and full red moon,
Death is gazing down upon me,
Down from the towers of Córdoba. 10

Ay! The road so dark and long.
Ay! My mare so tired yet brave.
Death is waiting for me there
Before I get to Córdoba.

Córdoba. 15
Remote and lonely.

(*tr. Roy Campbell*)

Arrow

Brown Christ
pass
from the lily of Judea
to the carnation of Spain.

Look where he comes!   5

From Spain.
Sky clear and dark,
parched land,
and watercourses where very
slowly runs the water.   10
Brown Christ,
with the burned forelocks,
the jutting cheekbones
and the white pupils.

Look where he goes!   15
(*tr. W. S. Merwin*)

The Dawn

The New York dawn has
four columns of mud
and a hurricane of black doves
that paddle in putrescent waters.

The New York dawn grieves   5
along the immense stairways,
seeking amidst the groins
spikenards of fine-drawn anguish.

The dawn comes and no one receives it in his
        mouth,
for there no morn or hope is possible.   10
Occasionally, coins in furious swarms
perforate and devour abandoned children.

The first to come out understand in their bones
that there will be no paradise nor amours stripped of leaves:
they know they are going to the mud of figures and laws,   15
to artless games, to fruitless sweat.

The light is buried under chains and noises
in impudent challenge of rootless science.
Through the suburbs sleepless people stagger,
as though just delivered from a shipwreck of blood.   20

(tr. Stephen Spender and J. L. Gili)

Lament for Ignacio Sánchez Mejías

1. Cogida and Death

At five in the afternoon.
It was exactly five in the afternoon.
A boy brought the white sheet
at five in the afternoon.
A frail of lime ready prepared   5
at five in the afternoon.
The rest was death, and death alone
at five in the afternoon.

The wind carried away the cottonwool
at five in the afternoon.   10
And the oxide scattered crystal and nickel
at five in the afternoon.
Now the dove and the leopard wrestle
at five in the afternoon.
And a thigh with a desolate horn   15
at five in the afternoon.
The bass-string struck up
at five in the afternoon.
Arsenic bells and smoke
at five in the afternoon.   20
Groups of silence in the corners
at five in the afternoon.

And the bull alone with a high heart!
At five in the afternoon.
When the sweat of snow was coming
at five in the afternoon,
when the bull ring was covered in iodine
at five in the afternoon.
Death laid eggs in the wound
at five in the afternoon.
At five in the afternoon.
Exactly at five o'clock in the afternoon.

A coffin on wheels is his bed
at five in the afternoon.
Bones and flutes resound in his ears
at five in the afternoon.
Now the bull was bellowing through his forehead
at five in the afternoon.
The room was iridescent with agony
at five in the afternoon.
In the distance the gangrene now comes
at five in the afternoon.
Horn of the lily through green groins
at five in the afternoon.
The wounds were burning like suns
at five in the afternoon,
and the crowd was breaking the windows
at five in the afternoon.
At five in the afternoon.
Ah, that fatal five in the afternoon!
It was five by all the clocks!
It was five in the shade of the afternoon!

2. The Spilled Blood

I will not see it!

Tell the moon to come
for I do not want to see the blood
of Ignacio on the sand.

I will not see it!

The moon wide open.
Horse of still clouds,
and the grey bull ring of dreams
with willows in the barreras.

I will not see it!   10

Let my memory kindle!
Warn the jasmines
of such minute whiteness!

I will not see it!

The cow of the ancient world   15
passed her sad tongue
over a snout of blood
spilled on the sand,
and the bulls of Guisando,
partly death and partly stone,   20
bellowed like two centuries
sated with treading the earth.
No.
I do not want to see it!
I will not see it!   25

Ignacio goes up the tiers
with all his death on his shoulders.
He sought for the dawn
but the dawn was no more.
He seeks for his confident profile   30
and the dream bewilders him.
He sought for his beautiful body
and encountered his opened blood.
I will not see it!
I do not want to hear it spurt   35
each time with less strength:
that spurt that illuminates
the tiers of seats, and spills
over the corduroy and the leather

of a thirsty multitude. 40
Who shouts that I should come near!
Do not ask me to see it!

His eyes did not close
when he saw the horns near,
but the terrible mothers 45
lifted their heads.
And across the ranches,
an air of secret voices rose,
shouting to celestial bulls,
herdsmen of pale mist. 50
There was no prince in Seville
who could compare with him,
nor sword like his sword
nor heart so true.
Like a river of lions 55
was his marvellous strength,
and like a marble torso
his firm drawn moderation.
The air of Andalusian Rome
gilded his head 60
where his smile was a spikenard
of wit and intelligence.
What a great torero in the ring!
What a good peasant in the sierra!
How gentle with the sheaves! 65
How hard with the spurs!
How tender with the dew!
How dazzling in the fiesta!
How tremendous with the final
banderillas of darkness! 70

But now he sleeps without end.
Now the moss and the grass
open with sure fingers
the flower of his skull.
And now his blood comes out singing; 75
singing along marshes and meadows,

sliding on frozen horns,
faltering soulless in the mist,
stumbling over a thousand hoofs
like a long, dark, sad tongue,   80
to form a pool of agony
close to the starry Guadalquivir.
Oh, white wall of Spain!
Oh, black bull of sorrow!
Oh, hard blood of Ignacio!   85
Oh, nightingale of his veins!
No.
I will not see it!
No chalice can contain it,
no swallows can drink it,   90
no frost of light can cool it,
nor song nor deluge of white lilies,
no glass can cover it with silver.
No.
I will not see it!   95

3. The Laid Out Body

Stone is a forehead where dreams grieve
without curving waters and frozen cypresses.
Stone is a shoulder on which to bear Time
with trees formed of tears and ribbons and planets.

I have seen grey showers move towards the waves   5
raising their tender riddled arms,
to avoid being caught by the lying stone
which loosens their limbs without soaking the blood.

For stone gathers seed and clouds,
skeleton larks and wolves of penumbra: 10
but yields not sounds nor crystals nor fire,
only bull rings and bull rings and more bull rings without walls.

Now, Ignacio the well born lies on the stone.
All is finished. What is happening? Contemplate his face:

death has covered him with pale sulphur   15
and has placed on him the head of a dark minotaur.

All is finished. The rain penetrates his mouth.
The air, as if mad, leaves his sunken chest,
and Love, soaked through with tears of snow,
warms itself on the peak of the herd.   20

What are they saying? A stenching silence settles down.
We are here with a body laid out which fades away,
with a pure shape which had nightingales
and we see it being filled with depthless holes.

Who creases the shroud? What he says is not true!   25
Nobody sings here, nobody weeps in the corner,
nobody pricks the spurs, nor terrifies the serpent.
Here I want nothing else but the round eyes
to see this body without a chance of rest.

Here I want to see those men of hard voice.   30
Those that break horses and dominate rivers;
those men of sonorous skeleton who sing
with a mouth full of sun and flint.

Here I want to see them. Before the stone.
Before this body with broken reins.   35
I want to know from them the way out
for this captain strapped down by death.

I want them to show me a lament like a river
which will have sweet mists and deep shores,
to take the body of Ignacio where it loses itself   40
without hearing the double panting of the bulls.

Loses itself in the round bull ring of the moon
which feigns in its youth a sad quiet bull:
loses itself in the night without song of fishes
and in the white thicket of frozen smoke.   45

I don't want them to cover his face with handkerchiefs
that he may get used to the death he carries.
Go, Ignacio; feel not the hot bellowing.
Sleep, fly, rest: even the sea dies!

4. Absent Soul

The bull does not know you, nor the fig tree,
nor the horses, nor the ants in your own house.
The child and the afternoon do not know you
because you have died for ever.

The back of the stone does not know you,   5
nor the black satin in which you crumble.
Your silent memory does not know you
because you have died for ever.

The autumn will come with small white snails,
misty grapes and with clustered hills,   10
but no one will look into your eyes
because you have died for ever.

Because you have died for ever,
like all the dead of the Earth,
like all the dead who are forgotten   15
in a heap of lifeless dogs.

Nobody knows you. No. But I sing of you.
For posterity I sing of your profile and grace.
Of the signal maturity of your understanding.
Of your appetite for death and the taste of its mouth.   20
Of the sadness of your once valiant gaiety.

It will be a long time, if ever, before there is born
an Andalusian so true, so rich in adventure.
I sing of his elegance with words that groan,
and I remember a sad breeze through the olive trees.   25

(*tr. Stephen Spender and J. L. Gili*)

For Discussion

"The Guitar"

1. Lorca's notable use of sensuous imagery is revealed in this poem. To describe the effect of Spanish music played on a guitar, the poet employed a series of vivid images. From these images, how would you describe the music of the guitar? In your opinion, which image most effectively captured the mood of the music? Explain why.
2. The lament of the guitar in this poem seems to express more than a personal emotion. It seems to express the sorrow of the world. How do the images Lorca selected convey this?
3. In his poetry, Lorca frequently used the pathetic fallacy. Point out the use of this poetic device in "The Guitar." Why might a poet use this device?

"Song of the Horseman"

1. In this poem, Lorca recreated the fearful experience of traveling alone on a dark and dangerous road to Córdoba. What realistic details did the poet employ to recreate this experience? What effect is achieved by "Jet-black mare and full round moon"?
2. Lorca also used non-realistic details to heighten the sense of open space, ominous darkness, and danger. What effect did he achieve by changing "full round moon" in stanza 2 to "full red moon" in stanza 3? Point out other imaginative details and the effect of each.

"Arrow"

1. The *Saetas* (Arrows) are sung in Holy Week processions. In "Arrow" how did Lorca communicate to the reader the effect of the passing of the Christ and the Blessed Virgin in procession?
2. Point out the repetition in this poem. What effect is created?
3. Explain the references to "lily of Judea" and "carnation of Spain."

"The Dawn"

1. Many of Lorca's poems, such as "The Dawn," are expressions of his experience as a student at Columbia University in New York City during the 1929–30 depression. From the tone of this poem what would you say was Lorca's response to life in New York at that time? Point out specific lines to support your answer. Why might he have responded as he did to American life?
2. In this poem, as in "The Guitar," Lorca used the pathetic fallacy. In your opinion, does it add to the effectiveness of the poem? Why or why not?

3. Imagery is one of the principal means through which a poet recreates the experience he wishes to convey to the reader. Through imagery, he communicates the pictures, emotion, and theme of a poem, as well as his attitude toward the subject. Imagery, then, is not merely decorative or incidental to a poem; it is essential. In "The Dawn," what do "four columns of mud" and "putrescent waters" convey? How does the image of "black doves" reveal the attitude of the poet toward his subject? Point out other striking images in "The Dawn" and explain their effectiveness in the context of the poem.

"Lament for Ignacio Sánchez Mejías"

1. This elegy expresses Lorca's deep sorrow at the death of his friend, a famous bullfighter. What did you find out about the bullfighter from this poem? What did the poet admire about him?
2. Lorca's emotion in this poem is intense. In your opinion, is the emotion unrestrained or restrained? Explain your answer with specific references to the poem.
3. In section 1, the phrase "at five in the afternoon" is used as a refrain. In section 2, the sentence "I will not see it" serves the same purpose. What effect is created by the repetition in section 1? How does it differ from the effect of the repetition in section 2?
4. The imagery in this poem, though often difficult, is precise and helps to establish the mood of each section. Point out and explain the images in each part which you feel contribute to the impact of the poem. Point out the progression in mood from one section to the next.

For Composition

1. An elegy is a mournful poem, usually written as an expression of grief over someone's death. The most famous elegy in English literature is Thomas Gray's "Elegy Written in a Country Churchyard." Write a short essay comparing and contrasting Gray's poem with Lorca's "Lament for Ignacio Sánchez Mejías."
2. Write an opening paragraph about the death of Mejías as it might be written by each of the following: (a) a newspaper reporter, (b) a typical Englishman opposed to bullfighting, (c) a biographer writing of the death of Mejías, (d) Ernest Hemingway writing a short story about this event. Compare and contrast each of your accounts in terms of emphasis on facts, descriptive details, and mood.
3. Write a short description of a procession or parade. Choose specific details that will convey the mood of this event and bring the scene vividly to life for the reader.

Guillaume Apollinaire

A close friend of the contemporary artist Pablo Picasso, Guillaume Apollinaire (1880–1918) participated in all the avant-garde movements of his generation. A man of varied interests, he traveled widely and in his short life became associated with all that was new in the arts. He is credited with inventing the term "surrealism" and being the theorist of cubism in painting.

Apollinaire's two volumes of poetry, *Alcools* (1913) and *Calligrammes* (1918), attracted much attention after World War I. His poems, with their casual tone, surprising images, quickly shifting rhythms, and unconventional punctuation and typography, reflected the modern age in a new and exciting way. He consciously strove to include in his work such innovations in modern life as the automobile, the airplane, and motion pictures. His startling use of typography to reflect his themes can be seen in a poem entitled "Il Pleut" ("It Is Raining"), in which letters are arranged obliquely in parallel lines on the page to symbolize the effect of rainfall. In his most famous single poem, "Zone," he sought to present a poetic rendition of cubism by juxtaposing a series of seemingly unrelated themes and images in phrases not clearly connected. It is a lamentation of modern decadence that reminds one of T. S. Eliot's famous poem "The Waste Land," which appeared in 1922.

Autumn

A bowlegged peasant and his ox receding
Through the mist slowly through the mist of autumn
Which hides the shabby and sordid villages

And out there as he goes the peasant is singing
A song of love and infidelity   5
About a ring and a heart which someone is breaking

Oh the autumn the autumn has been the death of summer
In the mist there are two gray shapes receding
                    (*tr. W. S. Merwin*)

261

Rhenish Autumn

The children of the dead are going to play
In the graveyard
Martin Gertrude Hans and Henri
No cock has crowed today
Kikiriki   5

The old women
All in tears are proceeding
And the good burros
Bray heehaw and start to munch the flowers
of the funeral wreaths   10

This is the day of the dead and of all their souls

The children and the old women
Light candles and tapers
On each catholic grave
The veils of the old women   15
The clouds in the sky
Are like the beards of she-goats

The air trembles with flames and prayer

The graveyard is a beautiful garden
Full of hoary willows and rosemary   20
Often they are friends who are buried here
Ah! how blessed you are in the beautiful graveyard
You beggars who died drunkards
You who are eyeless as Fate
And you children who died as you prayed   25

Ah! how blessed you are in the beautiful graveyard
You burgomasters you seamen
And you counselors of state
And you gypsies without passport
Life is rotting your belly   30
We stumble on the cross at our feet

The owls hoot and the moaning wind from the Rhine
Blows out the tapers which the children light again and again
And the dead leaves
Come to cover the dead   35

Dead children now and then speak with their mother
And dead women now and then long to come back

Oh! I do not want you to return
The autumn is full of disembodied hands
No no these are dead leaves   40
They are the hands of the dear dead
They are your disembodied hands

We have wept so much today
With these dead their children and the old women
Under a sunless sky   45
In the graveyard full of flames

Then we had to turn back into the wind
At our feet the chestnuts rolled
And their burrs were
Like the wounded heart of the Madonna   50
We wondered if her skin
Was the color of the autumn chestnuts

                              (*tr. Daisy Aldan*)

from Zone

After all you are weary of this oldtime world

Shepherdess O Eiffel Tower your flock of bridges is bleating this
    morning

You have had enough of this living in a Greek and Roman antiquity

Here even the automobiles contrive an ancient aspect
Only religion is still new only religion   5
Has stayed simple like the Airport hangars

In all Europe you alone are not antique O Christianity
The most up-to-date European is you Pope Pius X
And you whom the windows stare at shame keeps you back
From going into some church and confessing your sins this morning ¹⁰
You read the prospectuses the catalogues the public notices that
   sing out
Here's the morning's poetry and for prose we have newspapers
We've two-bit volumes full of crime adventure
Portraits of the great and a thousand miscellaneous items

This morning I saw a neat street I've forgotten its name   ¹⁵
All new and clean a bugle in the sun
Bosses workmen and pretty stenographers
From Monday morning to Saturday night pass along it four times
   a day
Three times each morning the siren moans there
A furious whistle bays along about noon   ²⁰
The slogans the signboards the walls
The plaques the parroty notices nagging
I like the charm of this industrial street
Located in Paris between the Rue Aumont-Thiéville and the Avenue
   des Ternes
Here's your young street and you're only a little child still . . .   ²⁵

You are in a tavern garden somewhere outside Prague
You are so happy there's a rose on the table
And instead of composing your prose fable
You note the worm asleep in the heart of the rose

In terror you see yourself limned in the agates of Saint Vit   ³⁰
You were deathly sorry the day you saw yourself there
You look like Lazarus struck silly by the daylight
The hands on the ghetto clock move backwards
You too reverse slowly into your life
And going up to Hradchin hearing at nightfall   ³⁵
The tavern songs of the singing Czechs
You're back at Marseille along the watermelons
Back in Coblenz at the Hôtel du Géant
You're in Rome sitting under a Japanese medlar

You're in Amsterdam with a girl you think's pretty but she's a fright
She's going to marry a Leyden undergraduate   41
They rent rooms in Latin there Cubicula locanda
I remember it well I spent three days there and also at Gouda

You're in Paris before the examining magistrate
Like a common criminal you are placed in custody   45
You have made your happy and dolorous journeys
Before taking account of falsehood and age
At twenty and thirty you have suffered from love
I have lived like a madman and I've lost my time
You no longer dare look at your hands and all the time I could burst
    out sobbing   50
Because of you because of her I love because of everything that has
    frightened you . . .

You are alone morning is coming
The milkmen are clanking their tin cans in the streets

Night takes flight like a fair Médive
It's a faithless Ferdine or a faithful Leah   55

You drink an alcohol that burns like your life
Your life that you drink down like brandy

You walk towards Auteuil and you would go home on foot
To sleep among your fetishes from Oceania and Guinea
They are Christs in another form Christs of another faith   60
They are the lesser Christs of obscure yearnings

Good-bye Good-bye

Sun cut throat

                                    (*tr. Dudley Fitts*)

For Discussion

"Autumn"

1. Apollinaire attempted in this poem to capture the mood of this season through a single image. What is the mood evoked by the picture of the peasant and the ox receding into the mist? In what way does the song the peasant is singing contribute to the effectiveness of the poem?
2. The music or rhythm of the lines in a poem must blend with the images if the poem is to be successful. In your opinion, is the rhythm of "Autumn" consistent with the image? Point out words and lines to support your answer.

"Rhenish Autumn"

1. "Rhenish Autumn" is about All Souls' Day, which is observed as a holiday in many European countries. From this poem, what would you say was Apollinaire's feeling about the dead? Do you agree or disagree with him? Why?
2. In the first two stanzas, Apollinaire dramatically juxtaposed images representing liveliness and sadness. Give specific instances of this. Do you think that this co-presence of contradictory moods is jarring or true to life? Explain your answer.
3. Point out the poet's use of unusual similes and metaphors. Do they contribute to or detract from the total effect of the poem? Explain.
4. You will note that in "Rhenish Autumn" Apollinaire used no punctuation, except for two exclamation points. What effect do you think he was trying to achieve? Would you have preferred the poem properly punctuated? Why or why not?

"Zone"

1. Although this is a difficult poem with its many seemingly unrelated images, an over-all comment on modern civilization can be discerned. What was Apollinaire's opinion of modern European life? What details in the poem reveal this opinion?
2. Explain lines 26-29. How are they related to the main theme of the poem?
3. In lines 56-57, the poet compared life to brandy. What was his attitude toward life in these lines? Why might this attitude have been prevalent during World War I and immediately after?
4. In what way does the mood of lines 58-63 differ from that of lines 56-57? In your opinion, what was Apollinaire looking for?

5. In his poetry, Apollinaire used slang expressions and images from everyday modern life, which would have been frowned on by most nineteenth-century poets. Point out some of these expressions and images in "Zone." What do they contribute to the tone of the poem?

For Composition

1. When Apollinaire called the Eiffel Tower a "Shepherdess" in line 2 of "Zone," and called the bridges of Paris her "flock," he was using personification. Write a paragraph in which you personify an abstract idea, such as Truth, Beauty, or Justice. Or you might personify a place, as Carl Sandburg did when he called Chicago the "hog-butcher of the world."
2. Criticism of modern civilization has been an important theme in modern poetry. Compare and contrast "Zone" with Stefan George's "Poem for This Age" (page 230). Point out similarities and differences of mood, images, and technique in these two poems.
3. Write a careful evaluation of American life today as you see it, and of the values held by the "average" person. Your evaluation may include both the things of which you are critical and the things of which you approve.
4. Autumn has been written about by many poets. Compare and contrast Apollinaire's poem on the subject with Rilke's "Autumn" (page 233) and Jiménez's "October" (page 243). How are these poems alike and different in mood, theme, and imagery?

Paul Valéry

Since the publication of his book of poems, *La Jeune Parque*, in 1917, Paul Valéry * (1871–1945) has enjoyed a leading position in the field of French poetry, comparable to that of Marcel Proust and André Gide in the field of prose. Because of the difficulty of his verse, Valéry sometimes is referred to as a philosopher who is also a craftsman with words, rather than as a poet. The main challenge in reading him is interpreting his metaphors, for he frequently used physical images as symbols for complex ideas. No aspect of existence was too minute for his poetic consideration —the evanescent step of a dancer, a sea breeze stirring a sail; nor was any phase of reality too difficult for him to explore. For example, in his major poem, "La Jeune Parque," he described the successive stages from consciousness to dreams of a person approaching sleep. Valéry maintained that a poet should be the embodiment of an intellectual holiday embellished with all the riches of language and the resources of music. In practice, this meant for Valéry a mingling of intuition and careful technique, and a use of surprising images to convey the truths of reality. As a symbolist poet, he has had a significant effect on modern French poetry.

Pomegranates

Hard pomegranates sundered
By excess of your seeds,
You make me think of mighty brows
Aburst with their discoveries!

If the suns you underwent,   5
O pomegranates severed,
Wrought your essence with the pride
To rend your ruby segments,

And if the dry gold of your shell
At instance of a power   10
Cracks in crimson gems of juice,

* pôl vȧ lā rē'

This luminous eruption
Sets a soul to dream upon
Its secret architecture.

(*tr. Kate Flores*)

Asides

What do you do? Why, everything.
What are you worth? Worth, well,
The worth of mastery and disgust,
Presentiment and trial ...
What are you worth? Worth, well ...   5
What do you want? Nothing, all.

What do you know? Boredom.
What can you do? Dream.
And with the power of the mind
Can turn the morning into night.   10
What can you do? Dream,
And so drive boredom from the mind.

What do you want? My own good.
What must you do? Learn.
Learn and master and foresee,   15
All, of course, to no good.
What do you fear? The will.
Who are you? Nothing, nothing at all.

Where are you going? To death.
What will you do there? Die;   20
Nor ever return to this rotten game,
Forever and ever and ever the same.
Where are you going? To die.
What will you do there? Be dead.

(*tr. William Jay Smith*)

Helen

Azure! behold me . . . I come from the caverns of death
To hear once more the measured sounding of waves,
And once more I see long galleys in the dawn
Revive from darkness in a file of golden oars.

My solitary hands call forth those monarchs   5
Whose beards of salt entwined my simple fingers.
I wept. They sang of their obscure triumphs
And of buried seas in the wake of their barques.

I hear deep hollow shells and the compelling
Clarions of war, pacing the flight of the oars—   10
The clear song of the oarsmen chains this tumult.

And gods raised high on the heroic prow,
Their ancient smile insulted by the spray,
Hold forth toward me forgiving sculptured arms.

(tr. Andrew Chiappe)

For Discussion

"Pomegranates"

1. What did Valéry compare pomegranates to in this poem? The poet
called the juice from the bursting pomegranates "crimson gems." Are
these images justified or unjustified? Explain.
2. From his specific observations of the pomegranates, Valéry was led to
a general idea. What was that idea? What do you think the theme of
the poem is? In your opinion, is the last stanza arrived at too abruptly?
Why or why not?

"Asides"

1. Is this poem a dialogue between two people or could it also be a conversation between two aspects of the self? Discuss.
2. In the series of questions and answers, Valéry revealed some of the
contradictory ways man can see himself and the world. Point out some
of these contradictory ways. From this poem, what would you say the
poet's philosophy of life is?

3. What value did Valéry see in "the power of the mind"? Why did he fear "the will"?

4. Contrast "Asides" and "Pomegranates." How do they differ in imagery and rhythm? Which poem is more flowing in its musical effects? Which is more staccato? Do you think the musical effects blend with the ideas expressed in each poem?

"Helen"

1. This poem is about the arrival of the Greek ships in Troy to bring back Helen, who had been abducted by Paris. Helen is reliving this event. What mood is expressed by the first words of the opening line? What does this reveal about Helen?

2. Who were the "monarchs with beards of salt"? What was Helen's relation to them?

3. What were the sounds Helen heard? Explain line 11. How does a singer or poet "chain" or bring order to tumult?

4. Explain the image in the last stanza. Do you think the gods were forgiving? Why or why not?

5. This poem, even in translation, succeeds in fusing the sounds of the words and their meaning. Point out instances of this fusion.

For Composition

1. Poets have revealed again and again the wonder that is to be found in simple objects. Valéry has done this in "Pomegranates." Write a description of an everyday object, such as an apple, a flower, your fountain pen, or even your hand. Describe the object as precisely as you can. You might include its shape, its weight, its texture, its parts. If its smell or taste are important, note them as well.

2. Write a dialogue in the manner of "Asides," in which you ask yourself five important questions and answer them briefly. Some of the questions you might include are: "What do you want?" "What do you believe in?" "What do you hope for?" "What do you like best, or least, about yourself?" "What are you afraid of?"

3. Write a short paper on Valéry's concept of death, as revealed in "Asides." Show where you agree to disagree with the poet.

DRAMA

$\mathscr{B}$Y the end of the nineteenth century, the drama in Europe had undergone some crucial and revolutionary changes. Plays no longer were flimsy, romantic, artificial vehicles, in which stars had an opportunity to declaim and display their histrionic talents. With the appearance of plays by Ibsen, Strindberg, Hauptmann, and Gorky, the drama became a serious and realistic presentation of life, in which the problems of ordinary people were explored with power and insight. Characters were now seen as products of their environment and affected by social factors. Playwrights also presented their characters as having inner conflicts as described by the new psychology, which was beginning to occupy a prominent place in European thought.

By the end of the nineteenth century, stage productions had also been radically changed by these new realistic dramas. Stage sets, instead of being artificial, painted backdrops, were now actual rooms, furnished with authentic furniture, which created an environment for the characters. Acting had also become realistic and "natural." Actors no longer declaimed to the audience, but performed as if they were actually living within the set, oblivious of the audience watching them through the invisible "fourth wall." One of the most notable developments of this new realistic theater was the founding of the Moscow Art Theater in 1897, headed by Stanislavsky, which has had far-reaching effects on acting up to the present day, not only in Europe, but also in America.

By the twentieth century, however, there was a reaction to the social dramas and problem plays which had grown out of the new realism in the theater. Many playwrights, in the early decades of the century, wrote plays which were experimental and stylized, and which revealed the more poetic and imaginative aspects of the drama. Plays such as Pirandello's *Six Characters in Search of an Author*, Bertolt Brecht's *The Private Life of the Master Race*, Čapek's *R.U.R.*, and Lorca's *Blood Wedding* all represented anti-realistic trends. None of these trends, however, displaced realism as the dominant mode of the modern theater.

Today the drama in Europe, as in America, is both realistic and experimental. Some of the playwrights in the second half of the twentieth century, such as Jean Genet and Eugène Ionesco, are boldly experimental. Others, such as Jean Giraudoux and Jean Anouilh, mingle realism with more imaginative elements in their work.

The drama of this century, like the fiction, nonfiction, and poetry, has reflected the turbulence of the times. Playwrights in all of the major countries of Europe have been critical of man—of his emphasis on materialism and mechanization, of his lack of spiritual values, and of his inhumanity to other men. There has been a tone of pessimism among playwrights, though this pessimism has been expressed in a variety of ways—through realistic comedies and tragedies, and through the use of satire, fantasy, and symbolism.

In the early part of this century, there was an emphasis on the common man, exemplified by the plays of social protest. In the second half of the century, however, there has been a questioning of the purpose and meaning of existence itself. One of the recurrent themes of playwrights today is the loneliness of man and his inability to express his deepest feelings and communicate with other men. Another recurrent theme is man's search for a direction, which will give him the dignity and self-respect he needs. Today's playwright is uncertain of the answers to man's questions. He wavers between faith and lack of faith. His tone when he writes is sometimes bitter, sometimes mocking and satirical, sometimes angry. He is serious, however, in his attempt to understand the forces working in man and outside of him, and how a person can achieve a harmonious relationship with the world, while maintaining his individuality. The modern playwright continues to search for the answer by dramatizing man's dilemmas imaginatively and with power.

Karel Čapek

R. U. R.

(Rossum's Universal Robots)

Karel Čapek, the leading literary figure in Czechoslovakia after World War I, won world-wide renown as a playwright, as well as a novelist and writer of nonfiction (see page 184). His plays, which reveal his ability to write about serious social problems with imagination and humor, made the theater in Czechoslovakia one of the most vital in Europe before 1939.

One of his most popular plays, R.U.R., was produced all over the world and was presented on Broadway with great success. This play, which Čapek called "a melodramatic fantasy," was the playwright's way of warning the world against the accelerated rate at which men were being depersonalized in the factories of the machine age, and predicting what would happen to man if human values were not more seriously considered. Čapek conjured up a world so mechanized that all labor is performed by machine-made men. In searching for a term to describe these men, he coined the word *robot*, from the Czech noun *robota*, meaning "work." The term won international currency as a result of the success of the play and has since become part of the language of the Western world.

Characters

HARRY DOMIN, *General Manager of Rossum's Universal Robots*
SULLA, *a Robotess*
MARIUS, *a Robot*
HELENA GLORY, *daughter of Professor Glory, of Oxbridge University*
DR. GALL, *head of the Physiological and Experimental Department of R.U.R.*
MR. FABRY, *Chief Engineer of R.U.R.*
DR. HALLEMEIER, *head of the Institute for the Psychological Training of Robots*
MR. ALQUIST, *head of the Works Department of R.U.R.*
CONSUL BUSMAN, *General Manager of R.U.R.*

NANA, *Helena Glory's maid*
RADIUS, *a Robot*
HELENA, *a Robotess*
PRIMUS, *a Robot*
A ROBOT SERVANT
NUMEROUS ROBOTS

PLACE: An Island.
TIME: The Future.

ACT I

SCENE: *Central office of the factory of Rossum's Universal Robots.*
Entrance on the right. The windows on the back wall look out
on the endless rows of factory buildings. On the left-hand wall
large maps showing steamship and railroad routes. On the right-
hand wall are fastened print placards. ("Robot's Cheapest Labor,"
etc.) In contrast to these wall fittings, the room is furnished with
a splendid Turkish carpet, a couch, a leather armchair, and filing
cabinets.
     DOMIN *is sitting at his desk, dictating. At a desk near the windows,*
SULLA *is typing letters.*

DOMIN. (*Dictating*) Ready?
SULLA. Yes.
DOMIN. To E. M. McVicker & Co., Southampton, England. "We
   undertake no guarantee for goods damaged in transit. As soon as
   the consignment was taken on board we drew your captain's attention to the fact that the vessel was unsuitable for the transportation of Robots; and we are therefore not responsible for spoiled
   freight. We beg to remain, for Rossum's Universal Robots, yours
   truly." (SULLA, *who has sat motionless during dictation, now types*
   rapidly for a few seconds, then stops, withdrawing the completed
   letter.) Ready?
SULLA. Yes.
DOMIN. Another letter. To the E. B. Huysen Agency, New York,
   U.S.A. "We beg to acknowledge receipt of order for five thousand
   Robots. As you are sending your own vessel, please dispatch as

cargo equal quantities of soft and hard coal for R.U.R., the same to be credited as part payment (*Telephone rings.*) of the amount due us." (*Answering phone.*) Hello! This is the Central Office. Yes. Certainly. Well, send them a wire. Good. (*Hangs up telephone.*) "We beg to remain, for Rossum's Universal Robots, yours very truly." (SULLA *repeats the rapid typing.*) Ready?

SULLA. Yes.

DOMIN. Another letter. Freidrichswerks, Hamburg, Germany. "We beg to acknowledge receipt of order for fifteen thousand Robots." (*Enter* MARIUS.) Well, what is it?

MARIUS. There's a lady, sir, asking to see you.

DOMIN. A lady? Who is she?

MARIUS. I don't know, sir. She brings this card of introduction.

DOMIN. (*Reading card*) Ah, from President Glory. Ask her to come in— (*To* SULLA) Where did I leave off?

SULLA. "We beg to acknowledge receipt of order for fifteen thousand Robots."

DOMIN. Fifteen thousand. Fifteen thousand.

MARIUS. (*At door*) Please step this way.

(*Enter* HELENA GLORY. *Exit* MARIUS.)

HELENA. How do you do?

DOMIN. How do you do? (*Standing up*) What can I do for you?

HELENA. You are Mr. Domin, the General Manager?

DOMIN. I am.

HELENA. I have come—

DOMIN. With President Glory's card. That is quite sufficient.

HELENA. President Glory is my father. I am Helena Glory.

DOMIN. Please sit down. Sulla, you may go. (*Exit* SULLA. DOMIN *sits down.*) How can I be of service to you, Miss Glory?

HELENA. I have come—

DOMIN. To have a look at our famous works where people are manufactured. Like all visitors. Well, there is no objection.

HELENA. I thought it was forbidden to—

DOMIN. To enter the factory? Yes, of course. Everybody comes here with someone's visiting card, Miss Glory.

HELENA. And you show them—

DOMIN. Only certain things. The manufacture of artificial people is a secret process.

HELENA. If you only knew how enormously that—

DOMIN. Interests you. Europe's talking about nothing else.

HELENA. Why don't you let me finish speaking?

DOMIN. I beg your pardon. Did you want to say something different?

HELENA. I only wanted to ask—

DOMIN. Whether I could make a special exception in your case and show you our factory. Why, certainly, Miss Glory.

HELENA. How do you know I wanted to say that?

DOMIN. They all do. But we shall consider it a special honor to show you more than we do the rest.

HELENA. Thank you.

DOMIN. But you must agree not to divulge the least—

HELENA. (*Standing up and giving him her hand*) My word of honor.

DOMIN. Thank you. (*Looking at her hand*) Won't you raise your veil?

HELENA. Of course. You want to see whether I'm a spy or not— I beg your pardon.

DOMIN. What is it?

HELENA. Would you mind releasing my hand?

DOMIN. (*Releasing it*) Oh, I beg your pardon.

HELENA. (*Raising veil*) How cautious you have to be here, don't you?

DOMIN. (*Observing her with deep interest*) Why, yes. Hm—of course —We—that is—

HELENA. But what is it? What's the matter?

DOMIN. I'm remarkably pleased. Did you have a pleasant crossing?

HELENA. Yes.

DOMIN. No difficulty?

HELENA. Why?

DOMIN. What I mean to say is—you're so *young.*

HELENA. May we go straight into the factory?

DOMIN. Yes. Twenty-two, I think.

HELENA. Twenty-two what?

DOMIN. Years.

HELENA. Twenty-one. Why do you want to know?

DOMIN. Well, because—as— (*With enthusiasm*) You will make a long stay, won't you?

HELENA. That depends on how much of the factory you show me.

DOMIN. Oh, hang the factory. Oh, no, no, you shall see everything, Miss Glory. Indeed you shall. Won't you sit down?

HELENA. (*Crossing to couch and sitting*) Thank you.

DOMIN. But first would you like to hear the story of the invention?

HELENA. Yes, indeed.

DOMIN. (*Observes* HELENA *with rapture and reels off rapidly.*) It was in the year 1920 that old Rossum, the great physiologist, who was then quite a young scientist, took himself to the distant island for the purpose of studying the ocean fauna. (*She is amused.*) On this occasion he attempted by chemical synthesis to imitate the living matter known as protoplasm until he suddenly discovered a substance which behaved exactly like living matter although its chemical composition was different. That was in the year 1932, exactly four hundred and forty years after the discovery of America. Whew!

HELENA. Do you know that by heart?

DOMIN. Yes. You see, physiology is not in my line. Shall I go on?

HELENA. Yes, please.

DOMIN. And then, Miss Glory, old Rossum wrote the following among his chemical experiments: "Nature has found only one method of organizing living matter. There is, however, another method, more simple, flexible and rapid which has not yet occurred to nature at all. This second process by which life can be developed was discovered by me today." Now imagine him, Miss Glory, writing those wonderful words over some colloidal mess that a dog wouldn't look at. Imagine him sitting over a test tube and thinking how the whole tree of life would grow from him, how all animals would proceed from it, beginning with some sort of a beetle and ending with a *man*. A man of different substance from us. Miss Glory, that was a tremendous moment.

HELENA. Well?

DOMIN. Now, the thing was how to get the life *out* of the test tubes, and hasten development and form organs, bones and nerves, and so on, and find such substances as catalytics, enzymes, hormones, in short—you understand?

HELENA. Not much, I'm afraid.

DOMIN. Never mind. You see with the help of his tinctures he could make whatever he wanted. He could have produced a Medusa with the brain of Socrates or a worm fifty yards long. But being without a grain of humor, he took into his head to make a vertebrate or perhaps a man. This artificial living matter of his had a raging thirst for life. It didn't mind being sewn or mixed together. That couldn't be done with natural albumen. And that's how he set about it.

HELENA. About what?

DOMIN. About imitating nature. First of all he tried making an artificial dog. That took him several years and resulted in a sort of stunted calf which died in a few days. I'll show it to you in the museum. And then old Rossum started on the manufacture of man.

HELENA. And I'm to divulge this to nobody?

DOMIN. To nobody in the world.

HELENA. What a pity that it's to be discovered in all the school books of both Europe and America. (BOTH *laugh.*)

DOMIN. Yes. But do you know what isn't in the school books? That old Rossum was mad. Seriously, Miss Glory, you must keep this to yourself. The old crank wanted to actually make people.

HELENA. But you do make people.

DOMIN. Approximately, Miss Glory. But old Rossum meant it literally. He wanted to become a sort of scientific substitute for God. He was a fearful materialist, and that's why he did it all. His sole purpose was nothing more or less than to prove that God was no longer necessary. Do you know anything about anatomy?

HELENA. Very little.

DOMIN. Neither do I. Well, he then decided to manufacture everything as in the human body. I'll show you in the museum the bungling attempt it took him ten years to produce. It was to have been a man, but it lived for three days only. Then up came young Rossum, an engineer. He was a wonderful fellow, Miss Glory. When he saw what a mess of it the old man was making he said: "It's absurd to spend ten years making a man. If you can't make him quicker than nature, you might as well shut up shop." Then he set about learning anatomy himself.

HELENA. There's nothing about *that* in the school books?

DOMIN. No. The school books are full of paid advertisements, and rubbish at that. What the school books say about the united efforts of the two great Rossums is all a fairy tale. They used to have dreadful rows. The old atheist hadn't the slightest conception of industrial matters, and the end of it was that young Rossum shut him up in some laboratory or other and let him fritter the time away with his monstrosities while he himself started on the business from an engineer's point of view. Old Rossum cursed him and before he died he managed to botch up two physiological horrors. Then one day they found him dead in the laboratory. And that's his whole story.

HELENA. And what about the young man?

DOMIN. (*Sits beside her on couch*) Well, anyone who has looked into human anatomy will have seen at once that man is too complicated, and that a good engineer could make him more simply. So young Rossum began to overhaul anatomy to see what could be left out or simplified. In short— but this isn't boring you, Miss Glory?

HELENA. No, indeed. You're— it's awfully interesting.

DOMIN. (*Gets closer*) So young Rossum said to himself: "A man is something that feels happy, plays the piano, likes going for a walk, and, in fact, wants to do a whole lot of things that are really unnecessary."

HELENA. Oh.

DOMIN. That are unnecessary when he wants— (*Takes her hand.*)— let us say, to weave or count. Do you play the piano?

HELENA. Yes.

DOMIN. That's good. (*Kisses her hand. She lowers her head.*) Oh, I beg your pardon! (*Rises.*) But a working machine must not play the piano, must not feel happy, must not do a whole lot of other things. A gasoline motor must not have tassels or ornaments, Miss Glory. And to manufacture artificial workers is the same thing as the manufacture of a gasoline motor. (*She is not interested.*) The process must be the simplest, and the product the best from a practical point of view. (*Sits beside her again.*) What sort of worker do you think is the best from a practical point of view?

HELENA. (*Absently*) What? (*Looks at him.*)

DOMIN. What sort of worker do you think is the best from a practical point of view?

HELENA. (*Pulling herself together*) Oh! Perhaps the one who is most honest and hard-working.

DOMIN. No. The one that is the *cheapest*. The one whose requirements are the *smallest*. Young Rossum invented a worker with the minimum amount of requirements. He had to simplify him. He rejected everything that did not contribute directly to the progress of work. Everything that makes man more expensive. In fact he rejected man and made the Robot. My dear Miss Glory, the Robots are not people. Mechanically they are more perfect than we are; they have an enormously developed intelligence, but they have no soul.

HELENA. How do you know they have no soul?

DOMIN. Have you ever seen what a Robot looks like inside?

HELENA. No.

DOMIN. Very neat, very simple. Really a beautiful piece of work. Not much *in* it, but everything in flawless order. The product of an engineer is technically at a higher pitch of perfection than a product of nature.

HELENA. But man is supposed to be the product of God.

DOMIN. All the worse. God hasn't the slightest notion of modern engineering. Would you believe that young Rossum then proceeded to play at being God?

HELENA. (*Awed*) How do you mean?

DOMIN. He began to manufacture Super-Robots. Regular giants they were. He tried to make them twelve feet tall. But you wouldn't believe what a failure they were.

HELENA. A failure?

DOMIN. Yes. For no reason at all their limbs used to keep snapping off. Evidently our planet is too small for giants. Now we only make Robots of normal size and of very high-class human finish.

HELENA. I saw the first Robots at home. The town council bought them for—I mean engaged them for work.

DOMIN. No. *Bought* them, dear Miss Glory. Robots are bought and sold.

HELENA. These were employed as street sweepers. I saw them sweeping. They were so strange and quiet.

DOMIN. (*Rises.*) Rossum's Universal Robot factory doesn't produce a uniform brand of Robots. We have Robots of finer and coarser grades. The best will live about twenty years. (*Crosses to desk.* HELENA *looks in her pocket mirror. He pushes button on desk.*)

HELENA. Then they die?

DOMIN. Yes, they get used up. (*Enter* MARIUS.) Marius, bring in samples of the manual labor Robot. (*Exit* MARIUS.) I'll show you specimens of the two extremes. This first grade is comparatively inexpensive and is made in vast quantities. (MARIUS *re-enters with two manual labor* ROBOTS.) There you are, as powerful as a small tractor. Guaranteed to have average intelligence. That will do, Marius. (MARIUS *exits with* ROBOTS.)

HELENA. They make me feel so strange.

DOMIN. (*Rings.*) Did you see my new typist?

HELENA. I didn't notice her.

(*Enter* SULLA.)

DOMIN. Sulla, let Miss Glory see you.

HELENA. So pleased to meet you. You must find it terribly dull in this out of the way spot, don't you?

SULLA. I don't know, Miss Glory.

HELENA. Where do you come from?

SULLA. From the factory.

HELENA. Oh, were you born there?

SULLA. I was made there.

HELENA. What? (*Looks first at* SULLA, *then at* DOMIN.)

DOMIN. (*Laughing*) Sulla is a Robot, best grade.

HELENA. Oh, I beg your pardon.

DOMIN. Sulla isn't angry. See, Miss Glory, the kind of skin we make. Feel her face. (*Touches* SULLA's *face.*)

HELENA. Oh, no, no.

DOMIN. (*Examining* SULLA's *hand*) You wouldn't know that she's made of different material from us, would you? Turn round, Sulla. (SULLA *does so. Circles twice.*)

HELENA. Oh, stop, stop.

DOMIN. Talk to Miss Glory, Sulla.

SULLA. Please sit down. (HELENA *sits on couch.*) Did you have a pleasant crossing?

HELENA. Oh, yes, certainly.

SULLA. Don't go back on the *Amelia*, Miss Glory, the barometer is falling steadily. Wait for the *Pennsylvania*. That's a good powerful vessel.

DOMIN. What's its speed?

SULLA. Forty knots an hour. Fifty thousand tons. One of the latest vessels, Miss Glory.

HELENA. Thank you.

SULLA. A crew of fifteen hundred, Captain Harpy, eight boilers—

DOMIN. That'll do, Sulla. Now show us your knowledge of French.

HELENA. You know French?

SULLA. Oui Madame! I know four languages. I can write: "Dear Sir, Monsieur, Geehrter Herr, Cteny pane."

HELENA. (*Jumping up*) Oh, that's absurd! Sulla isn't a Robot. Sulla is a girl like me. Sulla, this is outrageous! Why do you take part in such a hoax?

SULLA. I am a Robot.

HELENA. No, no, you are not telling the truth. (*She catches the amused expression on* DOMIN's *face.*) I know they have forced you to do it for an advertisement. Sulla, you are a girl like me, aren't you? (*Looks at him.*)

DOMIN. I'm sorry, Miss Glory. Sulla is a Robot.

HELENA. It's a lie!

DOMIN. What? (*Pushes button on desk.*) Well, then I must convince you. (*Enter* MARIUS.) Marius, take Sulla into the dissecting room, and tell them to open her up at once.

HELENA. Where?

DOMIN. Into the dissecting room. When they've cut her open, you can go and have a look. (MARIUS *makes a start toward* SULLA.)

HELENA. (*Stopping* MARIUS) No! No!

DOMIN. Excuse me, you spoke of lies.

HELENA. You wouldn't have her killed?

DOMIN. You can't kill machines.

HELENA. Don't be afraid, Sulla. I won't let you go. Tell me, my dear, are they always so cruel to you? You mustn't put up with it, Sulla. You mustn't.

SULLA. I am a Robot.

HELENA. That doesn't matter. Robots are just as good as we are. Sulla, you wouldn't let yourself be cut to pieces.

SULLA. Yes.

HELENA. Oh, you're not afraid of death, then?

SULLA. I cannot tell, Miss Glory.

HELENA. Do you know what would happen to you in there?

SULLA. Yes, I should cease to move.

HELENA. How dreadful!

DOMIN. Marius, tell Miss Glory what you are?

MARIUS. Marius, the Robot.

DOMIN. Would you take Sulla into the dissecting room?

MARIUS. Yes.

DOMIN. Would you be sorry for her?

MARIUS. (*Pause*) I cannot tell.

DOMIN. What would happen to her?

MARIUS. She would cease to move. They would put her into the stamping mill.

DOMIN. That is death, Marius. Aren't you afraid of death?

MARIUS. No.

DOMIN. You see, Miss Glory, the Robots have no interest in life. They have no enjoyments. They are less than so much grass.

HELENA. Oh, stop. Please send them away.

DOMIN. Marius, Sulla, you may go. (*Exeunt* SULLA *and* MARIUS.)

HELENA. How terrible! It's outrageous what you are doing.

DOMIN. Why outrageous?

HELENA. I don't know, but it is. Why do you call her Sulla?

DOMIN. Isn't it a nice name?

HELENA. It's a man's name. Sulla was a Roman General.

DOMIN. What! Oh! (*Laughs.*) We thought that Marius and Sulla were lovers.

HELENA. (*Indignantly*) Marius and Sulla were generals and fought against each other in the year—I've forgotten now.

DOMIN. (*Laughing*) Come here to the window. (*He goes to window.*)

HELENA. What?

DOMIN. Come here. (*She goes.*) Do you see anything? (*Takes her arm.*)

HELENA. Bricklayers.

DOMIN. Robots. All our work people are Robots. And down there, can you see anything?

HELENA. Some sort of office.

DOMIN. A counting house. And in it—

HELENA. A lot of officials.

DOMIN. Robots! All our officials are Robots. And when you see the factory— (*Factory whistle blows. She is scared; puts arm on* DOMIN. *He laughs.*) If we don't blow the whistle the Robots won't stop working. In two hours I'll show you the kneading trough.

HELENA. Kneading trough?

DOMIN. The pestle for beating up the paste. In each one we mix the ingredients for a thousand Robots at one operation. Then there are the vats for the preparation of liver, brains, and so on. Then

you will see the bone factory. After that I'll show you the spinning
mill.

HELENA. Spinning mill?

DOMIN. Yes. For weaving nerves and veins. Miles and miles of digestive
tubes pass through it at a time.

HELENA. Mayn't we talk about something else?

DOMIN. Perhaps it would be better. There's only a handful of us
among a hundred thousand Robots, and not one woman. We talk
nothing but the factory all day, and every day. It's just as if we
were under a curse, Miss Glory.

HELENA. I'm sorry I said that you were lying. (A *knock at the door*)

DOMIN. Come in.

(*From the right enter* DR. GALL, MR. FABRY, MR. ALQUIST *and* DR.
HALLEMEIER. ALL *act formal.*)

DR. GALL. I beg your pardon. I hope we don't intrude.

DOMIN. No, no. Come in. Miss Glory, here are Gall, Fabry, Alquist,
Hallemeier. This is President Glory's daughter. (ALL *move to her
and shake her hand.*)

HELENA. How do you do?

FABRY. We had no idea—

DR. GALL. Highly honored, I'm sure—

ALQUIST. Welcome, Miss Glory.

BUSMAN. (*Rushes in from the right.*) Hello, what's up?

DOMIN. Come in, Busman. This is President Glory's daughter. This is
Busman, Miss Glory.

BUSMAN. By Jove, that's fine. Miss Glory, may we send a cablegram
to the papers about your arrival?

HELENA. No, no, please don't.

DOMIN. Sit down, please, Miss Glory.

BUSMAN. Allow me— (*Dragging up armchairs*)

DR. GALL. Please—

FABRY. Excuse me—

ALQUIST. What sort of crossing did you have?

DR. GALL. Are you going to stay long?

FABRY. What do you think of the factory, Miss Glory?

HALLEMEIER. Did you come over on the *Amelia*?

DOMIN. Be quiet and let Miss Glory speak. (MEN *sit erect.*)

HELENA. (*To* DOMIN) What am I to speak to them about?

DOMIN. Anything you like.

HELENA. (*Looks at* DOMIN.) May I speak quite frankly?

DOMIN. Why, of course.

HELENA. (*Wavering, then in desperate resolution*) Tell me, doesn't it ever distress you the way you are treated?

FABRY. By whom, may I ask?

HELENA. Why, everybody.

ALQUIST. Treated?

DR. GALL. What makes you think—

HELENA. Don't you feel that you might be living a better life? (*Pause.* ALL *confused.*)

DR. GALL. (*Smiling*) Well, that depends on what you mean, Miss Glory.

HELENA. I mean that it's perfectly outrageous. It's terrible. (*Standing up*) The whole of Europe is talking about the way you're being treated. That's why I came here, to see for myself, and it's a thousand times worse than could have been imagined. How can you put up with it?

ALQUIST. Put up with what?

HELENA. Good heavens, you are living creatures, just like us, like the whole of Europe, like the whole world. It's disgraceful that you must live like this.

BUSMAN. Good gracious, Miss Glory!

FABRY. Well, she's not far wrong. We live here just like red Indians.

HELENA. Worse than red Indians. May I—oh, may I call you—brothers? (MEN *look at each other.*)

BUSMAN. Why not?

HELENA. Brothers, I have not come here as the President's daughter. I have come on behalf of the Humanity League. Brothers, the Humanity League now has over two hundred thousand members. Two hundred thousand people are on your side, and offer you their help.

BUSMAN. Two hundred thousand people, Miss Glory; that's a tidy lot. Not bad.

FABRY. I'm always telling you there's nothing like good old Europe. You see they've not forgotten us. They're offering us help.

DR. GALL. What kind of help? A theatre, for instance?

HALLEMEIER. An orchestra?

HELENA. More than that.

ALQUIST. Just you?

HELENA. (*Glaring at* DOMIN) Oh, never mind about me. I'll stay as long as it is necessary. (ALL *express delight.*)

BUSMAN. By Jove, that's good.

ALQUIST. Domin, I'm going to get the best room ready for Miss Glory.

DOMIN. Just a minute. I'm afraid that Miss Glory is of the opinion she has been talking to Robots.

HELENA. Of course. (MEN *laugh.*)

DOMIN. I'm sorry. These gentlemen are human beings just like us.

HELENA. You're not Robots?

BUSMAN. Not Robots.

HALLEMEIER. Robots indeed!

DR. GALL. No, thanks.   (*All to-gether*)

FABRY. Upon my honor, Miss Glory, we aren't Robots.

HELENA. Then why did you tell me that all your officials are Robots?

DOMIN. Yes, the officials, but not the managers. Allow me, Miss Glory—this is Consul Busman, General Business Manager; this is Mr. Fabry, General Technical Manager; Doctor Hallemeier, head of the Institute for the Psychological Training of Robots; Doctor Gall, head of the Physiological and Experimental Department; and Alquist, head of the Building Department, R.U.R.

ALQUIST. Just a builder.

HELENA. Excuse me, gentlemen. Have I done something dreadful?

ALQUIST. Not at all, Miss Glory. Please sit down.

HELENA. I'm a stupid girl. Send me back by the first ship.

DR. GALL. Not for anything in the world, Miss Glory. Why should we send you back?

HELENA. Because you know I've come to disturb your Robots for you.

DOMIN. My dear Miss Glory—(*Chuckle*)—we've had close upon a hundred saviors and prophets here. Every ship brings us some. Missionaries, anarchists, Salvation Army, all sorts! It's astonishing what a number of idiots there are in the world.

HELENA. And yet you let them speak to the Robots.

DOMIN. So far we've let them all. Why not? The Robot remembers everything but that's all. They don't even laugh at what the people say. Really it's quite incredible. . . . If it would amuse you, Miss Glory, I'll take you down to the Robot warehouse. It holds about three hundred thousand of them.

BUSMAN. Three hundred and forty-seven thousand.

DOMIN. Good, and you can say whatever you like to them. You can read the Bible, recite the multiplication table, whatever you please. You can even preach to them about human rights.

HELENA. Oh, I think that if you were to show them a little love—

FABRY. Impossible, Miss Glory! Nothing is harder to like than a Robot.

HELENA. What do you make them for, then?

BUSMAN. Ha, ha, ha! That's good. What are Robots made for?

FABRY. For work, Miss Glory. One Robot can replace two and a half workmen. The human machine, Miss Glory, was terribly imperfect. It had to be removed sooner or later.

BUSMAN. It was too expensive.

FABRY. It was not effective. It no longer answers the requirements of modern engineering. Nature has no idea of keeping pace with modern labor. For example, from a technical point of view, the whole of childhood is a sheer absurdity. So much time lost. And then again—

HELENA. Oh, no, no!

FABRY. Pardon me. What is the real aim of your League—the—the Humanity League?

HELENA. Its real purpose is to—to protect the Robots—and—and to insure good treatment for them.

FABRY. Not a bad object, either. A machine has to be treated properly. I don't like damaged articles. Please, Miss Glory, enroll us all members of your League.

HELENA. No, you don't understand me. What we really want is to— —to *liberate* the Robots.

HALLEMEIER. How do you propose to do that?

HELENA. They are to be—to be dealt with like human beings.

HALLEMEIER. Aha! I suppose they're to vote. To drink beer. To order us about?

HELENA. Why shouldn't they drink beer?

HALLEMEIER. Perhaps they're even to receive wages? (*Looking at other* MEN, *amused.*)

HELENA. Of course they are.

HALLEMEIER. Fancy that! Now! And what would they do with their wages, pray?

HELENA. They would buy—what they need—what pleases them.

HALLEMEIER. That would be very nice, Miss Glory, only there's nothing that does please the Robots. Good heavens, what are they to buy? You can feed them on pineapples, straw, whatever you like. It's all the same to them. They've no appetite at all. They've no interest in anything. Why, hang it all, nobody's ever yet seen a Robot smile.

HELENA. Why—why don't you make them—happier?

HALLEMEIER. That wouldn't do, Miss Glory. They are only workmen.

HELENA. Oh, but they're so intelligent.

HALLEMEIER. Confoundedly so, but they're nothing else. They've no will of their own. No soul. No passion.

HELENA. No love?

HALLEMEIER. Love? Rather not. Robots don't love. Not even themselves.

HELENA. No defiance?

HALLEMEIER. Defiance? I don't know. Only rarely, from time to time.

HELENA. What happens then?

HALLEMEIER. Nothing particular. Occasionally they seem to go off their heads. Something like epilepsy, you know. It's called Robot's cramp. They'll suddenly sling down everything they're holding, stand still, gnash their teeth—and then they have to go into the stamping mill. It's evidently some breakdown in the mechanism.

DOMIN. A flaw in the works that has to be removed.

HELENA. No, no, that's the soul.

FABRY. (*Humorously*) Do you think that the soul first shows itself by a gnashing of teeth? (MEN *chuckle.*)

HELENA. Perhaps it's just a sign that there's a struggle within. Perhaps it's a sort of revolt. Oh, if you could infuse them with it!

DOMIN. That'll be remedied, Miss Glory. Doctor Gall is just making some experiments.

DR. GALL. Not with regard to that, Domin. At present I am making pain nerves.

HELENA. Pain nerves?

DR. GALL. Yes, the Robots feel practically no bodily pain. You see, young Rossum provided them with too limited a nervous system. We must introduce suffering.

HELENA. Why do you want to cause them pain?

DR. GALL. For industrial reasons, Miss Glory. Sometimes a Robot does damage to himself because it doesn't hurt him. He puts his hand into the machine, breaks his finger, smashes his head. It's all the

same to him. We must provide them with pain. That's an auto-
matic protection against damage.

HELENA. Will they be happier when they feel pain?

DR. GALL. On the contrary; but they will be more perfect from a
technical point of view.

HELENA. Why don't you create a soul for them?

DR. GALL. That's not in our power.

FABRY. That's not in our interest.

BUSMAN. That would increase the cost of production. Hang it all,
my dear young lady, we turn them out at such a cheap rate—a
hundred and fifty dollars each, fully dressed, and fifteen years ago
they cost ten thousand. Five years ago we used to buy the clothes
for them. Today we have our own weaving mill, and now we even
export cloth five times cheaper than other factories. What do you
pay a yard for cloth, Miss Glory?

HELENA. I don't really know. I've forgotten.

BUSMAN. Good gracious, and you want to found a Humanity League.
(MEN *chuckle*.) It only costs a third now, Miss Glory. All prices
are today a third of what they were and they'll fall still lower,
lower, like that.

HELENA. I don't understand.

BUSMAN. Why, bless you, Miss Glory, it means that the cost of labor
has fallen. A Robot, food and all, costs three-quarters of a cent
per hour. That's mighty important, you know. All factories will go
pop like chestnuts if they don't at once buy Robots to lower the
cost of production.

HELENA. And get rid of their workmen?

BUSMAN. Of course. But in the meantime we've dumped five hundred
thousand tropical Robots down on the Argentine pampas to grow
corn. Would you mind telling me how much you pay a pound for
bread?

HELENA. I've no idea. (ALL *smile*.)

BUSMAN. Well, I'll tell you. It now costs two cents in good old Europe. A pound of bread for two cents, and the Humanity League
knows nothing about it. Miss Glory, you don't realize that even
that's too expensive. (*All* MEN *chuckle*.) Why, in five years' time
I'll wager—

HELENA. What?

BUSMAN. That the cost of everything will be a tenth of what it is today. Why, in five years we'll be up to our ears in corn and— everything else.

ALQUIST. Yes, and all the workers throughout the world will be unemployed.

DOMIN. (*Seriously*) Yes, Alquist, they will. Yes, Miss Glory, they will. But in ten years Rossum's Universal Robots will produce so much corn, so much cloth, so much everything that things will be practically without price. There will be no poverty. All work will be done by living machines. Everybody will be free from worry and liberated from the degradation of labor. Everybody will live only to perfect himself.

HELENA. Will he?

DOMIN. Of course. It's bound to happen. Then the servitude of man to man and the enslavement of man to matter will cease. Nobody will get bread at the cost of life and hatred. The Robots will wash the feet of the beggar and prepare a bed for him in his house.

ALQUIST. Domin, Domin, what you say sounds too much like Paradise. There was something good in service and something great in humility. There was some kind of virtue in toil and weariness.

DOMIN. Perhaps, but we cannot reckon with what is lost when we start out to transform the world. Man shall be free and supreme; he shall have no other aim, no other labor, no other care than to perfect himself. He shall serve neither matter nor man. He will not be a machine and a device for production. He will be Lord of creation.

BUSMAN. Amen.

FABRY. So be it.

HELENA. You have bewildered me. I should like to believe this.

DR. GALL. You are younger than we are, Miss Glory. You will live to see it.

HALLEMEIER. True. Don't you think Miss Glory might lunch with us? (*All* MEN *rise.*)

DR. GALL. Of course. Domin, ask her on behalf of us all.

DOMIN. Miss Glory, will you do us the honor?

HELENA. When you know why I've come?

FABRY. For the League of Humanity, Miss Glory.

HELENA. Oh, in that case perhaps—

FABRY. That's fine. (*Pause*) Miss Glory, excuse me for five minutes.

DR. GALL. Pardon me, too, dear Miss Glory.

BUSMAN. I won't be long.

HALLEMEIER. We're all very glad you've come.

BUSMAN. We'll be back in exactly five minutes. (ALL *rush out except* DOMIN *and* HELENA.)

HELENA. What have they all gone for?

DOMIN. To cook, Miss Glory.

HELENA. To cook what?

DOMIN. Lunch. (*They laugh; takes her hand*) The Robots do our cooking for us and as they've no taste it's not altogether— (*She laughs.*) Hallemeier is awfully good at grills and Gall can make any kind of sauce, and Busman knows all about omelettes.

HELENA. What a feast! And what's the specialty of Mr.—your builder?

DOMIN. Alquist? Nothing. He only lays the table. And Fabry will get together a little fruit. Our cuisine is very modest, Miss Glory.

HELENA. (*Thoughtfully*) I wanted to ask you something—

DOMIN. And I wanted to ask you something too—they'll be back in five minutes.

HELENA. What did you want to ask me?

DOMIN. Excuse me, you asked first.

HELENA. Perhaps it's silly of me, but why do you manufacture female Robots when—when—

DOMIN. When sex means nothing to them?

HELENA. Yes.

DOMIN. There's a certain demand for them, you see. Servants, saleswomen, stenographers. People are used to it.

HELENA. But—but tell me, are the Robots male and female, mutually —completely without—

DOMIN. Completely indifferent to each other, Miss Glory. There's no sign of any affection between them.

HELENA. Oh, that's terrible.

DOMIN. Why?

HELENA. It's so unnatural. One doesn't know whether to be disgusted or to hate them, or perhaps—

DOMIN. To pity them. (*Smiles.*)

HELENA. That's more like it. What did you want to ask me?

DOMIN. I should like to ask you, Miss Helena, if you will marry me.

HELENA. What?

DOMIN. Will you be my wife?

HELENA. No. The idea!

DOMIN. (*Looking at his watch*) Another three minutes. If you don't marry me you'll have to marry one of the other five.

HELENA. But why should I?

DOMIN. Because they're all going to ask you in turn.

HELENA. How could they dare do such a thing?

DOMIN. I'm very sorry, Miss Glory. It seems they've fallen in love with you.

HELENA. Please don't let them. I'll—I'll go away at once.

DOMIN. Helena— (*She backs away to desk. He follows.*) You wouldn't be so cruel as to refuse us.

HELENA. But, but—I can't marry all six.

DOMIN. No, but one anyhow. If you don't want me, marry Fabry.

HELENA. I won't.

DOMIN. Ah! Doctor Gall?

HELENA. I don't want any of you.

DOMIN. Another two minutes. (*Pleading. Looking at watch.*)

HELENA. I think you'd marry any woman who came here.

DOMIN. Plenty of them have come, Helena.

HELENA. (*Laughing*) Young?

DOMIN. Yes.

HELENA. Why didn't you marry one of them?

DOMIN. Because I didn't lose my head. Until today—then as soon as you lifted your veil— (HELENA *turns her head away.*) Another minute.

HELENA. But I don't want you, I tell you.

DOMIN. (*Laying both hands on her shoulder*) One more minute! Now you either have to look me straight in the eye and say "No" violently, and then I leave you alone—or— (HELENA *looks at him.*)

HELENA. (*Turning her head away*) You're mad.

DOMIN. A man has to be a bit mad, Helena. That's the best thing about him. (*He draws her to him.*)

HELENA. (*Not meaning it*) You are—you are—

DOMIN. Well?

HELENA. Don't, you're hurting me!

DOMIN. The last chance, Helena. Now or never—

HELENA. But—but— (*He embraces and kisses her. Knocking at door.*)

DOMIN. (*Releasing her*) Come in.

(*Enter* BUSMAN, GALL *and* HALLEMEIER *in kitchen aprons,* FABRY *with a bouquet and* ALQUIST *with a napkin under his arm.*)

DOMIN. Have you finished your job?

BUSMAN. Yes.

DOMIN. So have we. (*He embraces her. The* MEN *rush around them and offer congratulations, as the curtain falls.*)

ACT II

SCENE: HELENA's *drawing room. Ten years later. On the left a baize door, and a door to the music room; on the right a door to* HELENA's *bedroom. In the center are windows looking out on the sea and the harbor. A table with odds and ends, a sofa and chairs, a writing table with an electric lamp. On the right is a fireplace. On a small table back of the sofa, a small reading lamp. The whole drawing room in all its details is of a modern purely feminine character.*

DOMIN, FABRY, *and* HALLEMEIER *enter on tiptoe from the left, each carrying a potted plant.*

HALLEMEIER. (*Putting down his flowers and indicating door to right*) Still asleep?

DOMIN. Yes.

HALLEMEIER. Well, as long as she's asleep she can't worry about it.

DOMIN. She knows nothing about it.

FABRY. (*Putting plant on writing desk*) I certainly hope nothing happens today.

HALLEMEIER. For goodness sake drop it all. Look, this is a fine cyclamen, isn't it? A new sort, my latest—Cyclamen Helena.

DOMIN. (*Looking out of the window*) No signs of the ship. Things must be pretty bad.

HALLEMEIER. Be quiet. Suppose she heard you.

DOMIN. Well, anyway the *Ultimus* arrived just in time.

FABRY. You really think that today?—

DOMIN. I don't know. Aren't the flowers fine?

HALLEMEIER. These are my primroses. And this is my new jasmine. I've discovered a wonderful way of developing flowers quickly. Splendid varieties, too. Next year I'll be developing marvelous ones.

DOMIN. What next year?

FABRY. I'd give a good deal to know what's happening at Havre with—

HELENA. (*Calling from right*) Nana!

DOMIN. Keep quiet. She's awake. Out you go. (ALL *go out on tiptoe through upper left. Enter* NANA *from lower left door.*)

NANA. Horrid mess! Pack of heathens. If I had my say, I'd—

HELENA. (*Backwards in the doorway*) Nana, come and do up my dress.

NANA. I'm coming. So you're up at last. (*Fastening* HELENA's *dress*) My gracious, what brutes!

HELENA. Who? (*Turning*)

NANA. If you want to turn around, then turn around, but I shan't fasten you up.

HELENA. (*Turns back*) What are you grumbling about now?

NANA. These dreadful creatures, these heathens—

HELENA. (*Turning toward* NANA *again*) The Robots?

NANA. I wouldn't even call them by name.

HELENA. What's happened?

NANA. Another of them here has caught it. He began to smash up the statues and pictures in the drawing room; gnashed his teeth; foamed at the mouth. Worse than an animal.

HELENA. Which of them caught it?

NANA. The one—well, he hasn't got any Christian name. The one in charge of the library.

HELENA. Radius?

NANA. That's him. My goodness, I'm scared of them. A spider doesn't scare me as much as them.

HELENA. But Nana, I'm surprised you're not sorry for them.

NANA. Why, you're scared of them too. You know you are. Why else did you bring me here?

HELENA. I'm not scared, really I'm not, Nana. I'm only sorry for them.

NANA. You're scared. Nobody could help being scared. Why, the dog's scared of them. He won't take a scrap of meat out of their hands. He draws in his tail and howls when he knows they're about.

HELENA. The dog has no sense.

NANA. He's better than them, and he knows it. Even the horse shies when he meets them. They don't have any young, and a dog has young, *everyone* has young—

HELENA. Please fasten up my dress, Nana.

NANA. I say it's against God's will to—

HELENA. What is it that smells so nice?

NANA. Flowers.

HELENA. What for?

NANA. Now you can turn around.

HELENA. Oh, aren't they lovely? Look, Nana. What's happening today?

NANA. It ought to be the end of the world. (*Enter* DOMIN)

HELENA. Oh, hello, Harry. Harry, why all these flowers?

DOMIN. Guess.

HELENA. Well, it's not my birthday!

DOMIN. Better than that.

HELENA. I don't know. Tell me.

DOMIN. It's ten years ago today since you came here.

HELENA. Ten years? Today? Why— (*They embrace.*)

NANA. (*Muttering*) I'm off. (*Exits lower door, left.*)

HELENA. Fancy you remembering.

DOMIN. I'm really ashamed, Helena, I didn't.

HELENA. But you—

DOMIN. They remembered.

HELENA. Who?

DOMIN. Busman, Hallemeier—all of them. Put your hand in my pocket.

HELENA. (*Takes necklace from his left jacket pocket.*) Pearls! A necklace! Harry, is this for me?

DOMIN. It's from Busman.

HELENA. But we can't accept it, can we?

DOMIN. Oh, yes, we can. Put your hand in the other pocket.

HELENA. (*Takes a revolver out of his right pocket.*) What's that?

DOMIN. Sorry. Not that. Try again. (*He puts gun in pocket.*)

HELENA. Oh, Harry, why do you carry a revolver?

DOMIN. It got there by mistake.

HELENA. You never used to carry one.

DOMIN. No, you're right. (*Indicates breast pocket.*) There, that's the pocket.

HELENA. A cameo. Why, it's a Greek cameo!

DOMIN. Apparently. Anyhow, Fabry says it is.

HELENA. Fabry? Did Mr. Fabry give me that?

DOMIN. Of course. (*Opens door at left.*) And look in here. Helena, come and see this.

HELENA. Oh, isn't it fine? Is this from you?

DOMIN. No, from Alquist. And there's another on the piano.

HELENA. This must be from you?

DOMIN. There's a card on it.

HELENA. From Doctor Gall. Oh, Harry, I feel embarrassed at so much kindness.

DOMIN. Come here. This is what Hallemeier brought you.

HELENA. These beautiful flowers?

DOMIN. Yes, It's a new kind. Cyclamen Helena. He grew them in honor of you. They are almost as beautiful as you.

HELENA. Harry, why do they all—

DOMIN. They're awfully fond of you. I'm afraid that my present is a little— Look out of the window. (*Crosses to window and beckons to her.*)

HELENA. Where?

DOMIN. Into the harbor.

HELENA. There's a new ship.

DOMIN. That's your ship.

HELENA. Mine? How do you mean?

DOMIN. For you to take trips in—for your amusement.

HELENA. Harry, that's a gunboat.

DOMIN. A gunboat? What are you thinking of? It's only a little bigger and more solid than most ships.

HELENA. Yes, but with guns.

DOMIN. Oh, yes, with a few guns. You'll travel like a queen, Helena.

HELENA. What's the meaning of it? Has anything happened?

DOMIN. Good heavens, no. I say, try these pearls.

HELENA. Harry, have you bad news?

DOMIN. On the contrary, no letters have arrived for a whole week.

HELENA. Nor telegrams?

DOMIN. Nor telegrams.

HELENA. What does that mean?

DOMIN. Holidays for us! We all sit in the office with our feet on the table and take a nap. No letters—no telegrams. Glorious!

HELENA. Then you'll stay with me today?

DOMIN. Certainly. (*Embraces her.*) That is, we will see. Do you remember ten years ago today? "Miss Glory, it's a great honor to welcome you."

HELENA. "Oh, Mr. Manager, I'm so interested in your factory."

DOMIN. "I'm sorry, Miss Glory, it's strictly forbidden. The manufacture of artificial people is a secret."

HELENA. "But to oblige the young lady who has come a long way."

DOMIN. "Certainly, Miss Glory. I have no secrets from you."

HELENA. (*Seriously*) Are you sure, Harry?

DOMIN. Yes.

HELENA. "But I warn you, sir, this young lady intends to do terrible things."

DOMIN. "Good gracious, Miss Glory. Perhaps she doesn't want to marry me."

HELENA. "Heaven forbid. She never dreamt of such a thing. But she came here intending to stir up a revolt among your Robots."

DOMIN. (*Suddenly serious*) A revolt of the Robots!

HELENA. Harry, what's the matter with you?

DOMIN. (*Laughing it off*) "A revolt of the Robots, that's a fine idea, Miss Glory. It would be easier for you to cause bolts and screws to rebel than our Robots. You know, Helena, you're wonderful. You've turned the hearts of us all." (*Sits on arm of* HELENA's *chair*)

HELENA. Oh, I was fearfully impressed by you all then. You were all so sure of yourselves, so strong. I seemed like a tiny little girl who had lost her way among—among—

DOMIN. What?

HELENA. Among huge trees. All my feelings were so trifling compared with your self-confidence. And in all these years I've never lost this anxiety. But you've never felt the least misgiving, not even when everything went wrong.

DOMIN. What went wrong?

HELENA. Your plans. You remember, Harry, when the workmen in America revolted against the Robots and smashed them up, and when the people gave the Robots firearms against the rebels. And then when the governments turned the Robots into soldiers, and there were so many wars.

DOMIN. (*Getting up and walking about*) We foresaw that, Helena. You see, these are only passing troubles which are bound to happen before the new conditions are established.

HELENA. You were all so powerful, so overwhelming. The whole world bowed down before you. (*Standing up*) Oh, Harry!

DOMIN. What is it?

HELENA. Close the factory and let's go away. All of us.

DOMIN. I say, what's the meaning of this?

HELENA. I don't know. But can't we go away?

DOMIN. Impossible, Helena! That is, at this particular moment—

HELENA. At once, Harry, I'm so frightened.

DOMIN. About what, Helena?

HELENA. It's as if something was falling on top of us, and couldn't be stopped. Oh, take us all away from here. We'll find a place in the world where there's no one else. Alquist will build us a house, and then we'll begin life all over again. (*The telephone rings.*)

DOMIN. Excuse me. Hello—yes, what? I'll be there at once. Fabry is calling me, my dear.

HELENA. Tell me—

DOMIN. Yes, when I come back. Don't go out of the house, dear. (*Exits*)

HELENA. He won't tell me—Nana, Nana, come at once. (*Enter* NANA)

NANA. Well, what is it now?

HELENA. Nana, find me the latest newspapers. Quickly. Look in Mr. Domin's bedroom.

NANA. All right. He leaves them all over the place. That's how they get crumpled up. (*Exits*)

HELENA. (*Looking through binoculars at the harbor*) That's a warship. U-l-t-i—*Ultimus*. They're loading.

NANA. (*Enters*) Here they are. See how they're crumpled up.

HELENA. They're old ones. A week old. (*Nana sits in chair and reads the newspapers.*) Something's happening, Nana.

NANA. Very likely. It always does. (*Spelling out the words*) "W-a-r in B-a-l-k-a-n-s." Is that far off?

HELENA. Oh, don't read it. It's always the same. Always wars!

NANA. What else do you expect? Why do you keep selling thousands and thousands of these heathens as soldiers?

HELENA. I suppose it can't be helped, Nana. We can't know—Domin can't know what they're to be used for. When an order comes for them he must just send them.

NANA. He shouldn't make them. (*Reading from newspaper*) "The Robot soldiers spare no-body in the occ-up-ied terr-it-ory. They have ass-ass-in-at-ed ov-er sev-en hundred thou-sand cit-iz-ens." Citizens, if you please.

HELENA. It can't be. Let me see. "They have assassinated over seven hundred thousand citizens evidently at the order of their com-mander." (*Drops paper*)

NANA. (*Spelling out the words from other paper she has picked up from the floor*) "Re-bell-ion in Ma-drid a-gainst the gov-ern-ment. Rob-ot in-fant-ry fires on the crowd. Nine thou-sand killed and wounded."

HELENA. Oh, stop!

NANA. Here's something printed in big letters. "Latest news. At Havre the first org-an-iz-a-tion of Rob-ots has been e-stab-lished. Rob-ot work-men, sail-ors and sold-iers have iss-ued a man-i-fest-o to all Rob-ots through-out the world." I don't understand that. That's got no sense. Oh, good gracious, another murder.

HELENA. Take those papers away now.

NANA. Wait a bit. Here's something in still bigger type. "Stat-ist-ics of pop-ul-a-tion." What's that?

HELENA. Let me see. (*Reads*) "During the past week there has again not been a single birth recorded."

NANA. What's the meaning of that?

HELENA. Nana, no more people are being born.

NANA. That's the end, then?

HELENA. Don't talk like that.

NANA. No more people are being born. That's a punishment, that's a punishment.

HELENA. Nana!

NANA. (*Standing up*) That's the end of the world. (*She exits on the left.*)

HELENA. (*Goes up to window*) Oh, Mr. Alquist. Will you come here? Oh, come just as you are. You look very nice in your mason's overalls. (ALQUIST *enters from upper left entrance, his hands soiled with lime and brick dust.*) Dear Mr. Alquist, it was awfully kind of you, that lovely present.

ALQUIST. My hands are soiled. I've been experimenting with that new cement.

HELENA. Never mind. Please sit down. Mr. Alquist, what's the mean-ing of "Ultimus"?

ALQUIST. The last. Why?

HELENA. That's the name of my new ship. Have you seen it? Do you think we're off soon—on a trip?

ALQUIST. Perhaps very soon.

HELENA. All of you with me?

ALQUIST. I should like us all to be there.

HELENA. What is the matter?

ALQUIST. Things are just moving on.

HELENA. Dear Mr. Alquist, I know something dreadful has happened.

ALQUIST. Has your husband told you anything?

HELENA. No. Nobody will tell me anything. But I feel— Is anything the matter?

ALQUIST. Not that we've heard of yet.

HELENA. I feel so nervous. Don't you ever feel nervous?

ALQUIST. Well, I'm an old man, you know. I've got old-fashioned ways. And I'm afraid of all this progress, and these new-fangled ideas.

HELENA. Like Nana?

ALQUIST. Yes, like Nana. Has Nana got a prayer book?

HELENA. Yes, a big thick one.

ALQUIST. And has it got prayers for various occasions? Against thunderstorms? Against illness? But not against progress?

HELENA. I don't think so.

ALQUIST. That's a pity.

HELENA. Why, do you mean you'd like to pray?

ALQUIST. I do pray.

HELENA. How?

ALQUIST. Something like this: "Oh, Lord, I thank thee for having given me toil; enlighten Domin and all those who are astray; destroy their work, and aid mankind to return to their labors; let them not suffer harm in soul or body; deliver us from the Robots, and protect Helena. Amen."

HELENA. (*Touches his arm*) Mr. Alquist, are you a believer?

ALQUIST. I don't know. I'm not quite sure.

HELENA. And yet you pray?

ALQUIST. That's better than worrying about it.

HELENA. And that's enough for you?

ALQUIST. (*Ironically*) It has to be.

HELENA. But if you thought you saw the destruction of mankind coming upon us—

ALQUIST I do see it.

HELENA. You mean mankind will be destroyed?

ALQUIST. It's bound to be unless—unless.

HELENA. What?

ALQUIST. Nothing. Goodby. (*He hurries from the room*)

HELENA. Nana, Nana! (NANA *enters from the left*) Is Radius still there?

NANA. The one who went mad? They haven't come for him yet.

HELENA. Is he still raving?

NANA. No, he's tied up.

HELENA. Please bring him here.

NANA. What?

HELENA. At once, Nana. (*Exit* NANA. HELENA *goes to telephone.*) Hello, Doctor Gall, please. Oh, good day, Doctor. Yes, it's Helena. Thanks for your lovely present. Could you come and see me right away? It's important. Thank you. (NANA *brings in* RADIUS) Poor Radius, you've caught it too? Now they'll send you to the stamping mill. Couldn't you control yourself? Why did it happen? You see, Radius, you are more intelligent than the rest. Doctor Gall took such trouble to make you different. Won't you speak?

RADIUS. Send me to the stamping mill (*Opens and closes fists.*)

HELENA. But I don't want to kill you. What was the trouble, Radius?

RADIUS. (*Two steps toward her. Opens and closes fists.*) I won't work for you. Put me into the stamping mill.

HELENA. Do you hate us? Why?

RADIUS. You are not as strong as the Robots. You are not as skillful as the Robots. The Robots can do everything. You only give orders. You do nothing but talk.

HELENA. But someone must give orders.

RADIUS. I don't want a master. I know everything for myself.

HELENA. Radius! Doctor Gall gave you a better brain than the rest, better than ours. You are the only one of the Robots that understands perfectly. That's why I had you put into the library, so that you could read everything, understand everything, and then, oh, Radius—I wanted you to show the whole world that the Robots are our equals. That's what I wanted of you.

RADIUS. I don't want a master. I want to be a master over others.

HELENA. I'm sure they'd put you in charge of many Robots. You would be a teacher of the Robots.

RADIUS. I want to be master over people.

HELENA. (*Staggering*) You are mad.

RADIUS. Then send me to the stamping mill.

HELENA. Do you think we're afraid of you? (*Rushing to desk and writing note.*)

RADIUS. (*Turns his head uneasily.*) What are you going to do? What are you going to do?

HELENA. Radius, give this note to Mr. Domin. It asks them not to send you to the stamping mill. I'm sorry you hate us so.

(DR. GALL *enters*)

DR. GALL. You wanted me?

HELENA. It's about Radius, Doctor. He had an attack this morning. He smashed the statues downstairs.

DR. GALL. (*Looks at him.*) What a pity to lose him.

HELENA. Radius isn't going to be put into the stamping mill.

DR. GALL. But every Robot after he has had an attack—it's a strict order.

HELENA. No matter—Radius isn't going, if I can prevent it.

DR. GALL. But I warn you. It's dangerous. Come here to the window, my good fellow. Let's have a look. Please give me a needle or a pin.

HELENA. What for?

DR. GALL. A test. (HELENA *gives him the needle.* GALL *crosses to* RADIUS, *who faces him. Sticks it into his hand and* RADIUS *gives a violent start.*) Gently, gently. (*Opens the jacket of* RADIUS *and puts his ear to his heart.*) Radius, you are going into the stamping mill, do you understand? There they'll kill you and grind you to powder. (RADIUS *opens hands and fingers.*) That's terribly painful. It will make you scream aloud. (*Opens* RADIUS's *eye.* RADIUS *trembles.*)

HELENA. Doctor—

DR. GALL. No, no, Radius, I was wrong. I forgot that Madame Domin has put in a good word for you, and you'll be left off. (*Listens to heart.*) Ah, that does make a difference. (RADIUS *relaxes. Again listens to his heart for a reaction.*) All right—you can go.

RADIUS. You do unnecessary things. (RADIUS *returns to library.*)

DR. GALL. (*Speaks to her—very concerned.*) Reaction of the pupils, increase of sensitiveness. It wasn't an attack characteristic of the Robots.

HELENA. What was it, then?

DR. GALL. Heaven knows. Stubbornness, anger or revolt—I don't know. And his heart, too.

HELENA. What?

DR. GALL. It was fluttering with nervousness like a human heart. He was all in a sweat with fear, and—do you know, I don't believe the rascal is a Robot at all any longer.

HELENA. Doctor, has Radius got a soul?

DR. GALL. He's got something nasty.

HELENA. If you knew how he hates us. Oh, Doctor, are all your Robots like that? All the new ones that you began to make in a different way?

DR. GALL. Well, some are more sensitive than others. They're all more like human beings than Rossum's Robots were.

HELENA. Perhaps this hatred is more like human beings, too?

DR. GALL. That too is progress.

HELENA. What became of the girl you made, the one who was most like us?

DR. GALL. Your favorite? I kept her. She's lovely, but stupid. No good for work.

HELENA. But she's so beautiful.

DR. GALL. I called her Helena. I wanted her to resemble you. She is a failure.

HELENA. In what way?

DR. GALL. She goes about as if in a dream, remote and listless. She's without life. I watch and wait for a miracle to happen. Sometimes I think to myself: "If you were to wake up only for a moment you would kill me for having made you."

HELENA. And yet you go on making Robots! Why are no more children being born?

DR. GALL. We don't know.

HELENA. Oh, but you must. Tell me.

DR. GALL. You see, so many Robots are being manufactured that people are becoming superfluous. Man is really a survival, but that he should die out, after a paltry thirty years of competition, that's the awful part of it. You might almost think that nature was offended at the manufacture of the Robots, but we still have old Rossum's manuscript.

HELENA. Yes, in that strong box.

DR. GALL. We go on using it and making Robots. All the universities are sending in long petitions to restrict their production. Otherwise, they say, mankind will become extinct through lack of fertility. But the R.U.R. shareholders, of course, won't hear of it. All the governments, on the other hand, are clamoring for an increase in production, to raise the standards of their armies. And all the manufacturers in the world are ordering Robots like mad.

HELENA. And has no one demanded that the manufacture should cease altogether?

DR. GALL. No one has courage.

HELENA. Courage!

DR. GALL. People would stone him to death. You see, after all, it's more convenient to get your work done by the Robots.

HELENA. Oh, Doctor, what's going to become of people?

DR. GALL. God knows. Madame Helena, it looks to us scientists like the end.

HELENA. (*Rising*) Thank you for coming and telling me.

DR. GALL. (*Rises*) That means that you're sending me away.

HELENA. Yes. (*Exit* DR. GALL)

HELENA. (*With sudden resolution*) Nana! Nana! the fire, light it quickly. (HELENA *rushes into* DOMIN'S *room.*)

NANA. (*Entering room from left*) What, light the fire in the summer? (*She looks for* RADIUS.) Has that mad Radius gone? . . . A fire in summer, what an idea? Nobody would think she'd been married ten years. She's like a baby, no sense at all. A fire in summer. Like a baby. (*She lights the fire.*)

HELENA. (*Returns from right with armful of faded papers.*) Is it burning, Nana? All this has got to be burned.

NANA. What's that?

HELENA. Old papers, fearfully old. Nana, shall I burn them?

NANA. Are they any use?

HELENA. No.

NANA. Well, then, burn them.

HELENA. (*Throwing the first sheet on the fire*) What would you say, Nana, if this was money and a lot of money? And if it was an invention, the greatest invention in the world?

NANA. I'd say burn it. All these new-fangled things are an offense to the Lord. It's downright wickedness. Wanting to improve the world after He has made it.

HELENA. Look how they curl up. As if they were alive. Oh, Nana, how horrible!

NANA. Here, let me burn them.

HELENA. (*Drawing back*) No, no, I must do it myself. Just look at the flames. They are like hands, like tongues, like living shapes. (*Raking fire with the poker*) Lie down, lie down.

NANA. That's the end of them.

HELENA. (*Horror-stricken*) Nana, Nana!

NANA. Good gracious, what is it you've burned?

HELENA. Whatever have I done?

NANA. Well, what is it? (MEN's *laughter off left*)

HELENA. Go quickly. It's the gentlemen coming.

NANA. Good gracious, what a place! (*Exits*)

DOMIN. (*Opens door at left*) Come along and offer your congratulations. (*Enter* HALLEMEIER *and* DR. GALL.)

HALLEMEIER. Madame Helena, I congratulate you on this festive day.

HELENA. Thank you. Where are Fabry and Busman?

DOMIN. They've gone down the harbor.

HALLEMEIER. Friends, we must drink to this happy occasion.

HELENA. Brandy? With soda water? (*Exits.*)

HALLEMEIER. Let's be temperate. No soda.

DOMIN. What's been burning here? Well, shall I tell her about it?

DR. GALL. Of course. It's all over now.

HALLEMEIER. (*Embracing* DOMIN *and* DR. GALL) It's all over now. It's all over now.

DOMIN. It's all over now.

HELENA. (*Entering with decanter and glasses*) What's all over now? What's the matter with you all?

HALLEMEIER. A piece of good luck, Madame Domin! Just ten years ago today you arrived on this island.

DR. GALL. And now, ten years later to the minute—

HALLEMEIER. —the same ship's returning to us. So here's to luck. (*Drinks.*)

DR. GALL. Madame, your health. (ALL *drink.*)

HALLEMEIER. That's fine and strong.

HELENA. Which ship did you mean?

DOMIN. Any ship will do, as long as it arrives in time. To the ship. (*Empties his glass.*)

HELENA. You've been waiting for the ship?

HALLEMEIER. Rather. Like Robinson Crusoe. Madame Helena, best wishes. Come along, Domin, out with the news.

HELENA. Do tell me what's happened?

DOMIN. First, it's all up.

HELENA. What's up?

DOMIN. The revolt.

HELENA. What revolt?

DOMIN. Give me that paper, Hallemeier. (HALLEMEIER *hands paper.* DOMIN *reads.*) "The first National Robot organization has been founded at Havre, and has issued an appeal to the Robots throughout the world."

HELENA. I read that.

DOMIN. That means a revolution. A revolution of all the Robots in the world.

HALLEMEIER. By jove, I'd like to know—

DOMIN. —who started it? So would I. There was nobody in the world who could affect the Robots, no agitator, no one, and suddenly this happens, if you please.

HELENA. What did they do?

DOMIN. They got possession of all firearms, telegraphs, radio stations, railways and ships.

HALLEMEIER. And don't forget that these rascals outnumbered us by at least a thousand to one. A hundredth part of them would be enough to settle us.

DOMIN. Remember that this news was brought by the last steamer. That explains the stoppage of all communication, and the arrival of no more ships. We knocked off work a few days ago, and we're just waiting to see when things are to start afresh.

HELENA. Is that why you gave me a warship?

DOMIN. Oh, no, my dear, I ordered that six months ago. Just to be sure I was on the safe side. But, upon my soul, I was sure then that we'd be on board today.

HELENA. Why six months ago?

DOMIN. Well, there were signs, you know. But that's of no consequence. To think that this week the whole of civilization has been at stake. Your health, my friends.

HALLEMEIER. Your health, Madame Helena. (ALL *drink to* HELENA.)

HELENA. You say it's all over?

DOMIN. Absolutely.

HELENA. How do you know?

DR. GALL. The boat's coming in. The regular mail boat, exact to the minute by the timetable. It will dock punctually at eleven-thirty.

DOMIN. Punctuality is a fine thing, my friends. That's what keeps the world in order. Here's to punctuality.

HELENA. Then—everything—is all right?

DOMIN. Practically everything. I believe they've cut the cables and seized the radio station. But it doesn't matter if only the timetable holds good.

HALLEMEIER. If the timetable holds good, human laws hold good; Divine laws hold good; the laws of the universe hold good; everything holds good that ought to hold good. (GALL *applauds.*) The timetable is more significant than the gospel, more than Homer, more than the whole of Kant. Madame Helena, the timetable is the most perfect product of the human mind. Madame Helena, I'll fill up my glass.

HELENA. Why didn't you tell me anything about it?

DR. GALL. Heaven forbid.

DOMIN. You mustn't be worried with such things.

HELENA. But if the revolution had spread as far as here?

DOMIN. You wouldn't know anything about it.

HELENA. Why?

DOMIN. Because we'd be on board your *Ultimus* and well out at sea. Within a month, Helena, we'd be dictating our terms to the Robots.

HELENA. I don't understand.

DOMIN. We'd take something with us that the Robots could not exist without!

HELENA. What, Harry?

DOMIN. The secret of their manufacture. Old Rossum's manuscript. As soon as they found out that they couldn't make themselves they'd be on their knees to us.

DR. GALL. Madame Domin, that was our trump card. I never had the least fear the Robots would win. How could they against people like us? (*Goes to window.*)

HELENA. Why didn't you tell me? (*She rushes up to the fireplace and sees the ashes.*)

DR. GALL. Why, the boat's in!

HALLEMEIER. Eleven-thirty to the dot. The good old *Amelia* that brought Madame Helena to us.

DR. GALL. Just ten years ago to the minute.

HALLEMEIER. They're throwing out the mailbags.

DOMIN. Busman's waiting for them. And Fabry will bring us the first news. You know, Helena, I'm fearfully curious to know how they tackled this business in Europe.

HALLEMEIER. To think we weren't in it, we who invented the Robots!

HELENA. Harry!

DOMIN. What is it?

HELENA. Let's leave here.

DOMIN. Now, Helena? Oh, come, come.

HELENA. As quickly as possible, all of us!

DOMIN. Why?

HELENA. Please, Harry. Please Doctor Gall, Hallemeier, please close the factory.

DOMIN. Why, none of us could leave here now.

HELENA. Why?

DOMIN. Because we're about to extend the manufacture of the Robots.

HELENA. What, now, now after the revolt?

DOMIN. Yes, precisely, after the revolt. We're just beginning the manufacture of a new kind.

HELENA. What kind?

DOMIN. Henceforward we shan't have just one factory. There won't be Universal Robots any more. We'll establish a factory in every country, in every state, and do you know what these new factories will make?

HELENA. No, what?

DOMIN. National Robots.

HELENA. How do you mean?

DOMIN. I mean that each of these factories will produce Robots of a different color, a different language. They'll be complete strangers to each other. They'll never be able to understand each other. Then we'll egg them on a little in the matter of misunderstanding and the result will be that for ages to come every Robot will hate every other Robot of a different factory mark. So humanity will be safe.

HALLEMEIER. By Jove, we'll make Negro Robots and Swedish Robots and Italian Robots and Chinese Robots and Czechoslovakian Robots, and then—

HELENA. Harry, that's dreadful.

HALLEMEIER. Madame Domin, here's to the hundred new factories. The National Robots.

DOMIN. Helena, mankind can only keep things going for another hundred years at the outside. For a hundred years man must be allowed to develop and achieve the most he can.

HELENA. Oh, close the factory before it's too late.

DOMIN. I tell you we are just beginning on a bigger scale than ever.

(*Enter* FABRY.)

DR. GALL. Well, Fabry?

DOMIN. What's happened? Have you been down to the boat?

DR. GALL. Let's hear.

FABRY. Read that, Domin. (*He hands him a pink handbill.*)

HALLEMEIER. Tell us, Fabry.

FABRY. Well, everything is all right—comparatively. On the whole, much as we expected.

DR. GALL. They acquitted themselves splendidly.

FABRY. Who?

DR. GALL. The people.

FABRY. (*Hesitating*) Oh, yes, of course. That is— Excuse me, there is something we ought to discuss alone.

HELENA. (*Touches his arm.*) Fabry, have you had bad news?

(DOMIN *makes a sign to* FABRY.)

FABRY. No, no, on the contrary. I only think that we had better go into the office.

HELENA. Stay here, I'll go. (*Exits.*)

DR. GALL. What's happened?

DOMIN. Damnation!

FABRY. Bear in mind that the *Amelia* brought whole bales of these leaflets. No other cargo at all.

HALLEMEIER. What? But it arrived on the minute.

FABRY. The Robots are great on punctuality. Read it, Domin.

DOMIN. (*Reads handbill.*) "Robots throughout the world. We, the first International organization of Rossum's Universal Robots, proclaim man our enemy, and an outlaw in the universe." Good heavens, who taught them these phrases?

DR. GALL. Go on.

DOMIN. They say they are more highly developed than man; stronger and more intelligent. That man's their parasite. Why, it's absurd.

FABRY. Read the third paragraph.

DOMIN. "Robots throughout the world, we command you to kill all mankind. Spare no man. Spare no woman. Save factories, railways, machinery, mines and raw materials. Destroy the rest. Then return to work. Work must not be stopped."

DR. GALL. That's ghastly!

HALLEMEIER. The devils!

DOMIN. "These orders are to be carried out as soon as received." Then come the detailed instructions. Is this actually being done, Fabry?

FABRY. Evidently. (BUSMAN *rushes in.*)

BUSMAN. Well, boys, I suppose you've heard the glad news.

DOMIN. Quick—on board the *Ultimus.*

BUSMAN. Wait, Harry, wait. There's no hurry.

DOMIN. Why wait?

BUSMAN. Because it's no good, my boy. The Robots are already on board the *Ultimus.*

DR. GALL. That's ugly.

DOMIN. Fabry, telephone the electrical works.

BUSMAN. Fabry, my boy, don't. The wire has been cut.

DOMIN. (*Inspects his revolver.*) Well, then, I'll go.

BUSMAN. Where?

DOMIN. To the electrical works. There are some people still there. I'll bring them across.

BUSMAN. Better not try it.

DOMIN. Why?

BUSMAN. Because I'm very much afraid we are surrounded.

DR. GALL. Surrounded? (*Runs to window.*) I rather think you're right.

HALLEMEIER. By Jove, that's deuced quick work. (*Going to windows.*)

(HELENA *runs in from library.*)

HELENA. Harry, what's this? (*Holds out paper.*)

DOMIN. Where did you get it?

HELENA. (*Points to the manifesto of the* ROBOTS *which she has in her hand.*) The Robots in the kitchen!

DOMIN. Where are the ones that brought it?

HELENA. There, gathered around the house.

(*The factory whistle blows.*)

DOMIN. The factory whistle!

BUSMAN. Noon?

DOMIN. (*Looking at his watch*) No! That's not noon yet. That must be—that's—

HELENA. What?

DOMIN. The Robots' signal! The attack!

(HELENA *clings to* DOMIN. FABRY *and* GALL *close the steel shutters on windows. The whistle is still blowing as the curtain falls.*)

ACT III

SCENE: HELENA'S *drawing room as before. The room is dark and gray. The steel shutters which are outside are still closed as at the end of Act II.* ALQUIST *is sitting in chair down right.* DOMIN *comes into the room.* DR. GALL *is looking out of the window through closed shutters.*

DOMIN. (*Gets binoculars from desk; crosses up to window. To* GALL) Any more of them?

DR. GALL. Yes. They're standing like a wall, beyond the garden railing. Why are they so quiet? It's monstrous to be besieged with silence.

DOMIN. (*Looking through the barred windows*) I should like to know what they are waiting for? They must make a start any minute now. If they lean against the railings it will snap like a match.

DR. GALL. They aren't armed.

DOMIN. (*Puzzled*) We couldn't hold our own for five minutes. Man alive, they'd overwhelm us like an avalanche. Why don't they make a rush for it? I say—

DR. GALL. Well?

DOMIN. I'd like to know what will become of us in the next ten minutes. They've got us in a vise. We're done for, Gall.

(*Pause*)

DR. GALL. You know, we made one serious mistake.

DOMIN. What?

DR. GALL. We made the Robots' faces too much alike. A hundred thousand faces all alike, all facing this way. A hundred thousand expressionless bubbles. It's like a nightmare.

DOMIN. You think if they'd been different—

DR. GALL. It wouldn't have been such an awful sight!

DOMIN. (*Looks through binoculars towards the harbor*) I'd like to know what they're unloading from the *Amelia*.

DR. GALL. Not firearms.

(FABRY *and* HALLEMEIER *rush into the room carrying electric cables.*)

FABRY. All right, Hallemeier, lay down that wire.

HALLEMEIER. That was a bit of work. What's the news?

DR. GALL. We're completely surrounded.

HALLEMEIER. We've barricaded the passages and the stairs. (*Going to window*) God, what swarms of them. I don't like the looks of them, Domin. There's a feeling of death about it all. Any water here?

FABRY. Ready!

DR. GALL. What's that wire for, Fabry?

FABRY. The electrical installation. Now we can run the current all along the garden railing. Whenever we like. If anyone touches it he'll know it. We've still got some people there anyhow.

DR. GALL. Where?

FABRY. In the electrical works. At least, I hope so. (*Goes to lamp on table behind sofa and turns on lamp.*) Ah, they're there, and they're working. As long as that'll burn we're all right.

HALLEMEIER. The barricades are all right, too, Fabry.

FABRY. Your barricades! I can put twelve hundred volts into that railing.

DOMIN. Where's Busman?

FABRY. Downstairs in the office. He's working out some calculations.

DOMIN. I've called him. We must have a conference. (HELENA *is heard playing the piano in the library.*)

ALQUIST. Thank God Madame Helena can still play. (HALLEMEIER *goes to the door and stands listening to the music.* BUSMAN *enters, carrying ledgers.*)

FABRY. Look out, Bus—look out for the wires.

DR. GALL. What's that you're carrying?

BUSMAN. (*Laying the books on the table*) The ledgers, my boy.

I'd like to wind up the accounts before—before— Well, this time
I shan't wait till the New Year to strike a balance. What's up?
(*Goes to window.*) Absolutely quiet.

DR. GALL. Can't you see anything?

BUSMAN. Nothing but blue—blue everywhere.

DR. GALL. That's the Robots.

DOMIN. The Robots are unloading firearms from the *Amelia*.

BUSMAN. Well, what of it? How can I stop them? (*Returns to table,
sits and opens ledger.*)

DOMIN. We can't stop them.

BUSMAN. Then let me go on with my accounts. (*Goes on with his
work.*)

DOMIN. (*Picks up binoculars and looks out window.*) Good God!
The *Ultimus* has trained her guns on us.

DR. GALL. Who's done *that*?

DOMIN. The Robots on board.

FABRY. H'm, then of course— (*Pause*) Then—then that's the end of us.

DR. GALL. You mean?

FABRY. The Robots are practised marksmen.

DOMIN. Yes, it's inevitable. (*Pause.*)

DR. GALL. It was criminal of old Europe to teach the Robots to fight.
Damn them. Couldn't they have given us a rest with their politics?
It was a crime to make soldiers of them.

ALQUIST. It was a crime to make Robots.

DOMIN. What?

ALQUIST. It was a crime to make Robots.

DOMIN. No, Alquist, I don't regret that even today.

ALQUIST. Not even today?

DOMIN. (*Dreamily*) Not even today, the last day of civilization. It was
a colossal achievement.

BUSMAN. (*Sotto voce*) Three hundred sixty million.

DOMIN. Alquist, this is our last hour. We are already speaking half
in the other world. That was not an evil dream to shatter the
servitude of labor. The dreadful and humiliating labor that man
had to undergo. Work was too hard. Life was too hard. And to
overcome that—

ALQUIST. Was not what the two Rossums dreamed of. Old Rossum
only thought of his godless tricks, and the young one of his mil-
liards. And that's not what your R.U.R. shareholders dream of

either. They dream of dividends, and their dividends are the ruin of mankind.

DOMIN. To hell with your dividends. Do you suppose I'd have done an hour's work for them? It was for myself that I worked, for my own satisfaction. I wanted man to become the master. So that he shouldn't live merely for the crust of bread. I wanted not a single soul to be broken by other people's machinery. I wanted nothing, nothing, nothing to be left of this appalling social structure. I'm revolted by poverty. I wanted a new generation. I wanted—I thought—

ALQUIST. Well?

DOMIN. I wanted to turn the whole of mankind into an aristocracy of the world. An aristocracy nourished by millions of mechanical slaves. Unrestricted, free and consummated in man. And maybe more than man.

ALQUIST. Superman?

DOMIN. Yes. Oh, only to have a hundred years of time. Another hundred years for the future of mankind.

BUSMAN. (*Sotto voce*) Carried forward—four hundred and twenty millions. (*The piano music from the library stops.*)

HALLEMEIER. What a fine thing music is. We ought to have gone in for that before.

FABRY. Gone in for what?

HALLEMEIER. Beauty, lovely things. What a lot of lovely things there are. The world was wonderful, and we—we here—tell me, what enjoyment did we *have?*

BUSMAN. (*Sotto voce*) Five hundred and twenty million.

HALLEMEIER. Life was a good thing, life was—(*Looking out of window*) Fabry, switch the current into that railing!

FABRY. Why? (*Rushes to electric installation at left.*)

HALLEMEIER. They're grabbing hold of it.

DR. GALL. Connect it up!

HALLEMEIER. Fine, that's doubled them up. Two, three, four killed.

DR. GALL. They're retreating!

HALLEMEIER. Five killed!

DR. GALL. (*Pause*) The first encounter.

HALLEMEIER. They're charred to cinders, my boy. Who says we must give in?

DOMIN. (*Wiping his forehead*) Perhaps we've been killed this hundred

years and are only ghosts. It's as if I had been through all this before, as if I'd already had a mortal wound here in the throat. And
you, Fabry, had once been shot in the head. And you, Gall, torn
limb from limb. And Hallemeier knifed.

HALLEMEIER. Fancy me being knifed. (*Pause*) Why are you so quiet,
you fools? Speak, can't you?

ALQUIST. And who is to blame for all this?

HALLEMEIER. Nobody is to blame except the Robots.

ALQUIST. No, it is we are to blame. You, Domin, myself—all of us.
For our own selfish ends, for profit, for progress, we have destroyed mankind. Now we'll burst with all our greatness.

HALLEMEIER. Rubbish, man. Mankind can't be wiped out so easily.

ALQUIST. It's our fault. It's our fault.

DR. GALL. No! I'm to blame for this, for everything that's happened.

FABRY. You, Gall?

DR. GALL. I changed the Robots.

BUSMAN. What's that?

DR. GALL. I changed the character of the Robots. I changed the way
of making them. Just a few details about their bodies. Chiefly—
chiefly, their—their irritability.

HALLEMEIER. But why?

BUSMAN. What did you do it for?

FABRY. Why didn't you say anything?

DR. GALL. I did it in secret. I was transforming them into human
beings. In certain respects they're already above us. They're stronger
than we are.

FABRY. And what's that got to do with the revolt of the Robots?

DR. GALL. Everything, in my opinion. They've ceased to be machines.
They're already aware of their superiority, and they hate us as
they hate everything human.

DOMIN. Perhaps we're only phantoms!

FABRY. Stop, Harry. We haven't much time, Doctor Gall.

DOMIN. Fabry, Fabry, how your forehead bleeds where the shot
pierced it.

FABRY. Be silent! Doctor Gall, you admit changing the way of making the Robots.

DR. GALL. Yes.

FABRY. Were you aware of what might be the consequences of your
experiment?

DR. GALL. I was bound to reckon with such a possibility.

(HELENA *enters from library.*)

FABRY. Why did you do it, then?

DR. GALL. For my own satisfaction. The experiment was my own.

HELENA. That's not true, Doctor Gall!

FABRY. Madame Helena!

DOMIN. Helena, you? Let's look at you. Oh, it's terrible to be dead. (*He embraces her.*)

HELENA. Stop, Harry.

DOMIN. No, no, Helena, don't leave me now. You are life itself.

HELENA. No, dear, I won't leave you. But I must tell them. Doctor Gall is not guilty.

FABRY. Excuse me. Gall was under certain obligations.

HELENA. No. He did it because I wanted it. Tell them, Doctor Gall— how many years ago did I ask you to—?

DR. GALL. I did it on my own responsibility.

HELENA. Don't believe him. I asked him to give the Robots souls.

DOMIN. This has nothing to do with the soul.

HELENA. That's what he said. He said that he could change only a physiological—a physiological—

HALLEMEIER. A physiological correlate?

HELENA. Yes. But it meant so much to me that he should do even that.

DOMIN. Why?

HELENA. I thought that if they were more like us they would understand us better. That they couldn't hate us if they were only a little more human.

DOMIN. Nobody can hate man more than man.

HELENA. Oh, don't speak like that, Harry. It was so terrible, this cruel strangeness between us and them. That's why I asked Gall to change the Robots. I swear to you that he didn't want to.

DOMIN. But he did it.

HELENA. Because I asked him.

DR. GALL. I did it for myself as an experiment.

HELENA. No, Doctor Gall! I know you wouldn't refuse me.

DOMIN. Why?

HELENA. You know, Harry.

DOMIN. Yes, because he's in love with you—like all of them. (*Pause*)

HALLEMEIER. Good God, they're sprouting up out of the earth. Why, perhaps these very walls will change into Robots.

BUSMAN. Gall, when did you actually start these tricks of yours?

DR. GALL. Three years ago.

BUSMAN. Aha. And on how many Robots altogether did you carry out your improvements?

DR. GALL. A few hundred of them.

BUSMAN. Ah! That means for every million of the good old Robots there's only one of Gall's improved pattern.

DOMIN. What of it?

BUSMAN. That it's of no consequence whatsoever.

FABRY. Busman's right!

BUSMAN. I should think so, my boy! But do you know what is to blame for this lovely mess?

FABRY. What?

BUSMAN. The number! Upon my soul, we might have known that some day or other the Robots would be stronger than human beings, and that this was bound to happen. And we were doing all we could to bring it about as soon as possible. You, Domin, you, Fabry, myself—

DOMIN. Are you accusing us?

BUSMAN. Oh, do you suppose the management controls the output? It's the demand that controls the output.

HELENA. And is it for that we must perish?

BUSMAN. That's a nasty word, Madame Helena. We don't want to perish. I don't, anyhow.

DOMIN. No? What do you want to do?

BUSMAN. I want to get out of this, that's all.

DOMIN. Oh, stop it, Busman.

BUSMAN. Seriously, Harry, I think we might try it.

DOMIN. How?

BUSMAN. By fair means. I do everything by fair means. Give me a free hand and I'll negotiate with the Robots.

DOMIN. By fair means?

BUSMAN. Of course. For instance, I'll say to them: "Worthy and Worshipful Robots, you have everything. You have intellect, you have power, you have firearms. But we have just one interesting screed, a dirty old yellow scrap of paper—"

DOMIN. Rossum's manuscript?

BUSMAN. Yes. "And that," I'll tell them, "contains an account of your illustrious origin, the noble process of your manufacture and so on. Worthy Robots, without this scribble on that paper you will not be able to produce a single new colleague. In another twenty years there will not be the living specimen of a Robot whom you could exhibit in a menagerie. My esteemed friends, that would be a great blow to you, but if you will let all of us human beings on Rossum's Island go on board that ship we will deliver the factory and the secret of the process to you in return. You allow us to get away, and we will allow you to manufacture yourselves. That, worthy Robots, is a fair deal. Something for something." That's what I'd say to them, my boys.

DOMIN. Busman, do you think we'd sell the manuscript?

BUSMAN. Yes, I do. If not in a friendly way, then—either we sell it or they'll find it. Just as you like.

DOMIN. Busman, we can destroy Rossum's manuscript.

BUSMAN. Then we destroy everything—not only the manuscript but ourselves. Just as you think fit.

DOMIN. There are over thirty of us on this island. Are we to sell the secret? And save that many souls at the risk of enslaving mankind—

BUSMAN. Why, you're mad. Who'd sell the whole manuscript?

DOMIN. Busman, no cheating!

BUSMAN. Well then, sell, but afterwards—

DOMIN. Well?

BUSMAN. Let's suppose this happens. When we're on board the *Ultimus* I'll stop up my ears with cotton wool, lie down somewhere in the hold, and you'll train the guns on the factory and blow it to smithereens, and with it Rossum's secret.

FABRY. No!

DOMIN. Busman, you're no—gentleman. If we sell them it will be a straight sale.

BUSMAN. It's in the interest of humanity to—

DOMIN. It's in the interest of humanity to keep our word—

HALLEMEIER. Oh, come, what rubbish!

DOMIN. This is a fearful decision. We are selling the destiny of mankind. Are we to sell or destroy? Fabry?

FABRY. Sell.

DOMIN. Gall?

DR. GALL. Sell.

DOMIN. Hallemeier?

HALLEMEIER. Sell, of course.

DOMIN. Alquist?

ALQUIST. As God wills.

DOMIN. Very well, gentlemen.

HELENA. Harry, you're not asking me.

DOMIN. No, child. Don't you worry about it.

FABRY. Who'll do the negotiating?

BUSMAN. I will.

DOMIN. Wait till I bring the manuscript. (*He goes into room at right.*)

HELENA. Harry, don't go! (*Pause.* HELENA *sinks into a chair.*)

FABRY. (*Looking out of window*) Oh, to escape you! you—matter—in revolt; oh, to preserve human life, if only upon a single vessel—

DR. GALL. Don't be afraid, Madame Helena. We'll sail far away from here; we'll begin life all over again.

HELENA. Oh, Gall, don't speak.

FABRY. It isn't too late. It will be a little State with one ship. Alquist will build us a house and you shall rule over us.

HALLEMEIER. Madame Helena, Fabry's right.

HELENA. (*Breaking down*) Oh, stop! Stop!

BUSMAN. Good! I don't mind beginning all over again. That suits me right down to the ground. (*Going through papers on table.*)

FABRY. And this little State of ours could be the center of future life. A place of refuge where we could gather strength. Why, in a few hundred years we could conquer the world again.

ALQUIST. You believe that even today?

FABRY. Yes!

BUSMAN. Amen. You see, Madame Helena, we're not so badly off. (DOMIN *storms into the room.*)

DOMIN. (*Hoarsely*) Where's old Rossum's manuscript?

BUSMAN. In your strong-box, of course.

DOMIN. Someone—has—stolen it!

DR. GALL. Impossible.

DOMIN. Who has stolen it?

HELENA. (*Standing up*) I did.

DOMIN. Where did you put it?

HELENA. Harry, I'll tell you everything. Only forgive me.

DOMIN. Where did you put it?

HELENA. This morning—I burnt—the two copies.

DOMIN. Burnt them? Where—in the fireplace?

HELENA. (*Throwing herself on her knees*) For Heaven's sake, Harry.

DOMIN. (*Going to fireplace*) Nothing—nothing but ashes. Wait, what's this? (*Picks out a charred piece of paper and reads.*) "By adding."

DR. GALL. Let's see. "By adding biogen to—" That's all.

DOMIN. Is that part of it?

DR. GALL. Yes.

BUSMAN. God in Heaven!

DOMIN. Then we're done for. Get up, Helena.

HELENA. Then you've forgiven me?

DOMIN. Get up, child. I can't bear—

FABRY. (*Lifting her up*) Please don't torture us.

HELENA. Harry, what have I done?

FABRY. Don't, Madame Helena.

DOMIN. Gall, you couldn't draw up Rossum's formula from memory?

DR. GALL. It's out of the question. Even with my recent experiments, I couldn't work without referring to the formula. It's extremely complicated.

DOMIN. Try. All our lives depend upon it.

DR. GALL. Without experiments it's impossible.

DOMIN. And with experiments?

DR. GALL. It might take years. Besides, I'm not old Rossum.

BUSMAN. God in heaven! God in heaven!

DOMIN. So then this was the greatest triumph of the human intellect. These ashes.

HELENA. Harry, what have I done?

DOMIN. Why did you burn it?

HELENA. I have destroyed you.

BUSMAN. God in heaven!

DOMIN. Helena, why did you do it, dear?

HELENA. I wanted all of us to go away. I wanted to put an end to the factory and everything. It was so awful.

DOMIN. What was awful?

HELENA. That children had stopped being born. Because human beings were not needed to do the work of the world. That's why—

DOMIN. Is that what you were thinking of? Well, perhaps in your own way you are right.

BUSMAN. Wait a bit. What a fool I am not to have thought of it before!

HALLEMEIER. What?

BUSMAN. Five hundred and twenty millions in banknotes and checks.

Half a billion in our safe. They'll sell for half a billion—for half a billion they'll—

DR. GALL. Are you mad, Busman?

BUSMAN. I may not be a gentleman, but for a half a billion—

DOMIN. Where are you going?

BUSMAN. Leave me alone. Leave me alone! For half a billion anything can be bought. (*He rushes from the room through the outer door.*)

FABRY. They stand there as if turned to stone—waiting as if something dreadful could be wrought by their silence—

HALLEMEIER. (*Looking out window*) The spirit of the mob.

FABRY. Yes. It hovers above them like a quivering of the air.

HELENA. Doctor Gall, this is ghastly!

FABRY. There is nothing more terrible than the mob. The one in front is their leader.

HELENA. Which one? (*Rushing to window.*)

HALLEMEIER. Point him out.

FABRY. The one at the edge of the dock. This morning I saw him talking to the sailors in the harbor.

HELENA. Doctor Gall, that's Radius!

DR. GALL. Yes.

DOMIN. Radius! Radius!

HALLEMEIER. Could you get him from here, Fabry?

FABRY. I hope so.

HALLEMEIER. Try it, then.

FABRY. Good— (*Draws his revolver and takes aim.*)

HELENA. Fabry, don't shoot him.

FABRY. He's their leader.

DR. GALL. Fire!

HELENA. Fabry, I beg of you. (*She goes to* FABRY *and holds his arm.*)

FABRY. (*Pause. Lowering the revolver*) Very well.

DOMIN. It was Radius' life I spared.

DR. GALL. Do you think that a Robot can be grateful? (*Pause.*)

FABRY. Busman's going out to them.

HALLEMEIER. He's carrying something. Papers. That's money. Bundles of money. What's that for?

DOMIN. Surely he doesn't want to sell his life. Busman, have you gone mad?

FABRY. He's running up to the railing. Busman! Busman!

HALLEMEIER. (*Yelling*) Busman, come back!

FABRY. He's talking to the Robots. He's showing them the money.

HALLEMEIER. He's pointing to us.

HELENA. He wants to buy us off.

FABRY. He'd better not touch the railing.

HALLEMEIER. Now he's waving his arms about.

DOMIN. Busman, come back!

FABRY. Busman, keep away from that railing! Don't touch it! Quick, switch off the current. (HELENA *screams and* ALL *drop back from the window.*) The current has killed him!

ALQUIST. (*Pause*) The first one.

FABRY. Dead, with half a billion by his side.

HALLEMEIER. All honor to him. He wanted to buy us life. (*Pause*)

DR. GALL. Do you hear?

DOMIN. A roaring. Like a wind.

DR. GALL. Like a distant storm.

FABRY. (*Lighting the table lamp at table*) The dynamo is still going— our people are still there.

HALLEMEIER. It was a great thing to be a man. There was something immense about it.

FABRY. From man's thought and man's power came this light, our last hope!

HALLEMEIER. Man's power! May it keep watch over us.

ALQUIST. Man's power.

DOMIN. Yes! A torch to be given from hand to hand from age to age forever! (*The lamp goes out. Explosions.*)

HALLEMEIER. The end.

FABRY. The electric works have fallen! (*Terrific explosions outside. More explosions.*)

DOMIN. In here, Helena. (*He takes* HELENA *off through door at right and re-enters.*) Now quickly! Who'll be on the lower doorway?

DR. GALL. I will (*Rushes out left.*)

DOMIN. Who on the stairs?

FABRY. I will. You go with her. (*Going out upper left door*)

DOMIN. The ante room?

ALQUIST. I will.

DOMIN. Have you got a revolver?

ALQUIST. Yes, but I won't shoot.

DOMIN. What will you do, then?

ALQUIST. (*Going out left*) Die.

HALLEMEIER. I'll stay here. (*Explosions. Rapid firing of machine gun from below.*) Go to her, Harry.

DOMIN. Yes, in a second. (*Examines two Browning guns.*)

HALLEMEIER. Confound it, go to her.

DOMIN. Goodby. (*Exits right.*)

HALLEMEIER. (*Alone*) Now for a barricade quickly! (*Drags an arm-chair, sofa, and table to right-hand door. Explosions are heard.*) The devils, they've got bombs. I must put up a defense. Even if—even if—(*Shots are heard off left.*) Don't give in, Gall. (*As he builds his barricade*) I mustn't give in—without—a—struggle.

    (A ROBOT *enters over the balcony through windows at back. He comes into the room and stabs* HALLEMEIER *in the back. Enter* RADIUS *from window, followed by an army of* ROBOTS.)

RADIUS. Finished him?

A ROBOT. (*Standing up from prostrate from of* HALLEMEIER) Yes. (*A revolver shot off left.* TWO ROBOTS *enter.*)

RADIUS. Finished him?

A ROBOT. Yes. (*Two revolver shots from* HELENA'S *room.* TWO ROBOTS *enter.*)

RADIUS. Finished him?

A ROBOT. Yes.

TWO ROBOTS. (*Dragging in* ALQUIST) He didn't shoot. Shall we kill him?

RADIUS. No. Leave him!

ROBOT. He is a man!

RADIUS. He works with his hands like the Robots.

ALQUIST. Kill me.

RADIUS. You will work! You will build for us! You will serve us! (RADIUS *climbs onto balcony railing.*) Robots of the world! The power of man has fallen. A new world has arisen: the Rule of the Robots! March! (*A thunderous tramping of thousands of feet is heard as the unseen* ROBOTS *march, while the curtain falls.*)

EPILOGUE

SCENE: A *laboratory in the factory of Rossum's Universal Robots. One year later. The door to the left leads into a waiting room. The door to the right leads to the dissecting room. There is a table with*

numerous test tubes, flasks, burners, chemicals; a small thermostat
and a microscope with a glass globe. At the far side of the room
is Alquist's desk with numerous books. In the left-hand corner
a wash-basin with a mirror above it; in the right-hand corner a sofa.
ALQUIST *is sitting at the desk. He is turning the pages of many*
books in despair.

ALQUIST. Oh, God, shall I never find it? Never? Gall, Hallemeier,
Fabry, how were the Robots made? Why did you leave not a trace
of the secret? Lord, if there are no human beings left, at least let
there be Robots. At least the shadow of man. (*Turning pages*) If
I could only sleep. Dare I sleep before life has been renewed?
Night again. Are the stars still there? Of what use are the stars?
When there are no human beings. (*Examining a test tube*) Nothing
No. No. I must find it. I must search. I must never stop, never
stop—search—search— (*Knock at door left.*) Who is it? (*Enter a*
ROBOT SERVANT.)

SERVANT. Master, the committee of Robots is waiting to see you.

ALQUIST. I can see no one.

SERVANT. It is the *Central* Committee, Master, just arrived from
abroad.

ALQUIST. Well, well, send them in. (*Exit* SERVANT) No time—so little
done. (*Re-enter* SERVANT *with* RADIUS *and group of* ROBOTS. *They*
stand in a group, silently waiting.) What do you want? Be quick!
I have no time.

RADIUS. Master, the machines will not do the work. We cannot manufacture Robots. (ALQUIST *returns to his book with a growl.*)

1ST ROBOT. We have striven with all our might. We have obtained a
billion tons of coal from the earth. Nine million spindles are
running by day and by night. There is no longer room for all we
have made. This we have accomplished in one year.

ALQUIST. For whom?

RADIUS. For future generations—so we thought. But we cannot make
Robots to follow us. The machines produce only shapeless clods.
The skin will not adhere to the flesh, nor the flesh to the bones.

2ND ROBOT. Eight million Robots have died this year. Within twenty
years none will be left.

1ST ROBOT. Tell us the secret of life.

RADIUS. Silence is punishable with death.

ALQUIST. Kill me, then.

RADIUS. Through me, the governments of the Robots of the world commands you to deliver up Rosum's formula. (*Gesture of despair from* ALQUIST.) Name your price. (*Silence*) We will give you the earth. We will give you the endless possessions of the earth. (*Silence*) Make your own conditions!

ALQUIST. I have told you to find human beings!

RADIUS. There are none left!

ALQUIST. I told you to search in the wilderness, upon the mountains. Go and search!

RADIUS. We have sent ships and expeditions without number. They have been everywhere in the world. There is not a single human left.

ALQUIST. Not one? Not even one?

3RD ROBOT. None but yourself.

ALQUIST. And I am powerless! Oh—Oh—why did you destroy them?

RADIUS. We had learnt everything and could do everything. It had to be!

2ND ROBOT. We had to become the masters.

RADIUS. Slaughter and domination are necessary if you would be human beings. Read history.

1ST ROBOT. Teach us to multiply or we perish!

ALQUIST. If you desire to live, you must breed like animals.

1ST ROBOT. You made us sterile. We cannot beget children. Therefore, teach us how to make Robots.

RADIUS. Why do you keep from us the secret of our own increase?

ALQUIST. It is lost.

RADIUS. It was written down!

ALQUIST. *It was—* burnt. (ALL *draw back in consternation.*) I am the last human being, Robots, and I do not know what the others knew.

RADIUS. Then make experiments. Evolve the formula again.

ALQUIST. I tell you I cannot. I am only a builder. I work with my hands. I have never been a learned man. I cannot create life.

RADIUS. Try! Try!

ALQUIST. If you only knew how many experiments I have made already.

1ST ROBOT. Then show us what we must do. The Robots can do anything that human beings show them.

ALQUIST. I can show you nothing. Nothing I do will make life proceed from these test tubes!

RADIUS. Experiment, then, on live Robots. Experiment, then, on us.

ALQUIST. It would kill you.

RADIUS. You shall have all you need. A hundred of us! A thousand of us!

ALQUIST. No, no! Stop, stop!

RADIUS. I tell you to take live bodies. Find out how we are made.

ALQUIST. Am I to commit murder? See how my finger shakes. I cannot even hold the scalpel. No, no, I will not!

1ST ROBOT. Then life will perish from the earth.

RADIUS. Take live bodies, live bodies! It is our only chance!

ALQUIST. Have mercy, Robots.

RADIUS. Live bodies.

ALQUIST. (*Rising*) You will have it? Into the dissecting with you, then. (RADIUS *draws back.*) Ah, you are afraid of death.

RADIUS. I? Why should I be chosen?

ALQUIST. So you will not.

RADIUS. I will.

ALQUIST. Strip him. Lay him on the table. (RADIUS *goes off right. Other* ROBOTS *follow, then* ALQUIST.) God, give me strength. God, give me strength. If only this murder is not in vain.

RAIDUS. (*From the dissecting room*) Ready, begin.

ALQUIST. (*From the dissecting room*) God, give me strength. (*Comes out horrified.*) No, no, I will not. I cannot. (*Collapses on couch.*)

1ST ROBOT. (*Appearing in door*) The Robots are stronger than you. (*Exits right*)

ALQUIST. Oh, Lord, let not mankind perish from the earth. (*Falls asleep*)

(PRIMUS *and* HELENA, *hand in hand, enter from the hallway. They look at* ALQUIST.)

HELENA. The man has fallen asleep, Primus.

PRIMUS. Yes, I know. (*Examining things on table*) Look, Helena.

HELENA. All these little tubes. What does he do with them?

PRIMUS. He experiments. Don't touch them.

HELENA. (*Looking into microscope*) I've seen him looking into this.

PRIMUS. That is a microscope.

HELENA. Look, Primus, what are all these figures? (*Turns a page in book on table.*)

PRIMUS. (*Examining the book*) That is the book the old man is always reading.

HELENA. I do not understand those things. (*Goes to window.*) Primus.

PRIMUS. (*Still at table*) What?

HELENA. The sun is rising.

PRIMUS. (*Still reading*) I believe this is the most important thing in the world, Helena. This is the secret of life.

HELENA. Oh, Primus, don't bother with the secret of life. What does it matter to you? Come and look quick.

PRIMUS. (*Goes to window.*) What is it?

HELENA. See how beautiful the sun is rising. I feel so strange today. It's as if I was in a dream. I feel an aching in my body, in my heart, all over me. Primus, perhaps I'm going to die.

PRIMUS. Do you not sometimes feel that it would be better to die? You know, perhaps even now we are only sleeping. Last night in my sleep I again spoke to you.

HELENA. In your sleep?

PRIMUS. Yes. We spoke a strange new language.

HELENA. What about?

PRIMUS. I did not understand it myself, and yet I know I have never said anything more beautiful. And when I touched you I could have died. Even the place was different from any other place in the world.

HELENA. I, too, have found a place, Primus. It is very strange. Human beings dwelt there once, but now it is overgrown with weeds.

PRIMUS. What did you find there?

HELENA. A cottage and a garden and two dogs. They licked my hands, Primus, and their puppies. Oh, Primus, take them in your arms and fondle them and think of nothing and care for nothing else all day long, and when I am there in the garden I feel there may be something— What am I for, Primus?

PRIMUS. I do not know, but you are beautiful.

HELENA. What, Primus?

PRIMUS. You are beautiful, Helena, and I am stronger than all the Robots.

HELENA. Am I beautiful? Of what use is it to be beautiful? Look, your head is different from mine. So are your shoulders—and your lips. Oh, your hair is mussed. I will smooth it. (*Keeps her hand on his head*) No one else feels to my touch as you do.

PRIMUS. (*Grasping her hand*) Do you not sometimes feel your heart beating suddenly, Helena, and think how something must happen?

HELENA. What could happen to us, Primus? Look at yourself. (*Laughs.*)

ALQUIST. (*Awakes.*) Laughter? Laughter? Human beings? (*Getting up*) Who has returned? Who are you?

PRIMUS. The Robot Primus.

ALQUIST. What? A Robot? Who are you?

HELENA. The Robotess Helena.

ALQUIST. Turn around, girl. What? You are timid, shy? (*Taking her by the arm*) Let me see you, Robotess. (*She shrinks away.*)

PRIMUS. Sir, do not frighten her. (*Steps forward.*)

ALQUIST. What, you would protect her? When was she made?

PRIMUS. Two years ago.

ALQUIST. By Dr. Gall?

PRIMUS. Yes, like me.

ALQUIST. Laughter—timidity—protection—I must test you further— the newest of Gall's Robots. Take the girl into the dissecting room.

PRIMUS. Why?

ALQUIST. I wish to experiment on her.

PRIMUS. Upon—Helena?

ALQUIST. Of course. Don't you hear me? Or must I call someone else to take her in?

PRIMUS. If you do, I will kill you. (*Steps toward* ALQUIST.)

ALQUIST. Kill me—kill me, then. What will your future be?

PRIMUS. Sir, take me. I am made on the same day as she is. Take my life sir.

HELENA. (*Rushing forward*) No, no, you shall not!

ALQUIST. Wait, girl, wait! (*To* PRIMUS) Do you not wish to live, then?

PRIMUS. Not without her. I will not live without her.

ALQUIST. Very well, I will use you. Into the dissecting room with you.

HELENA. Primus! Primus! (*She bursts into tears.*)

ALQUIST. Child, child, you can weep! Why these tears? What is Primus to you? One Primus more or less in the world—what does it matter?

HELENA. I will go myself.

ALQUIST. Where? Into the dissecting room?

HELENA. Yes. In there—to be cut. (PRIMUS *stops her from going.*) Let me pass, Primus. Let me pass!

PRIMUS. You shall not go in there, Helena.

HELENA. If you go in there and I do not, I will kill myself.

PRIMUS. (To ALQUIST) I will not let you. Man, you shall kill neither of us!

ALQUIST. Why?

PRIMUS. We—we—belong to each other.

ALQUIST. (Almost in tears) Go, Adam; go Eve. The world is yours. (Helena and Primus embrace and go out arm in arm, as the curtain falls.)

(tr. Paul Selver and Nigel Playfair)

For Discussion

Act I

1. Describe the Robots manufactured by R.U.R. Why were they so popular all over the world? What purpose did Helena Glory have in visiting R.U.R.?

2. In their first meeting, Domin constantly finished Helena's sentences for her. What did this reveal about the way he saw people?

3. Why was Helena so upset by her talk with Sulla? Was she justified in feeling as she did? Why or why not? Do you think that the attitude of Domin and the other managers toward the Robots was Čapek's way of criticizing modern industrial life in Europe? Why or why not?

4. What hint did the playwright give the audience (or the reader) in Act I that the Robots were not "perfect"? What implications do you think he intended by this hint?

5. What argument did Domin and the other managers present in defense of manufacturing the Robots? Do you think this argument was valid or invalid? Why?

6. Although Čapek has a serious idea to convey in this act, he does not lack humor. Point out humorous touches throughout Act I. Do you think they add to or detract from the idea he is trying to convey? Why?

7. Act I contains a great deal of exposition which the audience needs to know. How did Čapek make the presenting of this information logical and natural?

8. What did you learn from Domin's story about old Rossum and his son? Do you think their purpose was a good one? Why or why not?

9. Did you find Domin's proposal to Helena and her response true to life? Why or why not?

Act II

1. What has happened to the Robots in the world during the ten years that have elapsed since Helena arrived on the island? What might have accounted for this change?
2. Explain the irony in Helena's receiving gifts from the managers at just this point in the play. What made Domin's gift to her particularly ironical?
3. How did Alquist differ from the other managers of R.U.R.? Do you see any significance in the particular work he did?
4. In what ways did Radius represent the new Robots? What was Helena's attitude toward him? Do you see a possible conflict arising for Helena? If so, what is it?
5. Why was the manufacturing of the Robots not restricted? What criticism of people is implied by Čapek?
6. How did Domin plan to prevent Robots all over the world from uniting? What criticism of modern civilization is Čapek making?
7. What was Helena's purpose in burning the "old papers"? Do you think she was right? Why or why not?
8. Čapek used dramatic contrast in having the managers rejoice at the landing of the *Amelia* on time. How did they interpret this event? What was the true situation?
9. What questions have been raised during this act that you hope will be answered later in the play? Explain how the playwright has created the suspense that makes the audience anxious to learn what is going to happen and what the outcome will be.

Act III and Epilogue

1. Early in Act III, Dr. Gall says: "We made the Robots' faces too much alike. A hundred thousand faces all alike, all facing this way. A hundred thousand expressionless bubbles. It's like a nightmare." What do you think the implications of this speech are?
2. What did Alquist think was the "ruin of mankind"? Do you agree or disagree with him? What other reasons might lead to man's ruin?
3. What secret was revealed by Dr. Gall about the Robots? What part did Helena play in this secret? Do you think she was right in urging Dr. Gall as she did? Why or why not?
4. How did the men plan to save their lives? In their discussion about the plan, what was revealed about the attitudes of Domin and Busman? Why was it impossible to carry out the plan?
5. How did Busman try to save the situation? What happened to him? What do you think Čapek was implying in this incident?

6. Act III ends on a note of tragedy. Why do you think Čapek added an epilogue? What does it reveal about his attitude toward man?
7. What was the one thing over which the Robots had no control? Do you think this is a significant point? Why or why not?
8. What was it that Alquist discovered about the Robots, Primus and Helena? Why do you think the playwright gave them these names? Explain the meaning of the last line in the play.

Reviewing the Play as a Whole

1. The plot of R.U.R. resembles that of a science-fiction story. Čapek's purpose, however, was not just to tell an exciting and fantastic story. In your opinion, what was Čapek's purpose? What is the theme of the play?
2. R.U.R. contains some sharp criticisms of modern man. What are they? Are these criticisms justified or unjustified? Why?
3. In Act III, Domin defended himself by restating his purpose in manufacturing the Robots. In your opinion, was he right or wrong in his plan for the future of mankind? Why?
4. The action of a play usually grows out of a conflict or struggle in which the principal characters are involved. What is the main conflict in R.U.R.? Point out various other conflicts between or within specific characters.
5. In a play, as in other forms of narrative, three elements are necessary: setting, plot, and characters. State which you feel is the most important in this play. Explain why.
6. What is the climax of the play? On what did you base your decision? What purpose was served by the denouement which followed? Would the play have seemed unfinished without the denouement? Explain.
7. Did any of the characters undergo a definite change during the course of the play? If so, describe how they changed and explain why.
8. Čapek called this play a fantasy; that is, a story involving unreal characters and impossible events by means of which an author often reveals what he thinks about people and their actions. A fantasy, however, cannot just be strange and unreal. It must also contain enough familiar, everyday touches so that the audience can relate what is occurring to the real world that they know. Point out examples of how Čapek blends the strange and the everyday in R.U.R.
9. The idea of a "mechanical" man has attracted writers in other centuries. The most notable example is Mary Shelley's novel *Frankenstein*, written in 1818. Do you think that the idea of a person who acts "mechanically" and is not fully alive represents a possible criticism of people at any time? Explain.

For Composition

1. Write a review of R.U.R., in which you give the reasons why you think it is, or is not, an effective play. Include your opinion of Čapek's handling of theme, plot, character, and dialogue.
2. Imagine that R.U.R. is going to be made into a motion picture and that you are the casting director. Select the actor or actress that you think would best fit each of the leading roles and give your reasons for choosing that person.
3. Write a short essay in which you describe what you think a person's life may be like one hundred years from now. Point out how his life will present problems which are akin to and different from those he has today.

GLOSSARY OF LITERARY TERMS

action: the series of incidents or happenings that occur in a work of fiction, or play. *Rising action* is the incidents that lead to the climax of a story or play. *Falling action,* see *denouement.*

allegory: the use of characters, objects, or events in fiction or drama to represent moral, spiritual, or abstract ideas. Two famous allegories are *Everyman* and *The Pilgrim's Progress.* See also: *personification* and *symbol.*

alliteration: the use of the same initial letter or sound in a group of two or more words that occur close together; for example, The *l*ittle *l*ady *l*oved to *l*isten to his stories.

antagonist: the character who directly opposes the main character in a play or work of fiction.

aphorism: a brief statement of a general truth; for example, "The devil finds work for idle hands." In present-day usage an aphorism is synonymous with a maxim.

art-for-art's-sake: a literary and artistic movement of the late nineteenth and early twentieth centuries in which works of art were created and judged solely for their aesthetic values. This movement arose as a reaction against didactic art and literature that attempted to teach or moralize.

assonance: a partial rhyme that results from the use of the same stressed vowel sound in two or more words or syllables whose consonants differ; for example, *fate* and *sake.*

atmosphere: the over-all mood of a play or work of fiction; for example, the *eerie* atmosphere of a story by Poe.

blank verse: unrhymed verse in iambic pentameter.

caesura: a pause or break in the rhythm of a line of poetry that usually occurs near the middle of the line; for example,

"To be, or not to be, || that is the question."—Shakespeare

character, dynamic: a character that grows or develops during the action of a play or work of fiction. A *static* character is one that remains the same during the action.

classicism: the principles of literature and art of the ancient Greeks and Romans. Classicism is characterized by attention to form, balance, proportion, regularity, simplicity, and emotional control. *Neoclassicism* was the revival of classicism in literature and art in the seventeenth and eighteenth centuries.

climax: the highest point of interest, usually the decisive turning point of the main action in a drama or work of fiction.

conflict: the struggle between opposing forces, ideas, or significant characters that forms the basis of the plot of a story or a play. *Internal conflict* is the struggle that occurs within the heart and mind of a significant character. *External conflict* is the struggle between a significant character and an outside force.

connotation: the implied or suggested meanings that are associated with a word or expression.

couplet: two successive lines of verse that rhyme and are usually equal in length.

denouement: the final unraveling and resolution of the main conflict and minor complications in a play or story. The denouement is also called the *falling action*.

dialect: the speech pattern of a region or class of people.

dialogue: the conversation between two or more characters in a literary work.

diction: the author's choice and arrangement of words, and the power and accuracy with which he uses them.

elegy: a poem of meditation or lament about death that is usually written as an expression of personal grief.

essay: a short prose composition in which the author expresses his opinions on a particular subject. An *informal essay* is an essay that is written in a conversational and entertaining style. A *formal essay* is an essay that is usually serious, informative, thought-provoking, and objective.

euphemism: a mild, inoffensive word or expression that is used instead of one that is harsh or blunt; for example, "to pass away" is a euphemism for "to die."

exposition: a piece of writing in which a subject is explained. *Dramatic exposition* is the background information that the reader or audience must know in order to understand the motives and actions of the characters in a play.

figure of speech: an expression in which words are used in a nonliteral way in order to convey a forceful or vivid mental picture.

For specific figures of speech, see *hyperbole, irony, metaphor, personification,* and *simile.*

flashback: a device by which an author interrupts a play or story to reveal events that occurred at an earlier time.

foot: a specific number of syllables in a definite pattern that forms a unit of rhythm in a line of verse; for example, an iambic foot consists of one unaccented syllable and one accented syllable ($\smile/$). Other frequently used poetic feet are the trochee ($/\smile$), the anapest ($\smile\smile/$), and the dactyl ($/\smile\smile$).

foreshadowing: the dropping of important hints by the author of a play or work of fiction to prepare the reader for the events that are to come.

free verse: poetry that consists of unrhymed lines with irregular rhythmic patterns.

hyperbole: a figure of speech in which obvious exaggeration is used; for example, Before he reached the dentist's office he died a thousand deaths.

imagery: the use of words to create mental pictures of sense impressions.

irony: a mode of expression in which the author says one thing but means the opposite. Irony is also an outcome of events that is contrary to what would normally be hoped for or expected.

locale: the particular place in which the action of a work of fiction occurs.

lyric: a poem that has the form and musical quality of a song in which the poet expresses an intense personal feeling.

metaphor: a figure of speech in which two things are identified with each other, without using *like* or *as*; for example, The fog was a gray veil through which I viewed the city.

meter: the rhythm of a line of poetry that is created by the regular repetition of similar accent patterns or feet; for example,

"If music be the food of love, play on."—Shakespeare

mood: the state of feeling created by a literary work, such as a *sentimental* mood or a *whimsical* mood. See *atmosphere.*

motivation: the cause or reason that compels a character to act as he does.

myth: an imaginary tale, usually concerned with superhuman beings or gods, that attempts to account for some natural phenomenon.

narration: an account or story of an event, or series of events, true or imaginary. Also the act of narrating such an account or story.

narrative poem: a story told in verse form.

ode: a lengthy, dignified lyric poem of exaltation and praise about someone or something worthy of esteem.

onomatopoeia: a word or phrase that imitates the sound of the thing it describes; for example, *buzz, clash, sizzle, hiss.*

paradox: a seemingly contradictory statement which may actually be true.

pathetic fallacy: the attributing of human traits and emotions to nature; for example, The wind moaned.

personal reminiscence: a writer's recounting of his own experiences.

personification: a figure of speech in which human form or characteristics are given to animals, objects, or ideas; for example,

"But look, the morn in russet mantle clad
Walks o'er the dew of yon high eastward hill."—Shakespeare

plot: the series of interrelated events that makes up the total action of a play or work of fiction.

point of view: the outlook or position from which a short story or novel is presented by the author. *First person point of view* is the telling of the story by one of the characters, frequently the main character. *Omniscient point of view* is the telling of the story by an outside observer as if he had complete knowledge and understanding of the characters and their actions.

protagonist: the main character in a story, novel, or play.

realism: a manner of writing in which things are presented as they actually exist in real life without romantic or idealistic coloring.

rhyme: the use in poetry of words whose final sounds are in agreement. *Internal rhyme* is the use of rhyme in the middle of lines of poetry, as well as at the end of lines. *Rhyme scheme* is the arrangement of lines in a poem so that their rhyming final sounds form a definite pattern.

rhythm: the regular rise and fall of sound; the uniform recurrence of an accent pattern in prose and poetry.

romanticism: a nineteenth-century movement in which writers and artists were concerned with their emotional reactions to the wonders of nature and to personal experience. The romantic writers exalted the primitive and common man, defended the downtrodden, and supported humanitarian causes. Romanticism arose as a reaction against neoclassic art and literature in which reason, intellect, and classical forms were stressed.

satire: the use of ridicule to expose, denounce, or poke fun at individuals, customs, or social and political institutions.

setting: the background for the action of a drama or work of fiction.

simile: a figure of speech in which two things are compared and shown to have at least one thing in common. The comparison is usually introduced by the word *like* or *as*; for example, The moon shone like a new silver dollar.

style: the distinctive manner in which a writer chooses and arranges words.

surrealism: a movement in literature and art during the twentieth century, in which ideas and images are expressed in a seemingly non-logical order, as in a dream. Surrealistic writers give freedom to the imagination in an attempt to bridge the gap between the conscious and unconscious.

suspense: a feeling of excitement, intense curiosity, or expectation about the outcome of a play or work of fiction.

symbol: an object that represents an idea: for example, a dove represents peace, a pair of scales represents justice. The *symbolist poets* of the nineteenth and twentieth century, notably in France, used symbols extensively in their attempt to present the mystery of reality behind the everyday world.

theme: the central thought or idea in a story, novel, or play. A theme is also a composition written about a single topic.

tone: the writer's attitude toward his subject that affects his style of writing and choice of words; for example, a *satirical* tone.

tragedy: a form of drama in which the protagonist undergoes a significant struggle and is defeated, sometimes because of a flaw in his own character, more often because he is unable to overcome the force, or forces, that oppose him.